Sons of Tubal-cain

A History of Artificers in the Royal Navy
1868–2010

Sons of Tubal-cain

A History of Artificers in the Royal Navy 1868–2010

John North

Matador
9 Priory Business Park,
Wistow Road, Kibworth Beauchamp,
Leicestershire, LE8 0RX
Tel: 0116 279 2299
Email: books@troubador.co.uk
Web: www.troubador.co.uk/matador
Twitter: @matadorbooks

ISBN 978 183859 151 9

British Library Cataloguing in Publication Data.
A catalogue record for this book is available from the British Library.

Printed and bound in the UK by TJ International, Padstow, Cornwall
Typeset in 11pt Caslon Pro by Troubador Publishing Ltd, Leicester, UK

Matador is an imprint of Troubador Publishing Ltd

MIX
Paper from
responsible sources
FSC® C013056

To my wife Sue, with my love and thanks for her patience, help and forebearance during the writing of this book

Contents

• • •

Foreword

• • •

As a technology-led Service, the Royal Navy has always been highly dependent on its engineering branches to deliver and sustain its capabilities. In the absence of reliable supply chains and the need to minimise dependencies on logistic support, the Artificer's abilities to maintain, diagnose faults and undertake repairs has been essential to our success and reputation. This book celebrates the niche role of the Artificer across each of the Navy's Fighting Arms and examines its evolution to keep pace with the ever-increasing complexity of equipment and systems in ships, submarines and aircraft. The need to adapt and overcome was engendered in the Artificer through schools such as HMS FISGARD, DAEDAULS, COLLINGWOOD and SULTAN with a proud ethos and self-belief that was passed on from instructor to apprentice and then sustained throughout the Fleet via the close network and camaraderie within the Branch. As an Air Engineer Officer operating in the most remote locations and under the harshest of environmental conditions, it always gave me reassurance to seek the sage advice and guidance of my "Chief Tiff" as my mobile encyclopaedia who would have seen the problem before, regardless of the unfathomable fault or operational pressures. Whenever the Royal Navy has been tempted to reduce the role of the Artificer or technician, in whatever form it has taken, the outcome has been negative. I do not see this changing in the near term, so we should always look to the lessons of the past when shaping the future, which makes this book so invaluable.

R C THOMPSON CBE
Rear Admiral
Chief Naval Engineer Officer

Acknowledgements

• • •

This book has been a labour of love and is dedicated to all those who passed through the gates of all the establishments where Artificers have been trained over the years and who are proud to call themselves "Tiffies". I wish to thank Rear Admiral Rick Thompson, the Chief Naval Engineer Officer, for writing the Foreword, which he made time to write despite his onerous workload. My thanks also go to everyone who has contributed memories, anecdotes, dits and musings about themselves or their relatives, in some cases long gone but not yet forgotten. Further, my apologies to anyone I have inadvertently omitted to mention; it was not intentional.

To all the serving and retired Artificers who have taken the time to write to me, my grateful thanks. These include: Rear Admiral Paul Bass (Retd), Commodore Alan Bennett RN (Retd), Commodore John Newell RN (Retd), Commodore Mark Cameron RN, Captain Steve Gosden RN (Retd), Captain Bill Oliphant RN (Retd), Captain Dick Hobbs RN (Retd), Captain Matt Bolton RN, Captain Mike Rose RN, Captain Peter Towell RN, Commander Ken Enticknap RN (Retd), Commander Mark Barton RN, Commander Jonathan Pearce RN, Commander Andy Donaldson RN, Lieutenant Commander Nick Cross RN, Lieutenant Commander Brett Giles RN, Lieutenant Sam Weaver RN (Retd), WO1 ET(WE) Andy Bibb, WO1 ET(ME) Steve Drayton, CPO ET(ME) Dawn Jennings, CPO ET(ME) Jumper Collings, CPO ET(ME) Andrew Grimes, CPO ET(ME) Jay House, CPO ET(ME) Steven Nelson, CPO ET(WE) Helen Robson, CPO ET(WE) Darren Hawkins, CPO ET(WE) Gerry Jones, Roger Bateman, Dr Gordon Morris, Jon Cray, Stan Beale, Ron Calverley,

David Beard, Nigel Jury, Melanie Ward, Robert Mitchell, Karen Phillips, Art Pearse, Stuart Wakefield, John Redican, Phillip Alder, Mary Baillie, David Barrett, John Barrett, Kirsty Rixon, Ricky Walters, Monty Callow, Reg Maitland, Fred Dugan, Dave Clark, Peter Bellamy, Derek Nadine, Dr Mike Doyle, Steve Galloway-Kirkland and Jacky MacDonald, The Fisgard Association, The Old Caledonia Artificer Apprentices Association and The Royal Naval Engineers Benevolent Society.

Introduction

• • •

That the Navy is "going to the dogs" has been a favourite thesis from the days of Drake and Frobisher; and this canine goal never seemed nearer of attainment than when steam and iron came to stay in the fleet, and wrested from the old seadogs what they had come to regard as their own particular heritage.[1]

The first ship fitted with steam propulsion in the Royal Navy was the 238-ton Comet, powered by 80 hp engines, a paddle steamer built in 1822 at Deptford by Mr Oliver Lang, and this was followed shortly after by *Lightning*.[2] By 1837 there were twenty-seven steam-powered vessels on the Navy List and all of these ships were fitted with side-lever engines and low-pressure boilers, operating only marginally above atmospheric pressure. They were built by such firms as Maudslay, Sons and Field, Fairbairn, Penn, Miller and Seaward.[3] These engines were neither efficient nor reliable and many in the naval establishment questioned their worth. All these vessels were paddle wheel-driven, not armed but used purely as auxiliaries to manoeuvre the main line of battleships, particularly when leaving and entering harbour in light winds.

That there was apathy towards steam propulsion may be attributed to several causes, firstly the natural reactionary response of seaman officers inured in the culture of sail and the seamanship required to command a large line of battleship, ships that had hardly changed since *Trafalgar*. Another reason was the superiority of the Royal Navy in the number of battleships

1

it could deploy over its rivals. This is summed up by the response of Lord Melville, while First Lord of the Admiralty, to a request for a steamer to carry mail from Malta to Corfu, where he stated categorically, "it is their bounden duty to discourage to the utmost of their ability the employment of steam vessels, as they considered that the introduction of steam was calculated to strike a fatal blow at the Naval Supremacy of the Empire".[4] There were still compelling reasons at the time to maintain the status quo of sail; clearly the Admiralty wished to avoid an arms race that would allow rivals to challenge British naval hegemony.

The paddlewheel was vulnerable to enemy gunfire and interrupted the broadside. The paddlewheels and the room needed for the boilers and engines would reduce the number of guns by nearly half, clearly unacceptable to deck officers. There was also the poor performance and reliability and a dockyard organisation with no experience of steam machinery. So, as Geoffrey Penn succinctly puts it, "The value of steam for fighting ships was therefore extremely doubtful".[5] This antipathy to steam propulsion was very slow to die out, with many officers who served into the 1880s and 90s still longing for the days of sail.[6] Such attitudes towards steam propulsion also led to the engineers required for the operation and maintenance of the machinery being discounted as a squalid nuisance that interfered with the orderly running of a warship that had for many centuries been the sole preserve of Executive Officers.

The original engineers of the very early steam navy were supplied by the machinery manufacturers and therefore not actually linked to the established navy and as a consequence wore no uniform, carried no rank and were, as Penn commented, "little more than engine drivers", and some were, indeed, taken up from the railways.[7] These early engineers seemed to be a rather intemperate, not to say uncouth bunch, with little to recommend them to Executive Officers,[8] something that may have produced a mindset in future executives that contributed to the social stigma that engineers took so long to dispel.

The appointment of a Comptroller of Steam Machinery and Packet Department,[9] Captain Edward Parry, on 19 April 1837, who was an Arctic explorer not an engineer, was a move in the right direction and with it the recognition that steam propulsion was becoming an important issue for the future direction the Navy would take as steam supplanted sail. It was not until 1837 that engineers were finally put on an official, though humble footing, when the Admiralty recognised engineers as Warrant Officers "next below Carpenters" by Admiralty Order in Council dated 19 July 1837,[10] possibly due to Parry's influence at the Admiralty. That they should be of warrant status and not commissioned is detailed in a minute from Rear Admiral Sir William Parker, Lord of the Admiralty, to Parry, once again highlighting the social inferiority of engineers to the executive.[11]

This Admiralty Order in Council detailed the duties and responsibilities of the engineers and the pay each grade of engineer could expect, as the three classes of engineer and four of boys had been in existence for some time.[12] This finally regularised the system on an official basis. Similarly, it laid down the duties that were to be expected, to maintain an engine room log, keep accounts, make machinery sketches and, of course, be able to effect repairs to the machinery in their charge.[13] Those engineers entering already qualified were further examined by suitable senior engineers such as John Dinnen, the foreman at Woolwich Dockyard, the first naval engineer to take up an appointment ashore, a post he held for the next thirty-seven years,[14] and Peter Ewart, Chief Engineer and Inspector of Machinery, and suitable passing certificates were issued that detailed the level of competence and expertise attained by each engineer passing into the fleet.[15]

Later in 1837 first class engineers were issued with a uniform, which their Lordships decided should be that of gunners, boatswains and carpenters, which included the trademark top hat of Warrant Officers. How that could be "suitable" in an engine room has not been recorded. A further refinement was the introduction of buttons peculiar to engineers, which had on them a steam engine, side-lever of course, with a crown above, a move that singled out the engineer from his peers, once again making clear the social distinction between engineer and executive. But none of these innovations, nor an increase in pay, acted as an inducement for engineers to stay in the Service; they were still seen as no different from other engine room staff that Tony Chamberlain describes as "Stokers – the lowest of the low?"[16] They were considered "coarse, uneducated men with a reputation for being trouble makers"[17] and the executive saw engineers as from the same mould.

It was the introduction of the screw propeller that finally laid to rest the belief that a steam ship could not be a fighting vessel, but this did not advance the engineers' position in the slightest. The superiority of screw propeller over paddlewheel was demonstrated in a trial between *Alecto*, paddlewheel, and *Rattler*, screw propeller, in 1844. Both ships were built with identical hulls of 1,140 tons and 176'6" long and in trials *Rattler* outperformed *Alecto* in all sea conditions and finally, in the totally unscientific but spectacular "Tug of War", *Rattler* totally dominated poor *Alecto*, who even with her engines at full ahead was towed backwards at a steady speed.[18] This was conducted as a public relations exercise to convince the general public as well as the Admiralty of the superiority of the propeller. [19]

Captain Edward Chappell, who had overseen the trials, commented that the "the screw propeller admits of the whole machinery being kept below the water line… the whole broadside battery is left unobstructed, and should every mast be shot away the propeller might still enable a ship to maintain an efficient fighting position".[20] This would seem to obviate all the previous objections towards steam propulsion that had been levelled at the paddle steamers and the Admiralty was obviously convinced as that year it ordered twenty screw engines. [21]

There were still objectors, but, perversely, some of them were the very people who advocated steam propulsion, there being a concern as to how a vessel with this means of propulsion at the stern could be steered. Conversely, the adherents to sail saw the screw vessel as giving a "new lease of life to sail propulsion".[22] Presumably this was because they saw the same problem of steerage and believed that sails would be the answer. There is little to commend either point of view as it was soon demonstrated that steering was more controllable with a propeller, something borne out by experience, trial and error and common sense, though there remained some who were unconvinced in the propeller's superiority.

The benefits of screw propulsion were well documented by Captain Edward Pellew Halsted, a respected supporter of the propeller and an Executive Officer, who wrote, "The objects to be obtained are two, The first was 'to restore that complete broadside which experience had ever shown to be the best adapted for all the exigencies of warfare', the second was 'to render this complete armament at all times available; and to secure for the ship the full co-operation of steam power whether in close or distant action, by disposing her machinery as to afford it a protection as effectual as of the magazine itself'." [23]

Despite the adoption of steam propulsion, it was necessary to maintain a full sailing rig as the fuel economy of early steam engines was poor; this was exacerbated by the relatively small amount of coal that could be carried on board, which is highlighted by Francis Wheeler, an engineer, who records in his journal an occasion in HMS *Gladiator* where they had to revert to sail "on account of there being only two tons and a half of coal in the ship".[24] There was also the further difficulty in accessing adequate coal stores away from friendly harbours and the difficulties in recoaling.

There remained a core of Executive Officers who still maintained that engineers were "manual workers" and, therefore, not suitable material for naval officers. Many of these officers were steeped in the lore of sail and had joined a service that knew no other method of propulsion and were now in some of the most important posts in the Royal Navy, many in their seventies and eighties.[25] They had learnt their profession at sea and saw no requirement for either education or science, both of which they had no experience of and even less inclination to embrace, and, as Penn notes, "the art and practice of seamanship which had become so deep-rooted, so much a devotion as to amount almost to a religion", particularly after centuries of reliance on sail. [26]

It might be expected that the introduction of the screw propeller might have led to a better understanding between engineer and executive, however this does not seem to have been the case and many Executive Officers continued to view the engineer as "a person of inferior status, poor education and little importance".[27] This is countered by the views of J. MacFarlane Gray, vice-president of the Institute of Marine Engineers, who stated that "If engineers will aim at so conducting themselves that they are never spoken of otherwise as being 'quite equal if not superior to the deck officers in their language and behaviour', and if it pertains to their highly intellectual calling that make themselves the masters of both of theory and the practice, the time would not be very distant when their importance in steamers would be fully recognised."[28] This is the engineer trying to fight his corner in the face of continuing obfuscation from the executive.

And, while the engineers' status remained, for the moment, much as it had been from the inception of steam propulsion, with only minor concessions, the advent of the screw propeller brought home to all but the most reactionary Executive Officers that steam was here to stay. However, many executives considered themselves "gentlemen" and "could never have practised as an engineer without opening himself to a charge of eccentricity"[29].

There were other executives with an eye to the future keen to embrace the new propulsion seeking to gain a working knowledge of it, even to the extent of visiting the best-known engineering firms of the time at their own expense.[30] One was the future First Sea Lord, Astley Cooper Key, who requested to serve in steam ships but was looked on with pity by his contemporary Executive Officers. These officers, who he had joined and trained with, considered him to have "taken leave of his senses"[31] and that it would be the end of his career. However, Cooper Key was unrepentant and saw the step as "regrettable, though advantageous, if not essential, to his future career".[32] But time would show that Cooper Key had taken the right course of action in espousing steam propulsion.

Of course, the expansion of the steam fleet meant that there was an increasing requirement for engineers: between 1849 and 1859 the number of vessels with steam propulsion increased from 151 to 218[33] but with the merchant fleets relying mainly on sail there was no ready pool of engineers that could be tapped into and consequently status was rapidly becoming a prime issue. This the Admiralty needed to address with some urgency so that their rank and status could be equal to and consistent with their importance to the efficient fighting capability of the fleet and not remain so inferior to the executive.

That there was seen the need to look at how engineers were viewed and why there was a problem with recruitment is illustrated by a paper presented to the Royal United Services Institution in which the author, H. Orpen, commented, "I cannot advise my friends to send the best class of boys into the Navy as Naval Engineers, knowing that they take such a secondary position at present, and that they are always beneath the executive." [34]

From the humble start of the naval engineer as "little more than engine drivers" and Warrant Officers "next below Carpenters", there had been progress – in rank, though not much in status – but there still remained the social divide between executive and engineer. There was now a realisation among many Executive Officers that steam propulsion was no longer a toy but a powerful and reliable means of propulsion that was here to stay; this, of course, meant that so was the engineer. There still remained the perennial problem of insufficient numbers of engineers and several panaceas had been tried; in 1868 the rate of Engine Room Artificer was introduced to take on much of the "hands-on" engineering and maintenance previously undertaken by assistant engineers.[35]

So on 28 March 1868 an Admiralty Order in Council was issued which allowed for engineers to be recruited into the Royal Navy directly from industry and for these engineers to be ranked as Chief Petty Officers with the title Engine Room Artificer.[36] There were further improvements to the conditions of service of Artificers. Artificer Engineers with the rank of Warrant Officer were created by Admiralty Order in Council in 1897[37] and while this was seen as a temporary measure it actually lasted for the next fifty years. Chief Artificer Engineers, later known as Commissioned Engineers, were introduced in 1900.[38] Electrical Artificers were introduced in 1913 and there were further additions, with Ordnance Artificers appearing in 1919,[39] Air Artificers in 1938,[40] Air Electrical in 1942[41] and Shipwrights in 1947.[42] There have been many establishments associated with Artificers, from the original hulks in Chatham and the Tamar through HMS *Caledonia* in Rosyth, HMS *Ariel* and *Daedalus*, HMS *Collingwood*, HMS *Condor* and HMS *Sultan*. But to the majority of Artificers their alma mater will always remain HMS *Fisgard* in whatever incarnation, even after its closure as a training establishment in 1983.

The modern Artificer was the brainchild of Admiral "Jackie" Fisher, who introduced the scheme for the training of Boy Artificers, the forerunners of Artificer Apprentices, in 1903,[43] with the first twenty-six boys, all from the Royal Hospital School, Greenwich, joining the reserve ship *Algiers* at Chatham. This was consolidated in 1905 with the commissioning of the hulks *Audacious* and *Erebus* as HMS *Fisgard*, a name which became synonymous with Artificers until their demise in 2010. There were further additions and in 1910 all Artificer training was consolidated at Portsmouth and Devonport and in 1920 the term Boy Artificer was changed to Artificer Apprentice. There were many different ships and venues associated with the training of Artificers, with Chatham being re-employed as Fisgard Block and HMS *Caledonia* opening at Rosyth, moving ashore from the old White Star Liner to shore accommodation in 1940.

There were many and varied venues during the Second World War, including the use of Stoke Damerel High School for Girls, but, finally, in 1940 a training establishment was purpose-built at Torpoint and commissioned as HMS *Fisgard* in 1946. In the following year the training was restructured with the introduction of the "Series" system, which continued till 1968 when craft training gave way to technician apprenticeships. In 1961 training at *Fisgard* was reduced from four to three terms.

In 1969 the old titles of ERA, OA and EA gave way to MEA, OEA, REA and CEA and 1970 saw the introduction of Fleet Chief Petty Officer, later changed to the more recognisable Warrant Officer. Finally, in 1983 HMS *Fisgard* closed and basic training moved to Fisgard Squadron in HMS *Raleigh*, while HMS *Caledonia* also closed, with training moving to HMS *Sultan*. In 1990, apprenticeships were opened to young women, with seventeen joining *Raleigh* in 903 entry. Mechanicians were amalgamated into the Artificer stream in 1994 and what was seen by many as the final nail was the loss of fore and aft rig in 1997, after 129 years. The end of the line was reached in 2010 when the last class of Artificer Apprentices and Artificer candidates passed out of HMS *Sultan*, so ending 142 years of Artificers in the Royal Navy.

chapter one

The Early Years

• • •

Tubal-cain, an instructor of every artificer in brass and iron.[1]

The term "Artificer" had been in existence in the Royal Navy for many years. As early as 1731 there were regulations and orders for HM Ships at sea that required captains "To have Artificers to assist in careening and repairing ships".[2] These men to have an extra payment of 1/6d a day. There is further mention of Artificers on a headstone in Gibraltar Botanical Gardens, dedicated to Sergeant Henry Richmond, who died on 4 May 1800, aged 44, while serving in the Royal Marine Artificers Company. This company was employed in the construction of the labyrinth of caves and tunnels that honeycomb the Rock.

With the rapidly expanding use of steam propulsion in the Royal Navy and the increased complexity of this machinery it was obvious that engineers were a necessary evil that the Executive Officer would have to live with. There remained the dichotomy of whether engineers could be both "engine drivers" and naval officers and to this end the Admiralty sought to differentiate between the supervisory and practical aspects of marine engineering. As well as the existing stokers and coal trimmers it was decided that a new system was required to alleviate the "hands-on" engineering that many junior Engineer Officers had to undertake and so the Artificer was introduced to the Royal Navy by an Admiralty Order in Council dated 28 March 1868. These ratings would be recruited from industry and would enter with the rank of Chief Petty Officer and would be titled Engine Room Artificers. The Order in Council stated, "Whereas we are of the opinion it will be advantageous to employ mechanics in the engine rooms of Her Majesties ships in lieu of junior officers and to substitute such mechanics whom we propose to designate Engine Room Artificers for the present class of Chief Stokers now borne in Her Majesties ships; giving them the rank of Chief Petty Officer".[3] By removing the stigma of manual labour from the Engineer Officers it was hoped that their status could be brought up to equal that of the Executive Officer.

There remained a problem, as was pointed out by the committee set up to look at the training and retention of engineers under the chairmanship of Admiral Sir Astley Cooper Key, an enthusiastic advocate of steam since his early days as a junior officer, As the report stated, "notwithstanding the high education to be given, and the position in which Engineer Officers will be placed on board ships as Commissioned Officers, a large portion of the Candidates are sons of artificers of various grades in the dockyards, of seamen and marines, or of others belonging to the same class of society".[4] So these Artificers would be recruited from the same lower-middle-class background as the junior engineers they were to replace.

Artificers were inextricably linked to their Engineer Officers since the officers considered that they were not being treated with the same respect by the executive as their commissioned status required and the introduction of Engine Room Artificers to carry out the day-to-day "hands-on" engineering would allow the officers to rid themselves of the "engine driver" image and hence elevate their position within the officer hierarchy and allow younger engineers "to concentrate on the supervisory and administrative functions of an officer".[5]

So, craftsmen would be recruited from industry, they would be between twenty-one and thirty-five years of age and suitably qualified as engine-fitters, boilermakers, smiths or coppersmiths. As well as those recruited from industry those ratings who were Chief Stokers at the time of the introduction of Engine Room Artificers would also be incorporated into the new rating.[6]

There was a third route to selection as an Engine Room Artificer and that was from those stokers below Chief Stoker who showed the aptitude, skill and knowledge and passed the exam set for this selection. There were seventy-six prospective candidates for the first exam sat on 10 May 1868 and one of the four successful candidates was Michael Harcourt.[7] Michael was born on 25 August 1837 at Bourton, Dorset, one of eight children of John Harcourt, a blacksmith, and his wife, Sarah. Despite a scanty education, though probably little different to many others in his station, he managed to learn the trade of engine smith at Bourton Foundry.[8]

Michael joined the Royal Navy as Boy 1st Class on 6 March 1856 and was rated Stoker on 18 May 1857.[9] By this time he was already abroad on the China Station and was involved in the Second Opium War, where he served in HMS *Clown*, a wooden screw gunboat of two guns. He was present at the capture of Canton, the taking of the Taku Forts, Tientsin and in 1860 Pekin. He was awarded the Second China Medal with two clasps.[10] In the following twelve years Michael served ashore in HMS *Princess Charlotte* between December 1861 and November 1862.[11] He then joined HMS *Asia*, the Portsmouth depot ship for ERAs and stokers, and remained there until he sat the Engine Room Artificers exam. On 11 May 1868, the following day, he was rated Engine Room Artificer and so became one of the very earliest ERAs.[12] From Leading Stoker on 10 May to Engine Room Artificer with the rank of Chief Petty Officer the next day: swift promotion indeed and one quite likely to cause animosity amongst those ratings in the Executive Department, where promotion was tediously slow.

After his promotion he was drafted to HMS *Seraphis*, an iron-hulled troopship. *Seraphis* was used to transport troops from England to India right up until 1886. Michael stayed with her for just over a year so may well have completed several voyages to and from India, the passage taking seventy days. During this period he would have been heavily involved in the running and maintenance of the ships main engines, which during his period on board were changed from a four-cylinder horizontal single-expansion engine to a two-cylinder single-expansion engine of similar indicated power.[13]

Michael then served for two years in HMS *Hector*, an armoured frigate that was by 1870, when Michael joined, employed as guard ship of the Southern District of the Fleet Reserve. This included acting as sovereign's guard ship when Queen Victoria was in residence at Osborne House.[14] After this Michael returned to HMS *Asia*, where, apart from a short commission in HMS *Sultan*, a centre-battery ironclad, he seems to have served out his engagement, leaving the Royal Navy in June 1876, having served twenty-one years. He was awarded the Naval Long Service and Good Conduct Medal and his pension.[15] Among the very last acts in his career was to be asked to give evidence to the Cooper Key Committee and this will be examined later. HMS *Sultan* also has a future role to play in the history of Artificers.

During the final years of his service Michael was involved in an unsavoury incident while serving in HMS *Sultan*, a broadside ironclad launched in 1870 and serving in the Channel Fleet. It appears from the report in the *Naval and Military Gazette and Weekly Chronicle of the United Service* that a stoker named Henry Pearce took exception to his engineer, Mr R.B. Turner, and roundly abused him. He then seems to have completely lost his temper and struck ERA Harcourt and to further compound his offences assaulted the Royal Marine escort called to take him away. At his subsequent court martial, Pearce pleaded guilty to all the charges. The fact that this was a repeat offence did not help his cause, he already having served twelve months' imprisonment for a similar offence, and he was sentenced to five years' penal servitude.[16]

While still a young Stoker Michael had married Jane Slugg on 17 December 1862 at the parish church of St Thomas of Canterbury (this is now Portsmouth Cathedral). It was a particularly fecund marriage, there being nineteen children in the next twenty-two years, all but one of the nine girls and ten boys reaching adulthood. Of the boys, six joined the Royal Navy and two the army.[17] On leaving the Royal Navy Michael took employment as an engineer at Gale's Brewery, Hordean, and retired from there in 1904.[18] He continued to live in Cowplain in retirement and shortly after being interviewed by the *Hampshire Telegraph* he passed away aged ninety-one.

Also among the early recruits was William John Barrett, born on 2 September 1845 in Surrey Street in Portsmouth. The life of William Barrett has been well chronicled by his grandson John Barrett and his great-grandson David Barrett and seems to be one of the only personal histories available from this early period of the Artificer story. For this reason it is worth dwelling on William for an insight into the Artificers of the Victorian Royal Navy.[19]

Portsmouth at the time of William's twenties had only recently had its fortifications levelled and mains sewage and piped water provided. With the removal of the old fortifications, Portsmouth, Portsea and the Royal Dockyards were able to join with Landport and the other surrounding environs at the mouth of Portsmouth harbour to provide a town that would be recognisable today. William started work at thirteen, as was common for boys of his station in life at that time. His first job in engineering was as a ship smith apprentice at Whites Heaving Up Slip in Broad Street, which over time became Vosper Thorneycroft,[20] which is now part of BAE Systems. He then spent five years working as an engine smith at Charles Lungley's shipyard in Deptford Green.[21]

He returned to Portsmouth in 1865 and secured employment installing gas pipes in Portsmouth Dockyard, something of a come-down from his previous work as an engine smith, though he did gain work in that position in the dockyard but was made redundant in 1867, along with many others in Portsmouth during a time of high unemployment. He took to the road and finally gained employment in Salisbury, at the T H Lucas Engineering Works. He stayed there for a year, then moving to the Fishertons Ironworks nearby.[22]

William was by this time married to Mary Ann Truscott and the father of two sons, so steady employment and a regular income were of paramount importance. With this in mind and work prospects in Portsmouth improving, William and his family moved back to Portsmouth from Salisbury in 1870 and he gained a position in the dockyard as a smith. It was at this time and with an eye to steady employment that William prepared for entry into the Royal Navy as an Engine Room Artificer.[23]

On 23 February 1871 he was examined by a board of senior dockyard and naval officers "Touching his qualifications for Acting Engine Room Artificer".[24] The board consisted of a Chief Inspector of Machinery Afloat (Captain Equivalent), an Inspector of Machinery Afloat (Commander Equivalent) and the Commander of HM Steam Reserve, "acting for the Captain on duty", and was accepted.[25] Within only four days he joined HMS *Asia*, missing Michael Harcourt by a matter of months. That he joined his first ship, which we know was the Portsmouth depot ship for ERAs and stokers, begs the question as to how much military training Artificers joining directly from industry were subjected to and may suggest the lack of appreciation of the necessity of military discipline that dogged Engineers and Artificers during this period. However, in their history of William his descendants surmise that, in the sixteen months that William spent in *Asia*, "he would no doubt have been employed on a variety of engineering tasks much wider than his primary trade of Engine Smith and been trained in the ways and procedures of the navy".[26] Though it is fair to say that one of the hulks was HMS *Excellent*, the gunnery school.

William had little service to his credit when he became involved with the founding of the *Royal Naval Engineers Benevolent Society*, which mirrored the *Royal Naval Engineers Club*, formed in 1851 by Engineer Officers. This society had humble beginnings with just two branches in Portsmouth and Plymouth. But from these humble beginnings it became in the twentieth century a very large and influential organisation for the welfare of all Artificers and, though it has become much smaller now, it still provides support for Artificers and their dependants. This society was following in the footsteps of the Naval Warrant Officers Friendly Society, originally founded in 1792,[27] and in the course of the 1880s many more were set up for seamen, stokers and writers and in the following decade even more such that by the end of the century there were twelve such societies.

These societies were originally intended to provide a type of insurance for the wives of men killed in action, who, at the time, received no pension or any aid whatsoever from the state. Over time these societies took on the role of addressing grievances in pay and conditions and, as Carew notes, "The chosen method of pressing for reform was to issue petitions or memorials to the Admiralty or to Parliament through the medium of civilians or MPs. The practice of petitioning was deeply rooted."[28] Needless to say, the Admiralty saw things in a different light and sought to ban such petitioning and to this effect issued a circular letter in 1860, incorporated into Queens Regulations as Article 10, which is very clear: "Henceforth it was illegal to meet to discuss or take action on any collective grievance, and the maximum penalty for breaking the regulation was death."[29] Such were the conditions that constrained the societies and as a means of bypassing Article 10 they employed retired members to press their cases. However, it is clear that this petitioning almost universally had little success and the status quo was maintained.

William's service, in contrast to Michael Harcourt, who seems to have spent most of his time as an ERA in home waters, was spent mainly on foreign stations. It is easier to follow his career through the comprehensive history recorded by his grandson and great-grandson, whereas Michael's career can only be followed through his service record. After his time in *Asia* William moved to a similar berth in HMS *Indus* in Plymouth, which lasted a mere three weeks before he was drafted to HMS *Black Prince*, the sister ship of the more famous HMS *Warrior*. Here he had four voyages around the British Isles, including Ireland, around the south coast and eventually to the Clyde, where he made his way back to *Indus*. He was not to stay there long; within twelve days he joined HMS *Thalia*, a corvette on its way to the China Station to provide relief crews for HMS *Ringdove* and *Midge*, both small gunboats. William was of the opinion that his involvement with the *RNEBS* may have prompted the Admiralty to send him to a very small ship a long way away.

His time in *Ringdove* followed the pattern of gunboats on the China Station, with much time spent around the rivers of China, but also including a comprehensive voyage around Japan. Early in his time on board William was examined for confirmation as Engine Room Artificer and satisfying all the criteria was duly confirmed. During the voyage around Japan two fine swords came into William's possession, apparently retrieved from some rebels who were in revolt near Nagasaki. The ship's log makes no mention of any unrest but as the swords are still in the Bennett family this would suggest the truth of the story. It was also during this commission that William was admitted to hospital in Yokohama. No details survive, though the use of quinine may suggest that William had contracted malaria. Whatever the reason, shortly after his admission to hospital he and another of the ship's company were sent to HMS *Iron Duke* "invalided" to return home.[30]

On his return home William spent a month in the depot ship HMS *Adelaide* before returning once again to *Asia*. Here he was ideally placed to be called as a witness to the enquiry into conditions in the Engine Room Department. This enquiry was chaired by Vice Admiral Sir Astley Cooper Key, who was to look at all aspects pertaining to the recruitment, training and retention of Engineer Officers and Engine Room Artificers.

After 1857 Executive Officers began their naval careers on board a training ship, as a result of a working party under Commodore F.T. Pelham.[31] The original hulk *Illustrious* was soon superseded by the larger hulk, *Britannia*, and after brief stays at Portsmouth and Portland *Britannia*[32] finally settled at Dartmouth in 1863. The use of a training ship for naval cadets was deemed a success. As an enthusiastic advocate of steam since his early days as a junior officer, it was Cooper Key and the committee under his chairmanship that mooted that a similar scheme be introduced for engineering students as that already in place for Executive Officers, something likely to introduce conformity between executive and engineer. The committee consisted of Captain William Dowell, Captain Sir John Commerell and James Wright, the Engineer-in-Chief.[33] They gathered evidence from sixty-eight witnesses, senior Executive Officers, senior engineering staff and senior figures from the merchant marine and industry and Engine Room Artificers, in all a well-balanced blend of engineer and executive.[34] Their remit was wide-ranging, covering rates of pay, ranks, promotions and retirement,[35] but there were also comments on recruitment, retention and training.

One of the telling comments of Cooper Key's report concerns the perceived consanguinity between Engineer Officers and Artificers. On training it was their belief that the existing regime met the requirements of the service,[36] but they did have reservations as to the quality of those who entered as engineers. As the report stated, "notwithstanding the high education to be given, and the position in which Engineer Officers will be placed on board ships as Commissioned Officers, a large portion of the Candidates are sons of artificers of various grades in the dockyards, of seamen and marines, or of others belonging to the same class of society". Once again, social origins seem more important than suitability for the job.[37] It was further recommended that the number of Engineer Officers in each ship could be reduced by the expansion of the number of Engine Room Artificers.[38] In the committee's own words, "We find that the Engine Room Artificers already entered are considered to be fair average workmen, capable not only of conducting repairs in their respective trades with celerity and efficiency, but of soon learning to assist each other in every description of work; they are also considered well qualified to take charge of the watch in the stoke hold, and, after a few years' experience, to keep watch in the Engine Room of small ships, under the supervision of the Engineer in charge".[39] There were some issues the committee saw as a result of the recruitment of ERAs direct from industry and in a telling paragraph it identified the lack of military appreciation of these men:

Engine Room Artificers who have served their apprenticeship as fitters or boiler makers, and have thus placed themselves in a certain position of independence, join the Naval Service at an age of between twenty and thirty, having already contracted the habits of their class on shore; they have been accustomed to regular limited hours of work, to pass their Sundays at home, and on returning from their work daily to find their meals ready, their house cleaned for them, and themselves relieved from all supervision and work other than that of their trade. On board a ship of war they find themselves surrounded by men who have been brought up to a different system from boyhood, and who cannot therefore understand that the habits of their own ordinary course of life may prove a hardship to others, who for many years have been accustomed to an entirely different mode of living.[40]

Another very important recommendation was the proposal to introduce a new rate, that of Chief Engine Room Artificer. What the committee does not stipulate is the exact duties and responsibilities of the new rate; however, it does suggest that "The Chief Engine Room Artificers should rank next after the Writers, 1st class",[41] perhaps not the most glowing testimonial. There were other recommendations concerning pay, uniform and the need for a separate mess, near the engine room, for all ERAs, which should be implemented as soon as practicable. It is worth looking at what the committee had to say on the subject of separate messing.

We are of opinion that it is entirely in the power of the Commanding Officer to make this useful class of men comfortable when afloat, and in a short time reconciled to the inconveniences inseparable from a life on board ship, without any relaxation of that strict discipline which is absolutely necessary in a ship of war. Bearing in mind the habits of life to which the Artificers have been accustomed on shore, the age at which they join the Navy, and the important nature of their duties, it will be very desirable to make a few simple regulations respecting the mode of obtaining leave to go on shore, the care of their mess-place, their hammocks, and their washing arrangements, and to place them in these and all other respects as much as possible under the control of the Chief Engineer, who is best acquainted with the duties they are required to perform, and whether they can be spared from the Engine Room. We recommend, therefore, that directions be given to ensure that these apparently minor points are carefully attended to by Commanding Officers, as we believe that the benefits which should result from the employment of Engine Room Artificers are mainly dependent on them.[42]

There were other minor recommendations that would impinge little on the overall lot of the ERA, such as the size of clothes chest, uniform, and employment on ships not their own.

William gave evidence at length to the committee on 29 October 1875. After establishing his length of service and ship served in, Captain Dowell asked about his messing arrangements. William said he had been particularly unimpressed with his messing arrangements in most of the ships in which he has served. His evidence as stated in the report is as follows:

> 4631. Where do you mess in the "Excellent"?
> With the chief petty officers.
> 4632. Have you a comfortable mess?
> Yes, very comfortable indeed; it is an exception to the general rule.
> 4638. Where did you mess in the "Black Prince"?
> With the chief petty officers, on the lower deck.
> 4634. Were you comfortable there?
> No, not at all comfortable; sometimes when I came off watch from the stokehold there would be no food laid for me, and I had to get it the best way I could, or go without it.
> 4635. Where did you mess in the "Thalia"?
> In the blue jacket chief petty officers' mess; the master-at-arms by himself, the ship's steward by himself, and the schoolmaster by himself.
> 4636. Were you comfortable there?
> No, very uncomfortable indeed.
> 4637. Where did you mess in the "Ringdove"?
> With the corporal of marines, the ship's steward, chief gunner's mate, chief carpenter's mate, and ship's cook.
> 4638. Were you comfortably there?
> No, very uncomfortable there,
> 4639. (Captain Commerell) You have been unfortunate?
> Yes, very; my present time is the pleasantest time I have had since I have been in the service.[43]

These sentiments on messing arrangements were echoed by the next witness, William Walker, who took the same route to Engine Room Artificer as Michael Harcourt, having been a Leading Stoker:

4706. Where did you mess in the "Immortalité"?
In the second mess, right forward on the starboard side.
4707. Who were your messmates?
The school-master
4708. Anybody else?
No.
4709. Were you comfortable?
Not very.
4710. How many more engine-room artificers were there?
Only one besides myself.
4711. Why were you not comfortable?
Because we sometimes had to clean our own mess out, and the mess was such a long way from the stokehold that we were continually being found fault with for making a mess in going from the stokehold to it.
4712. In the way of a mess place, what would you like?
A place secluded from the rest of the ship's company.[44]

It is worth noting that when asked about his present employment he stated that he was employed in the maintenance of the Whitehead torpedo. This is an interesting statement that will be clarified later.

The sentiments as regards messing is reiterated by all the Engine Room Artificers, but it is clear that those with many years' service and those who rose from Leading Stoker have a far better appreciation of what their messing arrangements would be like, as Michael Harcourt stated in his evidence:

4474. How many engine-room artificers are there?
Three besides me.
4475. Are they all, like yourself, men of long standing in the service No; the other three have only just joined, and had never been to sea before.
447C. How do they get on in the mess?
They are rather awkward at present.
4477. Do they complain of their treatment on board?
It is not exactly what they expected.
4478. What did they expect; are you aware?
They thought that they would have rather better accommodation than they have got.

4479. Are not they satisfied with the mess?
No.
4480. Do you know what they expect?
They thought they should have a mess berth.[45]

There is further comment on the lack of discipline in the newly joined ERAs that cements the ill-feeling that was felt, not only by Executive Officers for Engineer Officers but of long-standing executive senior ratings for these newcomers and Michael continued in his evidence when pressed about relations between engineer and Executive Chief Petty Officers.

4506. Have you, since you have been in the service as an engine-room artificer, found that the executive chief petty officers were down on you or interfered in any way with the engine-room artificers?
I do not know.
4507. I suppose you are aware that there is a certain amount of ill-feeling between them?
Yes.
4508. Can you give any explanation of that?
The engine-room artificers have only just joined the service, and are not acquainted with its rules, and the little technical things on board ship they are not up to; little matters of discipline and such like; the other people who have been in the service nearly all their lives take notice of that, and there is a certain amount of ill-feeling between them on that score.
4509. Have you found that the engine-room artificers, taking into consideration that they have come on board a man-of-war, have been unreasonable in their little difficulties?
Sometimes.
4510. They have not considered sufficiently that there is discipline in a man-of-war, and that everything must give way to it?
Sometimes they have not. I have noticed that several times.
4511. There has not been quite that give and take principle on both sides that there might have been?
No.[46]

Evidence was also given by the Engine Room Artificers, who apart from Barrett, Harcourt and Walker included William Bateman, James Bolase,

Liagham Ennis, George Nancarrow, Robert Urquhart and John Wilkes. The Commissioned Engineers called were also asked their opinion on the standard of Artificer being recruited, and stated that, in the main, the standard was very high. However, it was the commonly stated belief that better messing arrangements and better pay would not only raise the standard of those recruited but mitigate the lack of numbers coming forward to enter the Service.

The Cooper Key Report was the first comprehensive investigation into the grievances of both Engineer Officers and ERAs since the introduction of Engineers in 1837, grievances that were both known about and long-standing. As Penn points out, "That the proposals were not received kindly by the military officers is hardly surprising, and the suggestions as to pay, promotion, rank and military status were not put into effect".[47] There was an increase in the establishment of both officers and ERAs and – what Penn considers to be of the greatest importance – the establishment by Order in Council of the new rating of Chief Engine Room Artificer,[48] who would take on the more mundane duties of junior officers that were seen as incompatible with their aspirations to be accepted by Executive Officers.

The importance of the Cooper Key Report cannot be overemphasised. It was a genuine attempt to change the perception of Engineer Officers and their social acceptance by the executive and:

> It was obvious that the intention of these changes was to underline further the change in the position of the junior engineer officers to that of the immediate equivalent of their contemporaries in other branches of the service, by further removing from them the practical side of their duties and simultaneously creating a class of senior rating capable of taking over the more responsible part of these duties, while reducing the number of junior officers to a figure more commensurate with the new supervisory nature of their duties.[49]

The Cooper Key Report was presented to Parliament in 1877, by which time Michael Harcourt had been discharged to pension. William Bennett still had some years left to serve and continued to be employed in *Asia*, which seems suitable recompense for his three years on the China Station. He stayed there until June 1876, when he was drafted to the ironclad HMS *Warrior*, though by this time *Warrior* was well past her glory days and was employed as first reserve in the coastguard service, hardly onerous duties.

Warrior had to steam south to Gibraltar when Russia indulged in a bit of periodic sabre rattling, but this soon subsided and *Warrior* returned to home waters.

William returned once again to *Asia*. It was during this spell in the Steam Reserve that he was involved in boiler trials onboard HMS *Thunderer*. This ship had been launched in 1872; it was during trials in the Solent that a serious accident happened. On 14 July in preparation for a maximum speed run a boiler exploded, killing fifteen instantly, including the Commanding Officer, and injuring another seventy, thirty of whom subsequently died. Tests were carried out on the surviving boiler in that stoke hold and the cause was attributed to a broken pressure gauge. It had gone round the dial and stuck on the stop pin, thus indicating to a casual observer that there was no pressure in the boiler. It was also found that the safety valves had corroded and jammed, allowing a catastrophic build-up of steam pressure and consequent explosion.

Once a replacement boiler had been installed, a steam trial was ordered, to which William was ordered to attend. This was much to the horror of his wife, Mary Ann, who feared that William would not come back alive.[50] Fortunately the trial was successful and William returned home unscathed; shore time is not necessarily all plain sailing. William continued in the Steam Reserve for a further six months before being drafted to HMS *Defence*, a smaller ironclad to *Warrior* but of similar design. William joined *Defence* in Lisbon on 9 February 1877. How he got to Lisbon is not recorded and by 8 April the ship had returned to Plymouth and after exercises around Great Britain the ship deployed to the Mediterranean, where it remained until returning to Plymouth on 7 August 1879. By November William once again joined the Steam Reserve in *Asia*, having spent nearly three years in *Defence*.

William's career followed this pattern, with service in HMS *Griffon* on the North America and West Indies Station. To join his new ship he travelled in the troopship *Crocodile* to Bermuda, where he had a wait of some five weeks before he finally joined *Griffon* and served in her for three years and eight months.[51] Once again William returned to the Steam Reserve, though only briefly, before joining HMS *Penelope*, a twin-screw ironclad. Again, *Penelope*'s duties were not onerous, involving coastguard duties based at Harwich. This at least allowed William to arrange accommodation in Harwich, which allowed his wife to visit when his ship was in harbour.

Penelope remained in Harwich with brief trips down the channel for exercises and training until 4 May 1887, when she paid off in Portsmouth.

William then served in HMS *Hotspur*, which carried out the same role as *Penelope* with a break to take part in Queen Victoria's Golden Jubilee Fleet Review at Spithead. For reasons that are not apparent from William's service record, he seems to have had a "Pier Head Jump"[52] from *Penelope* to HMS *Dolphin*, where he remained for three years, spending the time in the Mediterranean and Red Sea. He then returned to *Asia* and this was near the end of William's engagement and he was discharged to pension on 30 April 1891.

After leaving the Royal Navy William continued in engineering, establishing his own business at Rowlands Castle and with the help of his son William George continued working until he retired in 1925 at the age of eighty.[53] William remained a staunch supporter of the *RNEBS* and even in retirement he was fondly remembered as one of the founders of the society. In 1922 the society celebrated its golden anniversary and on 21 April that year a dinner was held to celebrate the occasion and the society invited William. The invitation is very clear: "I am requested by the Branch to solicit the honour of your attendance at the function, in fact, the celebration will be robbed of all interest if you are not present." It continues in the same vein: "a Jubilee feast without the oldest member gracing the board would be barren indeed of all that will give it significance".[54]

William reached his one hundredth birthday on 2 September 1945 and received a telegram from King George VI and Queen Mary, a letter from Mr A.V. Alexander, First Lord of the Admiralty, another letter from Vice Admiral Sir Geoffrey Layton, the Commander-in-Chief, Portsmouth, and, naturally, one from the *Royal Naval Engineers Benevolent Society*. William passed away peacefully on 24 May 1946, a long and illustrious life indeed.

William Walker in his evidence to the Cooper Key Committee stated that he was employed in the maintenance of the Whitehead torpedo. This was an ad hoc arrangement that was regularised by an Admiralty Circular issued on 1 November 1877. This made the Engineer responsible "for the efficiency of the Whitehead torpedoes and submerged torpedo-tubes, together with their stores and storerooms".[55] This was not the only area in which the ERA was active: as guns became more technically advanced and their size increased it was necessary to provide means of moving the weapons mechanically and the obvious medium was steam.

As well as existing ERAs there was also a requirement to use ratings already familiar with these new big guns. This led to another method of recruiting ERAs; those ratings with the necessary skills could transfer from the Armourers Branch directly to ERA. One such was Cardigan Dann. He joined as an Armourer in 1864 and was selected for Acting Engine Room Artificer on 8 September 1874, when he also signed to complete a pensionable engagement. This he completed in November 1883 when he left the Service.

Despite the recommendations and good intentions of the Cooper Key Committee, there remained much that needed to be done to ensure the recruitment of sufficient, suitably skilled Engineers and Artificers. Much was written on the subject of the "Engineer Question" in the next few decades, but without much being resolved. It remained difficult to recruit sufficient numbers and just as difficult to retain those that were recruited. As well as the scrutiny that the Cooper Key Committee had given to the subject of naval engineers, there was increasing attention from a number of sources far removed from both the Admiralty and Service press. There were various professional institutes who showed an interest in naval engineers. The Institution of Civil Engineers was founded in 1847, as was the Institute of Mechanical Engineers; the Institute of Marine Engineers was founded in 1888. These bodies were founded to promote the status, education and welfare of engineers and promote the importance of engineering to the nation. These and others forwarded, in 1901, a memorandum to the Admiralty "summarising their grievances and demanding that naval engineers be reclassified as military rather than civil officers and that their rank structure should be brought into line with their executive counterparts",[56] echoes of Cooper Key twenty-five years earlier.

Further support was forthcoming from an unlikely source, the Incorporated Institution of Headmasters, who represented the public schools. Their support seems to have been fostered by the desire to enhance the status and standing of naval engineers. As Dickinson points out, "in 1900 a career as a naval engineer was unlikely to bring credit to any institution whose principal aim was to produce 'gentlemen'".[57]

Further comment was made by the "undistinguished naval officer". He said of the Engineering Branch that it had "been enveloped in a mass of prejudice, and regarded with disfavour, dislike and contempt – some deserved – a great deal the result of pure snobbishness".[58] While there was still this lack of empathy by Executive Officers for engineers it would remain difficult to recruit the right calibre of entrant and keep them after training, consequently there remained a shortfall in numbers. Various panaceas were tried, such as diluting junior engineer billets with Engine Room Artificers, but again it was difficult to recruit and retain Artificers.

Another attempt was tried in 1897, when by an Admiralty Order in Council of 18 May Artificer Engineers were introduced with the rank of Warrant Officer,[59] and while this was seen as a temporary measure it actually lasted for the next fifty years. The introduction was welcomed by serving ERAs and many benefitted from this new rank:

I think that most of us know that the Engine Room Artificer (ERA) came into being on 28th March 1868. This was brought about by an Order in Council (OIC) and is also documented in the Navy List for 1870, page 472. But, did you ever wonder what happened next? After a number of years service, as an ERA, it was then possible to be promoted to the position of Chief Engine Room Artificer but what were the prospects of promotion on from there?

Was there any chance of becoming an Engineer Officer? Yes there was. In 1897 it was decided that a new rank would be created, that of the Artificer Engineer. This was brought about by an OIC dated 18th May of that year and details are given on page 668 in the Navy List for 1897. The Artificer Engineer was to hold a Warrant Rank and on promotion would receive the princely sum of 8/6d per day. Pretty good I would say for 1897. His rig changed to an eight button reefer jacket, he had a different cap badge and above the buttons on his sleeves he brandished a purple cloth ring to distinguish him from other warrant officers like the Carpenter and Gunner. After 10 years in the rank he would wear a thin gold ring above the purple cloth and become commissioned.

It was not long after this, 28th March 1903, that a further rank was established, that of a Chief Artificer Engineer, more money and now a thick gold ring above the purple cloth ring. It is interesting to note that at this time all Engineer Officers came under the heading of Royal Navy Civil Branch and were different from other Officers in that they did not have a curl in the first ring of their respective ranks.

The unification of officer rank badges did not come about until 1915.

At the same time the Chief Artificer Rank was created it was made possible by OIC No 24 for him to be promoted to the rank of Engineer Lt. and would now wear two gold stripes with the purple cloth between them. It was now possible to rise from an ERA right through to the rank of Engineer Lt. though I suspect it would have taken most of the young tiffies naval career. It is worthy of note that most of this was going on about the same time as Jackie Fisher was creating the Boy Artificer.[60]

There was also the introduction in 1903 of the commissioned rank of Chief Artificer Engineer, later refined to Commissioned Engineer, which, at last, provided an avenue for ERAs to gain commissioned status in the same manner as had been available to the seaman branch for some time.[61] So numbers did increase but, while in 1898 there was a total engineering complement in the Navy of 1,050 and this increased to 1,506 in 1902, this was still 400 short of the numbers required.[62] Penn is of the opinion that the Admiralty's intention was to divide the branch into two distinct entities, one professional and one practical.[63] But this does not seem borne out by the evidence; the separation between professional and practical was similar in the other branches of the Service, where ratings carried out the practical tasks while the officers ensured the smooth running of operations.

While Admiral Sir Arthur Wilson VC's declaration in 1901 that submarines were "Underhand, unfair and damned un-English"[64] is often quoted, it can lead to an unfair impression. Indeed, while the Royal Navy, as the leading navy in the world, was concerned and wanted to discourage the world from adopting anything that threatened that status quo and thus there was a desire to prevent research as such developments would be seen by other navies and enable them to challenge; a similar approach can be seen with respect to mine warfare.

However, as other navies were developing submarines the Royal Navy followed suit and launched its first one in 1901, the *Holland 1*. The first Inspecting Captain of Submarines, Reginald Bacon, made a list[65] of the very first officers and ratings to volunteer for service with submarines that year. This means the names of those first three engineer submariners are known:

Engineer Robert Spence
William J Robinson ERA 3rd Class
William Muirhead ERA 3rd Class

Within the Submarine Service there were also Electrical ERAs, who reported to the Engineer Officer rather than the Torpedo Officer until the introduction of Electricians and Electrical Artificers.[66]

One further action was necessary in light of the growing amount of electrical machinery and the increased generating capacity this required. To ensure that there was sufficient expertise to maintain this equipment, the rank of Electrician was introduced in November 1901. [67]The men were recruited in the same manner as ERAs, already trained by industry, and had the same rank of Chief Petty Officer, they remained in the Artisan Branch and were therefore not strictly Artificers, though they enjoyed the same conditions of service. It was not until 1913 that all Electricians below warrant rank were recategorised as Electrical Artificers.[68]

It would require radical steps to ensure that both Engineer Officers and Artificers were seen in a light that was an inducement to recruitment and retention such that the Engineering Establishment could be brought up to full strength. Such a man was about to arrive at the Admiralty.

chapter two

1903, Jackie Fisher, The Boys and *Fisgard*

• • •

Fisher arrives next week. Heaven knows what he may not attempt to run. Any wild cat scheme finds a supporter in him.[1]

There had been several initiatives to improve the status of engineers over the years, yet none had managed to break down the hostility of the Executive Branch to assimilating the engineer as a military officer. Admiral Sir John Fisher, while Commander-in-Chief of the Mediterranean Fleet, had devised a scheme that he believed would, at one stroke, solve this long-running conundrum of how best to assimilate the engineer and still maintain the position of the executive. It was a tall order and one that led to heated and partisan objections and arguments from all sides. When Fisher arrived at the Admiralty on 9 June 1902 to take up his appointment as Second Sea Lord, there were many in the Navy who looked on his arrival with dread. One was Rear Admiral Sir Reginald Custance, Director of Naval Intelligence, who wrote the letter to his friend, Vice Admiral Sir Cyprian Bridge, outlining his views on Fisher. Fisher was an acquired taste: he was either loved or loathed and in return he would look after his supporters, the so-called "Fishpond", and be ruthless in his castigation of his opponents.

Shortly after his arrival at the Admiralty he had persuaded the First Lord of the Admiralty that a change in the policy and method of recruiting and training naval officers was of paramount importance to the well-being of the Navy. The result of this was published on Christmas Day 1902, only six months after Fisher had arrived, and is referred to as the Selborne Memorandum. [2] This set out in great detail a total change of direction in the way naval officers would be selected, recruited and trained. In the opening *Précis* is the statement "In the old days it sufficed if a Naval Officer were a seaman. Now he must be sailor, gunner, soldier, engineer and man of science as well." [3] This prepared the ground for the main thrust of the Memorandum, that there would be common training of all cadets up until the time they are promoted to Sub-Lieutenant, meaning that engineering training would start considerably later.

There were three main strands to Fisher's proposals The first was a reduction in the age of entry, and this was lowered from fourteen or fifteen and a half to twelve or thirteen. The method of selection was also completely revised: no longer would there be a competitive selection process based on an examination; now selection would be by nomination and interview. Immediately there is an impediment to those of the lower middle classes, from whom engineers had traditionally been found. It would seem that who you knew and how much money you had was of greater importance than your suitability for entry as an Engineer Officer, as had been the case before the introduction of selection by open competition. Next, all cadets, whether Executive, Engineer or Royal Marine, would have a common training at either Dartmouth or the new college to be established at Osborne House on the Isle of Wight, which would act as a preparatory school for Dartmouth. [4]

Fisher had first outlined his plan for a new training regime for naval officers in a letter to Lord Selborne early in 1902 in which he opened with the observation that "we have been slow to appreciate the alteration in the status of the engineer consequent on the abolition of masts and sails". [5] He believed that an "alteration in training so essential for the efficiency of the Navy can be readily brought about by following precisely the same method as was employed to make navigation of his Majesty's ships more efficient". [6] He also discounted the pressure that had been applied by engineers within the service and the press and engineering institutions outside the Navy. He saw this scheme as essential to the future fighting efficiency of the fleet, as always Fisher had, in his opinion, the best interests of the Navy as his ultimate goal.

Among many to criticise this "unwarranted elevation" of engineers was David Boyle, Seventh Earl of Glasgow, who, in a speech to the House of Lords on 8 May 1903 made various critical comments against the new scheme. He initially made the observation that, despite the scheme having gained acceptance from many, including *The Times*, and "the tacit approval of the country, not to speak of the support of a majority in another place – I am not without hope that this discussion may lead to some modification."[7] He believed that the Admiralty had been forced into this precipitous action by agitation, both inside the Royal Navy and without. He mentioned the deputation from the engineering institutions in 1901, with which the First Lord remained unimpressed. How then had engineers been allowed to gain so much at the apparent detriment of the Executive Branch since "the opinion of the executive officers has not, as far as I am aware, been ascertained". Clearly in his view such opinion would be invaluable.[8]

He commented that the rationale of the scheme, "One System of Supply. One System of Entry. One System of Training",[9] put the scheme in a very favourable light. But he saw the future of the scheme to be the gradual abolition of the whole Engineering Branch and its supposed replacement by Artificers and Mechanicians to carry out the practical work while being supervised by officers of a more lofty social background. It was supposed that these Artificers and Mechanicians would be recruited from the same social class as existing naval engineers; snobbery raises its head again. This snobbery is reiterated when he made the totally spurious argument that the rank of Admiral should be reserved exclusively for Executive Officers. This, he claimed, was based on historical precedent "that title that is so bound up with all the glorious memories of the past, which our departed naval heroes were proud to bear".[10] He seems to totally miss the point that under the new scheme Nelson would have had the greatest difficulty in being accepted.

Despite all the opposition, Fisher was not a man to be thwarted once his mind was set. As he wrote to a friend, the journalist and keen supporter of the *Navy League* Arnold White, "Naval Rip Van Winkles – may vilify me and identify it as my work alone, so as to discredit it! It would be disastrous to the prestige of the scheme if it were in any way otherwise than what it is, which is *the unanimous decision of the whole of the Board of Admiralty*, and therefore I send this line of caution."[11] The scheme was approved and was implemented in 1905 with the publication of the Cawdor Memorandum of 30 November 1905. Even then there were those who wished to stop or at least delay it implementation. In the House of Commons Mr Bellairs, the Member for Lyme Regis, asked:

> *I beg to ask the Secretary to the Admiralty whether Lord Cawdor's memorandum of 30th November, 1905, is considered by the present Board of Admiralty to be binding in its decisions in regard to the future careers of the Osborne cadets and the future duties of the engine-room artificers; whether the Board has made an application for sanction by Order in Council of the changes affecting the officers and the engine-room artificers which were embodied in Lord Cawdor's memorandum; and, if so, will a copy of such Order in Council be laid upon the Table; whether any protests against Lord Cawdor's memorandum have been received from officers commanding our principal fleets, and also from other admirals in high positions who have commanded fleets; and, as the decisions in Lord Cawdor's memorandum were only made public during the recess, will the Admiralty defer action on it until the financial year 1906–7?*[12]

Naturally there was much written in the papers and many letters to their editors. One to the editor of the *Spectator* takes issue with the dilution of Artificers with the new rate of Mechanician with respect to their watch-keeping duties and the relevant cost this will bring to the Navy Estimates:

> *The next paragraph of "Another Naval Officer's" letter charges me with confusing the engine-room artificers with engineers. Certainly they are engineers drawn from exactly the same class as the engineer officers of the mercantile marine, performing watch-keeping duties in charge of one engine-room in a very large number of warships up to the largest types, and in sole charge of the machinery in eighty-four vessels of over two hundred tons. The slightest examination of the Report of the Douglas Committee will show your correspondents that the policy is to supersede the artificers entirely in watch-keeping duties, and it is so stated in Lord Cawdor's Memorandum on p. 4. That the present Board are only entering one hundred stokers a year is simply due to the failure of the policy, and does not in any way touch the absurd intentions of that policy. It is found that many of the selected men have to be rejected, as any capable engineer could have forecasted, and the low standard involves more men. Thus in the Exmouth' ten stoker-mechanicians are substituted for six engine-room artificers, so in reality*

I have understated the requirements of the policy at three thousand stoker-mechanicians for watch-keeping. As for cost, I cannot publish the two pages of closely typewritten figures giving the cost of the establishments in vessels prepared for the instruction of the stoker-mechanicians, the lathes, drilling machines, engines, motors, boilers. On the other hand, I include loss of the stoker's services for the period under training, and wastage due to the number of men rejected has to be taken into account. The increased cost to the State is fully £1,800,000.[13]

But this is exactly what Fisher envisaged as he wrote in 1905: "The rating to whom it is proposed to entrust the engine-driving is the mechanician. If an engine-room artificer can learn his engine-driving in one year, a mechanician can learn it by the time he has reached that rank."[14] It must be assumed that Fisher was well aware of any cost that this might entail and was sure it would be for the greater benefit of the Service, always his top priority. He sees this scheme as essential to the future fighting efficiency of the fleet; as always, Fisher has, in his opinion, the best interests of the Navy as his ultimate goal.

It is also worthwhile remembering that Fisher was a mercurial figure; he had little interest outside the Navy and always sought to establish what was in the best interests of the Service, as he saw it, and would brook no dissension once he saw the path he believed to be in those best interests. So it was with the Selborne scheme: he identified where there were deficiencies and sought to mitigate them and ensure the most effective fighting fleet possible. He believed that under his proposed scheme the amount of training devoted to engineering "should in a large measure, *at least half the time*, be devoted to engineering".[15]

While the scheme for Engineer Officers foundered over time, in what became known as the "Great Betrayal" of 1925, there was one initiative that did last: that of the introduction of the Boy Artificer, who would be recruited directly from school and trained in-house and progress through the ranks to Chief Petty Officer in an accelerated manner. There had been for some time the view that some of the men recruited from industry were of variable quality and also that to train these skilled craftsmen from scratch would ensure that they were inculcated in the mores and discipline of the service, something that had been a constant bone of contention with those recruited from industry. As well as the introduction of the Boy Artificer there was also the introduction of the rank of Chief Artificer Engineer, which, at last, gave Artificers an avenue to commissioned rank. There remained the warrant rank of Artificer Engineer, but in 1904, in another concession, these men and the Chief Artificer Engineers became eligible for promotion to Engineer Lieutenant, but only for acts of gallantry, not the most rewarding concession.

Another seldom realised aspect of the Selborne reform was the introduction of the seamen to the boiler room. As a prerequisite for his promotion to AB the ordinary seaman was required to accumulate six weeks' service in the stokehold and to achieve a certain proficiency at stoking and coal trimming. This was popular with the stokers, who relished being able to "get a real day's work" out of the seamen, but, as the stokers were better paid than they, it was resented by the seamen. This practice seems to have been discontinued by 1906.

The first Boy Artificers were entered in March 1903. The first entry of twenty-six boys (drawn exclusively from the Royal Hospital School, Greenwich) was accommodated at Chatham in the Reserve ship *Algiers*. They were initially instructed ashore at the Steam Reserve Factory, later to become the Mechanical Training Establishment. They were followed by a second class of twenty-six, also from the Royal Hospital School, Greenwich.

By July 1903 it was necessary to expand the accommodation and training facilities at Chatham to include *Hecla* (later replaced by *Triumph*) and *Pembroke*. There then followed the establishment of a training facility on the River Tamar near Torpoint and in April 1904 the first boys entered HMS *Indus* and in February 1905 the Hulks *Audacious* and *Erebus* were moored in Fareham Creek and commissioned as the Boy Artificer Training Establishment HMS *Fisgard*. This name would always be associated with Boy Artificers and later Artificer Apprentices until its demise in 1983.

These first recruits were the pick of the students at the Royal Hospital School and, apart from changing their Square Rig to the Fore and Aft Rig, which were to become synonymous with Boy Artificers and, later, Artificer Apprentices, they continued the ethos of a minor public school that remained right up until the very last days of Artificer Apprentices. Once the training and accommodation had been established, entry was opened to any suitably qualified boy, aged between fourteen and sixteen, from secondary schools throughout the country, though naval port areas were looked on particularly favourably. Another addition was introduced in October 1905, whereby suitable boys would be given the rate of Petty

Officer or Chief Petty Officer Boy, to maintain mess-deck discipline and with a small allowance of 4d a day for CPO Boys and 3d a day for PO Boys, a worthy reward at the time.[16]

It was then decided that entry would be by passing the Civil Service Commission open competitive examination, held in the spring for entry in August. This consisted of maths (three papers), science (two papers), English, geography, history and freehand drawing. or by passing the Admiralty maths and science examination sat by those boys nominated by their local education authority. As was noted in a book published by the editorial board of the *Fisgardian* in 2003:

In a Navy only waking up to the value of skilled, well-educated, disciplined and motivated engineers, Boy Artificers were the only lower deck recipients of a sixth form education which effectively qualified them academically for commissioned rank. They were also trained as highly skilled craftsmen capable of keeping ships fully operational at sea. Furthermore, during their long training, whatever athletic or sporting prowess they possessed was developed to the highest possible competitive standard by dedicated professionals. They were also actively aided and encouraged to "learn the Calculus" and to take up artistic and cultural pursuits such as the presentation of all-apprentice shows and Gilbert and Sullivan operas. Tenedos, Indus and Fisgard soon developed a public school ethos of pride in achievement in every sphere, self-reliance and an esprit de corps. Happy in the knowledge that they would be Chief Petty Officers by the age of 23 and had good prospects of promotion to Warrant and Commissioned Engineer Officer, they knuckled down to four years of pretty basic living conditions, tough discipline, barely adequate victuals, (for active growing lads), long working hours, low pay and restrictive liberty.[17]

Prior to attempting the civil service examination the boys were to be given a rigorous medical examination and those successful in both the medical and technical examinations and as was detailed in the instructions for the "New Training Scheme for Officers and Men":

Successful candidates will be entered on the books of one of the Naval Depots, and will be trained for four years in the Reserve Workshops and Vessels of the Dockyard Reserves.

At the end of this period they will be sent, on passing a technical examination, to sea-going ships (i.e., Repair Ships, Home sea-going Ships; Channel Fleet, &c) as "Artificers" with the rating of 2ⁿᵈ Class Petty Officer, for one year's practical sea training.[18]

Of those boys who joined in these early days from the Royal Hospital School, some names have survived. Arthur Gillingham Pedder was born on 22 October 1888 at Greenwich and joined *Pembroke* in January 1904 and served as an ERA until 1918, when his service record notes: "Discharged: Officers Section". His training was at *Tenedos*. This was an amalgamation of *Triumph* (*Tenedos I*), *Pembroke* (*Tenedos II*) and in 1906 *Ganges* (*Tenedos III*). In January 1908 he was rated ERA 5th Class. It had been necessary with the introduction of the Boy Artificer to incorporate suitable ranks for them, as noted below.

Artificers *[Note: Artificers, 5th class ranked as Petty Officer 2nd Class, 4th class ranked as Petty Officer 1st Class, 3rd Class and above as Chief Petty Officers, but without trade badges]*
Chief Engine Room Artificer, 1st Class
Chief Engine Room Artificer, 2nd Class
Artificer, 1st Class
Artificer, 2nd Class
Artificer, 3rd Class
Artificer, 4th Class
Acting Artificer, 4th Class
Artificer, 5th Class
Boy Artificer

He served in HMS *Duncan*, a pre-dreadnought battleship, as a 5th Class and was promoted to Acting ERA 4th Class on 27 August 1908, while still on board. After service ashore in *Pembroke*, *Tenedos* and *Pembroke II*, all part of the Steam Reserve, Arthur was then sent to serve on HMS *Lord Nelson*, the last of the Royal Navy's pre-dreadnought battleships and as such obsolete before she was even launched. He served in this ship for over two years and once more returned ashore to *Pembroke II* and the Steam Reserve. His service record now shows he spent time in HMS *Triton*. The only vessel of this name at the time was not in commission and was an ancient paddlewheel survey vessel, built in 1882. This ship was briefly recommissioned in 1914 to survey Plymouth Sound. Its appearance on Arthur's service record can only be an administrative exercise as at this time he was promoted to Engine Room Artificer 3rd Class. He remained in the Steam Reserve until February 1916, when he became an ERA 2nd Class.

He then saw service in HMS *Dido*, which was an old second-class protected cruiser, completed in 1898 and during the First World War used as a destroyer depot ship. As noted on Arthur's service record, he was seconded first to HMS *Linnet* and then to HMS *Sylph*, both quite modern destroyers. It was during this time he reached the rank of Chief Engine Room Artificer 2nd Class and it was in this rank he saw the end of the war and promotion to commissioned rank.

Another of Arthur's school mates at the RHS was Lionel Gordon Shipcott, born a day before Arthur on 21 October 1888 at New Romney in Kent. His training seems to have followed a slightly different path to Arthur Pedder. His service record saw him joining HMS *Firequeen* in January 1904 and then *Victory II* in April 1905. Neither of these training establishments has featured in Boy Artificer training until now, however in January 1906 he joined HMS *Fisgard*, now established as the Boy Artificer Training Establishment at Portsmouth. He completed his training at *Fisgard* in January 1908 and was duly rated Engine Room Artificer 5th class. He then consolidated his training in HMS *Goliath*, a pre-dreadnought battleship, and saw service with the Mediterranean Fleet. However, this service was somewhat curtailed when the ship suffered a fractured propeller shaft that required repairs that took four months. It was during this time that Lionel was rated Acting ERA 4th Class and left *Goliath* in February 1909, just prior to *Goliath* being paid off at Portsmouth the same year. She met her end during the Dardanelles campaign when she was torpedoed and sunk by the Turkish destroyer *Muâvenet-i Milliye*.

His career followed a familiar pattern with time ashore spent at *Victory II*, *Fisgard* and *Pembroke III*. His time at sea was spent, firstly, in HMS *Iphigenia*, an old and venerable second-class cruiser, launched in 1891 and converted to a minelayer in 1910, just after Lionel left. She ended her days as a blockship in the Zeebrugge raid in 1918.

His next ship was HMS *Argonaut*, another old protected cruiser of 1898 vintage. This ship has a somewhat strange claim to fame. During her time on the China Station 1900–1904 there was one Captain who achieved notoriety as a stern disciplinarian, issuing some 600 punishment warrants while in command.

He also ruled the wardroom in the same manner and earned the disapprobation of the officers, who had medals struck by Gamages of London, to be awarded to all those who suffered under this man, Captain George Cherry. The medal read on the obverse "Argonaut China 1900–1904" and showed a foul anchor (for the Royal Navy), a fleece (for Argonaut) and a dragon (for China); on the reverse were a cherry tree and a representation of the officers who survived the commission. It was, of course known as the "Cherry Medal" and an honorary medal was even presented to King George V, though what he thought of it is not recorded.[19]

Lionel's last seagoing draft was in HMS *Prince of Wales*, a Formidable-class pre-dreadnought battleship launched in 1902. The ship served in the Atlantic Fleet and at the beginning of the First World War changed to the Channel Fleet and was used to ferry Royal Marines to Belgium. During this time Lionel was rated ERA 3rd Class. Following his time in *Prince of Wales* he returned to *Pembroke III*. It is now that his career takes a strange turn. His service record notes his rate as CPO Mech 3 on 1 July 1914 and CPO II on 1 July 1915. In April 1915 he is on the books of *President II*, which was an accounting base for the Royal Naval Air Service, and in June 1916 he is on the books of *Daedalus*, which is recorded as the nominal depot ship for the Royal Naval Air Service. It should be noted that in brackets after *Daedalus* is written Cranwell (at this time a naval establishment) and his rate is now CPO 1.[20] This seems a complete change of direction and on 1 October 1917 is recorded his entry into the Royal Naval Air Service with the rank of Warrant Officer Class 2.[21] Here the trail seemed to end and it would be reasonable to suppose that he was commissioned into the Royal Flying Corps and would subsequently have joined the newly formed Royal Air Force. In fact it is recorded that Lionel was promoted from Pilot Officer to Flying Officer (Grade A) on 1 October 1919[22] and was placed on the retired list, due to ill health, on 11 January 1922.[23]

There have been few men who have joined as Artificers and risen to the rank of Admiral. the first was Sydney Oswell Frew, born on 4 January 1890 at Sculcoates in Yorkshire. He joined the Royal Navy as a Boy Artificer in June 1905, being sent to *Pembroke II* and later *Tenedos* at Chatham. He completed his training and was rated ERA 5th Class in July 1909 and was sent to sea for further training in HMS *Formidable*, another pre-dreadnought battleship that was commissioned in 1904. Here he was rated Acting ERA 4th Class on 16 June 1910. He returned to *Pembroke II* in April 1911 with a brief period onboard HMS *Bulwark*, while this pre-dreadnought battleship was preparing to begin a refit. He remained ashore until November 1911 when he joined HMS *Pelorus*, which seems to have been part of the Home Fleet. He stayed with this ship after he became ERA 3rd Class and once more returned to *Pembroke II* in September 1913 and stayed there or with HMS *Tyne*, a destroyer flotilla depot ship, until he was selected for promotion to commissioned rank in 1916, when he was promoted to Mate (E), a somewhat archaic rank that would soon be subsumed as Sub-Lieutenant.[24] He was promoted to Lieutenant in 1918, Lieutenant Commander in 1926, Commander in 1929, Captain in 1936 and Rear Admiral in 1945. His final honour was to be knighted in 1949. Admiral Frew retired in 1950 and died in 1972. He was the first Boy Artificer to reach flag rank; he had a division at *Fisgard* named after him in 1966.

In 1911 a young boy named Cecil Reginald Percival Bennett, known in the family as Reg, was accepted as a Boy Artificer. He was born on 29 July 1896 in Morchard Bishop, a small village near Crediton in Devon, and was educated at Crediton Grammar School, having won a scholarship. He joined the Royal Navy on 29 December 1911 and started his training in HMS *Indus* in Plymouth. This had been *Tenedos*, but in 1910 *Tenedos* had been decommissioned when it was decided to concentrate Boy Artificer training in Portsmouth and Plymouth. The hulks were moved to Plymouth where they became *Indus I, II, II, IV* and *V*. He has left a substantial journal of his service as a Boy Artificer and subsequent service, recording much of the day-to-day activity and ship's routine of the period. As he wrote at the start of his journal,

> *Our living ship was HMS "Indus V". She was an old wooden man-of-war originally called HMS "Ganges" and was built of teak. The guns had been removed and the gun ports fitted with windows. She had four decks–Upper, main, Lower and Orlop. The Orlop deck of course had no gun ports, and at the time that I joined the ship was only used for such purposes as Cloak Rooms for hanging our overcoats or oilskins, hammock nettings and for sundry baggage. Later it was used as a chest flat. Being more or less on the water level it was also used for the embarkation and disembarkation of heavy goods. The Junior classes occupied the Lower Deck and the Senior Classes the Main Deck. Each boy had*

a sea chest, which he took to sea with him up to the 1914 war when the practice was discontinued. The sea chest which was made of a good quality and well seasoned soft wood and was the Apprentices own property, and I still have mine in my possession after 55 years. We slept in hammocks and to-day the conditions under which we lived would be regarded as overcrowded; indeed this was the main reason given at a later date for removing accommodation to the shore.[25]

The accommodation can only be imagined today but surely would have been very spartan by modern standards. Though that would be of no comfort for the young boys who had only recently left more comfortable accommodation at home. Those boys from the RHS would have had no difficulty with such austere accommodation when they joined.

Bennett continues his journal with a description of the introduction to the layout and routine of the establishment and his initial issue of kit:

Our first day on board was occupied in being shown round the establishment, and instructed in the matters of routine. For the second the Tailor arrived to measure us for our contract uniforms, which took three weeks to mature. During this period we were not allowed on shore except to the recreational ground, and we were kitted up with such things as Underclothing etc not forgetting suits of overalls, boots which were hard and no Apprentice ever wore a pair after working hours. Our working shirts were patterned with a line pattern of thin stripes of alternate white and blue. They were very practical for a working shirt and had a soft detachable collar. Black ties were issued for wear with these shirts. Our shore-going shirts were of the white boiled variety, and these were worn with a semi Eton type collar and a Bow Tie. These were highly impractical and on our rate of pay expensive to maintain.[26]

It must have been very difficult to maintain his kit in good order. The washroom he describes could only be considered fit for the most basic routine of kit upkeep. He also made no mention of any laundry facilities, which must have made the upkeep of "boiled shirts" and collars all but impossible. But as he mentioned the cost of upkeep of these items it must be assumed that some form of contract laundry services was available:

In the after end of the Lower Deck was the wash room. This was fitted out with tip-up bowls of galvanised iron over a trough of similar material. I suppose there were about two hundred of these bowls the bowls were used for washing the person, bathing, washing clothes, etc.[27]

He continues by relating how he was occupied for several weeks in marking up kit with "our name stamp which was a wooden hand-cut type with about half inch letters with our names and initials on them".[28] It echoes memories of many Apprentices through the years who spent the first days and weeks in training similarly occupied. It was after this initial three weeks that he was ready to commence his workshop training and he details the daily routine:

0600. Lash up and stow Hammocks.
0630. Breakfast.
0700. Divisions and Prayers.
0730. Turn to in the Workshops.
1200. Cease work. Dinner.
1300. Turn-to.
1700. Cease work. Tea.
1800. Evening School.
2000. Cease School. Supper (A cup of cocoa and a bun).
2100. Junior Apprentices Turn In.
2200. Pipe Down. All Apprentices turned in.[29]

He continues that Wednesday night was free, allowing those who wished to, or could afford to, to have shore leave until 2100 as a junior boy and 2130 after the first year and 2200 in the final year. He also mentioned that smoking was not allowed until the age of eighteen, with a beating the punishment for being caught smoking under this age, something that as a non-smoker did not worry him.[30]

Much is made in his journal about sport, both competitive and individual. Saturday afternoons were set aside for team games, with those not participating attending as spectators for the "five soccer teams, Two Rugger fifteens, and the Padre created a diversion by taking some of the boys on a long walk".[31] As well as the organised sport, there was a personal hurdle to overcome for those less than proficient in the swimming pool, an activity known to Apprentices down the years: the Naval Swimming Test. In Cecil's day this test consisted of being able to swim three lengths of the swimming pool and then treading water for five minutes, all this while wearing a sailor's white duck uniform suit, which in Cecil's case was considerably oversized in trouser length. He does not say how long the swimming pool was but he did complete the test successfully.[32]

So ended his first term as a Boy Artificer. Now he says that once their trades had been allocated at Easter training began in earnest, but during the summer there still seemed to be ample time for cricket and rowing on the river with "six-oared gigs" from the Royal Naval Engineering College at Keyham, which had shut in 1910 as a result of the Selborne–Fisher scheme, which had been the catalyst for Reg's joining the Royal Navy. It appears that there were no examinations or trade tests at the end of the summer term so Reg could look forward to a carefree leave.[33]

As he moved into "B" Class he mentioned that there were reports of bullying at *Fisgard* at Portsmouth, a phenomenon not unknown in most public schools and commonly referred to as "fagging" and in *Fisgard* in later years as "sprogging". This was a widespread method of maintaining the status quo of the senior classes and though officially frowned upon was not actively discouraged for many years. He is particularly disparaging of the Petty Officer Boys who though they were supposed to help maintain discipline did little to merit their advancement and they were ineffective because, in his view, the wrong Boys were selected. This view might be coloured by the fact he was not himself selected, something that did not affect his future.

That he looked to the future is evident from his entries in 1913. It was during this time that a system of promotion from ERA to commissioned rank was introduced in response to the system introduced a year earlier for seamen. He is very clear about his objectives:

> *Also I had a few thoughts about my future. It seemed to me that if a Commission from the Lower Deck was a feasible object to obtain, I should attempt it. This would depend largely at what age one could attempt this goal. Anyway I had a few years to see how the matter worked, and so I returned from leave for once with a target to aim at.*[34]

It was to this end that Reg applied himself diligently over the coming months, applying to the University of London for the syllabus for gaining a BSc as an external student and meanwhile he sat and passed the Admiralty Examination and test at the end of the Autumn term and, as he said, "I therefore worked a bit harder during 'D' Class and at Christmas had the satisfaction of finding myself in the first ten for both Workshop skill and Academic attainment."[35] He could go on Christmas leave with a sense of satisfaction with his training progress, a Christmas leave that was to be the last that he would be able to spend together with his family or some years. We will rejoin Reg in the coming years of conflict.

Also joining as a Boy Artificer at the same time as Reg, but going to *Fisgard* in Portsmouth, was a young boy by the name of Herbert Edward Phillip Burwell, born 21 January 1896. He sat the entrance exam in October 1911, had the medical examination in November and joined *Fisgard* on 29 December 1911.

His training followed the same pattern as Reg and he was rated ERA 5th Class on 1 January 1916, when he was serving in *Victory II*; this was followed by time in HMS *Cochrane*, a Warrior-class armoured cruiser, including at the Battle of Jutland. Rated Acting ERA 4th Class in December 1916 he was again in *Victory II*. This was followed by a transfer to the Submarine Service, with service in HMS *Dolphin*, HMS *Titania* and finally submarine *J6*. This is a sorry tail of incorrect identification that today is referred to as "Blue on Blue". On 15 October 1918 *J6* was on patrol off the coast of Northumberland when she was sighted by a British Q-Ship, the *Cymric*, commanded by Lieutenant F. Peterson. The "J" on the conning tower of *J6* was mistaken for a "U" and the Q-Ship assumed it was a U-Boat and raised the white ensign and opened fire. The fire was accurate and the direct hits caused extensive damage to *J6* and she sank. It was only when some survivors were picked out of the sea that the mistake was realised; there were only fifteen who escaped from the stricken submarine. Those in the engine room had no chance of escape and drowned when the submarine sank; those lost included the young Herbert Burwell, who had only married five months earlier and whose young wife was pregnant. A very sorry end to a short life.

As mentioned previously there was seen to be a requirement for specialist electrical ratings. Electricity was first used in Royal Navy warships in the early 1870s, when a primitive pile battery was used for gun-firing circuits. The battleship HMS *Inflexible* saw the introduction, in 1881, of the first electrical supply system, having a single 800v DC generator supplying series–parallel circuits of arc lamps in main machinery spaces and incandescent lamps elsewhere. The choice of 800v DC was not a wise choice for the technology of the time and led to the first fatal accident involving electricity onboard HM Ships; subsequently the voltage was reduced to 80v DC. The voltage was increased in 1900 to 100v DC and the ring main system was introduced. The voltage in larger ships was again increased to 220 DC and despite a certain reluctance to replace steam and hydraulic auxiliary machinery with electric motors the generating capacity continued to rise and this voltage of 220v DC remained the standard until the late 1940s and later.

Notwithstanding the reluctance to utilise electric motors, there was a trial carried out on board HMS *Barfleur*, where the forward 10" mounting right gun elevation motion was adapted for electric drive. The trials were less than satisfactory as the gun would continually overshoot the required position. When the drive was modified in later trials the overshoot was eliminated by shorting out the armature of the shunt wound 80v DC motors, thus showing that electric drive was feasible for smaller-calibre guns.[36]

As has been stated earlier, the need for specialised electricians, rather than relying on the ERA, was apparent as early as the 1890s and to this end the Electrician was introduced. By 1910 an avenue for promotion to Warrant Officer was introduced by Admiralty Order in Council[37] and with it limited promotion to commissioned rank. It was clear that the position of Electrician was at odds with that of ERA: similar recruitment, abilities and promotion prospects and so those Electricians below warrant rank were reclassified in 1913 as Electrical Artificers. As well as those electrical aspects of his duties, the EA was also involved with both the mechanical as well as electrical aspects of the Whitehead torpedo, previously the domain of the Armourer and ERA.[38]

With storm clouds of war forming, there was bound to be change, both in numbers required and the quality of training that could be provided for the young Boy Artificers. For Reg Bennett there was initial upheaval, with uncertainty as to where and how his training would continue and what the Royal Navy would require of him in wartime.

chapter three

The First World War
and the Price of Peace

• • •

*Artificer: An artist; a mechanic or manufacturer; one whose
occupation requires skill or knowledge of a particular kind.*[1]

The requirements of the Royal Navy saw a vast increase in personnel
between 1914 and 1918. The majority of these were "hostilities only"
seaman ratings, but, of course, there was also a requirement for engineers
and these had to be recruited from industry, with the concomitant loss of
this expertise to those industries vital to the war effort.

Penn makes the observation that "When war broke out in August 1914
the state of the Engineering Branch was decidedly unsatisfactory. Yet the
timely action of Lord Fisher in placing the old-entry Engineer Officers
within the military branch had a most salutary effect, and it is probably
true to say that almost overnight the position became completely reversed
and that the branch was never before in its history more satisfied with its
position or contented with its lot."[2]

For Reg Bennett things had remained the same throughout the spring
term and it was not until he returned after leave that rumours started their
inevitable round of fact and fallacy. Within a week of war being declared
the boys were told to pack their personal possessions into their sea chests

ready to move at a moment's notice. In fact, they were on the move the following morning. They and their possessions were disembarked and loaded onto a train, which took them to Portsmouth, and from the station onto "commandeered" paddle steamers, which took them alongside HMS *Fisgard* at the Hardway Gosport. Cecil takes up the story:

> *This was rather an amazing move, for there was no real room for us so we had to double-bunk on meals, and the workshop arrangements were really crowded. I remember little about our stay in Portsmouth – something had evidently gone wrong with the organisation. The only thing that remains firmly in my mind is that one night I went with a friend to the Theatre Royal and saw the Arcadians. It was a wonderful show…*
>
> *I suppose we must have been in Portsmouth for about three weeks, when we got the order to pack up again, and we returned to Plymouth by the same route as we had come. On this occasion our destination was the Royal Naval Barracks, as the five ships of the "Indus". establishment had been dispersed. Two of them were west about to Invergordon, but one foundered in bad weather on the way.*[3]

It seems that their workshop training now continued in the Dockyard; in a matter of weeks a settled routine with adequate facilities had been lost and an at best ad hoc system of training had been cobbled together under the tutelage of recalled pensioner Petty Officers well out of date with modern training methods. The officers Reg refers to as retired "Ranker" Officers were equally out of date. While their training continued in the Dockyard it soon became clear that this arrangement was unsatisfactory to both the Dockyard and the Boy Artificers, interfering as it did with the day-to-day running of a dockyard geared up for war. By the end of summer leave *Indus* was returned to her old mooring at Wilcove and two of the factory ships were tied up to her, in fact an arrangement that was almost as it was before the advent of the war but with the unfortunate loss of training in that year.

Now, at last, Reg Bennett was about to start on the last term of training before joining the fleet. He recalled the final stages of his training and the tests and exams he faced during this period:

> *Time now seemed to pass more rapidly than ever, and soon the Passing Out procedure was upon our class. Firstly we had a fortnight's revision of school and technical subjects in preparation for the Examinations. This was*

a forenoon affair. In the afternoon we prepared tools and equipment for our Trade Test. This included the accumulation of Crosscut and Flat Chisels and a variation of files, for the majority of the work was hand work. The checking of lathes etc were also part of the routine and of course the assembly of reliably tempered lathe tools.

At the end of the revision period came the Examination. This started on the Monday morning and lasted until Wednesday morning and afternoon. On Thursday the Trade Test started and for the best part of three weeks that the Test took it was hard slogging. One wondered why so much hand work, why not use machines to greater advantage. The answer was invariably that in some classes of ship machines were not available. Many silly mistakes were made by the examinees at the start by over anxiety but after a few days things settled down and the men began to separate from the boys so to speak, and there were seldom any surprises.[4]

The results of all this testing and examining was published prior to the Boys going on Christmas leave and Reg reported with some satisfaction that all in his class made the grade. They would now go on Christmas leave and on their return would pack up all their kit and equipment and report to the Royal Naval Barracks for onward drafting to sea. In due course Reg was sent to HMS *Iron Duke*, a dreadnought battleship launched in 1912 and at this time the flagship of the Grand Fleet under the command of Admiral Sir John Jellicoe. This was clearly a prestigious posting but firstly it required a long and tiring train journey from Plymouth to Scapa Flow, where the Grand Fleet was anchored. Here after the usual formalities he was shown to the ERA's mess, where he met the CERA. Now, for ERA 5th Class Reg Bennett, having been promoted on 1 January 1916, a new chapter in his naval career lay before him.

The early years of the twentieth century had seen much change in the Royal Navy. There were the personnel changes already alluded to but also changes in materiél. Triple expansion engines had given way to the Parsons turbine, so elegantly displayed by *Turbinia* at Queen Victoria's Diamond Jubilee Fleet Review at Spithead on 26 June 1897, where she sped through the anchored ranks of warships at over thirty-four knots. Coal was also giving way to oil and armour and armaments were getting heavier and more powerful, such that the ships were almost unrecognisable to those of ten years before.[5]

As well as the improvements provided by technology, war bought further demands on men and machinery. As Penn commented,

War it is said, brings out the best and the worst in all of us. As far as the naval engineer is concerned the change from peace to war conditions means much. Long periods of continuous high-speed steaming with little or no chance to rectify defects or carry out long-overdue examinations; long hours at Action Stations; almost incessant watchkeeping for juniors, eternal vigilance and repeatedly disturbed nights for seniors; and when a ship is lucky enough to go to a properly equipped dockyard it is almost certain that it will be only to be told that defects cannot be rectified unless they are of such a character as to definitely to prevent the ship from going to sea or fighting an engagement.[6]

This is graphically illustrated by the experience of HMS *Kent*, which was in dockyard hands when war was declared and rushed out without the usual peacetime allowances. This rush led to only 18,000 horsepower being available, rather than the 22,000 horsepower that should have been available. Despite this and other teething troubles the ship sailed to join the South Atlantic Squadron, where it was involved in the Battle of the Falkland Islands.[7]

When the German Cruisers *Gneisenau* and *Nürnberg* were sighted, the British cruisers sailed quickly out of Port William in pursuit. In order to close the range on *Nürnberg* before darkness allowed her to escape, everything possible was done to ensure maximum speed was maintained for as long as possible. The main engine relief valves were screwed down to allow more steam pressure to the boilers and anything not required and that was flammable should have been broken up and passed down to the boiler rooms. *Kent* managed to close the range and the ships opened fire at a range of 11,000 yards. As Penn noted,

The ship was hit repeatedly from the opening of the engagement to its conclusion, one shell landing in the forward boiler-room funnel casing and another in the middle boiler-room; a small fire was reported from No. 4 funnel casing.

At about this time it became apparent that some of the main engine holding-down bolts (the bolts which hold the engines into the bottom of the ship) had carried away, and the engine frames were straining in the most abnormal manner.[8]

The action was published in great detail in the *London Gazette* of March 1915:

> *The engineers, with a careful eye on the vanishing fuel, tightened up a valve here and opened a steam pipe there, coaxing the 22,000 horse power engines as a jockey coaxes a racehorse. As one of the stokers put it afterwards, "It was a case of either getting the Nürnberg or busting up in trying to". Little by little the Kent increased her pace. Her record speed in ten years of service was a shade over twenty-four knots, but before long Engineer Commander Andrew and his perspiring band of artificers and stokers had her doing well over twenty-five, an achievement which can, perhaps, only be adequately appreciated by an engineer.*
>
> *It was therefore decided to eke out the coal with anything combustible that could be found on board. Wooden boats were taken out of their cradles, broken up, and taken below to feed the furnaces. Wooden spars, companionways and ladders shared a similar fate, and even the wooden planking of the decks was torn up and passed down to the stokeholds.[9]*

Following a furious gun battle, starting at range and reducing to close quarters, the *Kent* was victorious and the *Nürnberg* sank. The *Kent* had been hit thirty-six times. The *Gazette* stated that the greatest credit for the victory:

> *must be accorded to the men down below. They saw nothing of the fight; but had it not been for their magnificent efforts, giving their ship a speed more than two knots above that for which she was built, the gunners up above would never have got within striking distance of the enemy.[10]*

It seems incredible that a ship that was rushed out of refit and which failed to achieve its rated horsepower in trials should be able, so soon afterwards to chase, overhaul and subsequently sink the *Nürnberg* despite the damage to her main engines and this must be rated a very fine achievement and reflects well on the professionalism of all of those, both officer and rating, in the Engineering Department. That this is one incident in many during the war is down to the fact that much that went on in the machinery spaces went unreported and unrewarded in the maelstrom that was war; Penn put it very well when he wrote,

But it is aid that the bravest deeds in war often go unsung, for there is frequently
no witnesses to report them, and this is probably particularly true of the officers
and men of the engineering branch. There is a natural tendency, of course, for the
work of those down below, out of sight, to be taken for granted, and it is all the
more pleasing therefore when they figure prominently in the reports of those in
a position best to judge.[11]

Reg Bennett, having joined HMS *Iron Duke*, was ready to start his contribution to the war effort. He may have only been a lowly ERA 5th Class but he had much to offer and he was soon finding his feet in a large capital ship that must have appeared rather daunting. On his first morning onboard he reported to the engineer's workshop and the Senior Engineer detailed Reg to assist the CERA of the boiler rooms, a man called Harris, who is variously described as "the most ignorant man he ever knew" by the Engineer Commander and as a "kindly soul" by Cecil, who "got on well with him".[12] However he was viewed by his fellow engineers, Harris seems to have been a conscientious and diligent worker, though Reg does mention that all the dirty jobs seemed to come his way, doubtlessly as he was the most junior Artificer. Further to his daywork, Reg was detailed to stand watches in the boiler rooms on a three-watch system, a system that can become quite arduous, with two days of six hours on watch and the third with twelve on watch, with daywork as well.

Soon after joining, Reg recounts his terrible seasickness when the ship first sailed into a gale around the Pentland Firth and how the Chief Stoker suggested that chewing a lump of coal was an infallible cure. Reg did not find it in the least efficacious and the episode sounds like the Chief Stoker was having fun at Reg's expense: an occupational hazard for young Artificers then as in more modern times.[13] His ordeal continued and was compounded when the ship hit a particularly large wave and a considerable amount of water came down the forced draught fan trunking and drenched him in ice-cold water. Fortunately this was at the end of his watch and he was able to have a hot shower and crawl into his hammock.[14]

HMS *Iron Duke* was still burning coal and this made work in the boiler rooms dirty, tiring and unpleasant. Moving the coal from the bunkers to the boilers was hard physical work and had to be maintained continuously to keep the boilers producing steam. As well as moving the coal, there was all the clinker to be removed periodically, which meant the boiler had to be allowed to die down and the clinker removed with a ninety-pound bar known as a "slice". Clearly such an implement was not for the faint-hearted and, as Reg remarks, "quite often the Petty Officer would have to come to the rescue".[15]

Working in the boiler rooms also had the potential pitfall of how an ERA 5th Class stood in respect of the Chief Stoker. Reg seems to have approached this in a very pragmatic way:

> I soon put this matter right by telling the Chief Stoker that as he was in charge of the Boiler Room I was subordinate to him, and would carry out his orders. From then on there was no further questions and there was complete harmony of working.
>
> This question of the standing of a Fifth Class ERA was a tricky one as there was no clear definition. It was decided that I should be regarded as a Leading Hand, but that I should have the same privileges as an ERA, as regards leave and the signing of the leave book.[16]

It was shortly after this that he must have caught the eye of the Engineer Commander, who saw fit to inform Reg that he was to be given a course of training, "details of which would be disclosed to me in due course".[17] The man who was to mentor him in the engine room was a CERA named Fraser, who Reg maintains did not have one redeeming feature and "of all the people I have met in my lifetime there was none that I disliked more than Fraser".[18] And Reg saw him as a very dangerous man to deal with and one who would have no scruples in hazarding Reg's career.

The time spent in Scapa Flow was long, tedious and very monotonous, with constant exercises and sub-calibre gun-firing. These could be carried out in the anchorage, but for full-calibre firing it was necessary to carry these out while carrying out routine sweeps of the North Sea. There was the occasional change of scenery when ships visited Invergordon. This allowed the ships companies time for some rest and recreation. There was a canteen ashore and facilities for the men to play organised sport and the opportunity to walk ashore to stretch their legs. During this period of relative quiet and inaction Reg was provided with an unprecedented opportunity to improve himself, just as the Engineer Commander had promised:

> Engineer Commander Moorshead had arranged for me to use a canvas enclosed compartment on the Main deck known as the midshipman's study when it

was not occupied my midshipmen. I was also allowed access to all the Ship's Engineering Drawings which was a great boon. This caused a bit of jealousy as no other ERA or CERA was allowed this privilege. I learned much from these drawings besides the actual construction of the plant concerned. For instance the names of the contractors for the various components were given and the material and the composition thereof. Being of an enquiring tone of mind I tried to discover what this was all about. We had a very good reference library in the ship and this helped a lot.[19]

The reason why Reg had been chosen for this rare privilege can only be speculated on, but being the only young ERA 5th Class on board may have helped. It is clear, however, that he was favourably looked-upon by Engineer Commander Moorshead, who continued to show interest in the young man, requesting to see his notebooks and keeping abreast of his training.[20]

It was at this time that the Grand Fleet was called upon to justify the vast expenditure lavished upon it. Reg notes in his journal that there was a rumour on the grapevine that the German High Seas Fleet had finally ventured out of the safety of their base at Wilhelmshaven. The Grand Fleet immediately raised steam and left Scapa Flow to rendezvous with Admiral Beatty's battlecruisers in the hope of a decisive engagement with the Germans. This was the prelude to the Battle of Jutland.

The Battle of Jutland was the last and largest sea battle between massed fleets of dreadnought, fought in the North Sea some seventy miles off the Skagerrak, on 31 May 1916. Britain expected a second Trafalgar, but that was not the outcome; the ships were hardly back in port and the cordite smoke barely cleared before the acrimony, criticism and controversy started. Germany was far quicker off the mark to trumpet a great victory over the British Grand Fleet and the tardiness with which the Admiralty responded to the German announcement allowed the German report to gain a hold over the British press and public that was almost impossible to counter. This was one of many mistakes that were made before, during and after the battle.

As the Grand Fleet sailed from its anchorage in Scapa Flow and Beatty's battlecruiser squadron left Rosyth, two lapses in communications began the litany of mistakes. Firstly, the seaplane carrier HMS *Campania* either did not receive the order to sail[21] or possibly misinterpreted it;[22] this deprived Admiral Sir John Jellicoe of ten aircraft that might have provided significant reconnaissance in the build-up to the battle. The second failure in communications was the signal sent by Captain Thomas Jackson, director of the Operations Division in the Admiralty.

He asked Room 40, who had decoded German Naval signals, where they had picked up the call sign of Admiral Scheer's flagship *Friedrich der Große* and was told that it was still in harbour in the Jade and this was what he signalled to Jellicoe and Beatty. As both Osborne[23] and Nicholas Jellicoe[24] point out, there was a history of antipathy between Jackson and Room 40 and Jackson was not liked by the staff of Room 40. The outcome was that Jellicoe and Beatty proceeded at a speed designed to conserve fuel, with the outcome that it limited the hours of daylight the following day that were available for the battle and as the British had very little training in night fighting this severely limited Jellicoe's options once darkness fell.

Reg and the rest of the ship's company went to action stations at about three o'clock in the afternoon and later that afternoon there was a message passed down to the Engine room that the ship had passed some wreckage; this subsequently turned out to be from HMS *Queen Mary*, one of three battlecruiser casualties that afternoon, held by some to be the result of the adoption by the British of a policy to achieve and maintain as rapid a rate of fire as was possible with no regard for magazine safety.

Arthur J. Marder reached the conclusion that the Royal Navy lacked "a generally accepted, comprehensive, authoritative tactical doctrine in 1914".[25] This is disputed by Jon Tetsuro Sumida, who makes four points to refute Marder: firstly, there were many pre-war experiments with battlefleet tactics; secondly, that Jellicoe's perceived caution and defensiveness is at odds with his pre-war reputation; thirdly, that pre-war gunnery techniques and firing practice was all at medium range, that is, 7,000 yards to 10,000 yards; and, finally, there were arguments over the "relative merits of deliberate shooting at long range as opposed to rapid fire at medium range".[26] One result of these arguments was the adoption by the British of a policy to achieve and maintain as rapid a rate of fire as was possible. To this end there seems to be a consensus among modern historians that there were flagrant breaches of magazine safety such as storing excess cordite charges in turrets and passageways, the disregard for anti-flash door discipline and the fact that British cordite charges were in silk bags that easily caught fire and British cordite was inherently unstable.[27]

During the night Jellicoe reorganised his battleships so as to be ready to destroy the German fleet in the morning; however, once again, he was not apprised of the enemy's position by anybody and hence failed to prevent Scheer from making good his escape back to the safety of his home ports, the closeness of which gave the German Admiralty a significant head start over the British in issuing a report of the battle and being able to announce a great victory. This entered the public domain both on the continent and the British press and with nothing coming out of the British Admiralty it was all there was to report. Even when a communiqué was released, it was, as Osborne wrote, "tersely-worded and brutally-honest".[28] This led to speculation in the press that the Royal Navy had been defeated; further, it allowed the darling of the press, Beatty, to be feted as the hero of the hour who led the Germans onto the guns of Jellicoe's battleships only for Jellicoe to show too much caution and waste the opportunity.[29]

It is now that the divergence of opinion started. Firstly, indications to the Admiralty seemed to indicate that the battlecruisers had exploded because of the disregard for magazine discipline; these had been highlighted at Dogger Bank, but without a proper naval staff little was done, although the Commissioned Gunner aboard HMS *Lion*, Alexander Grant, did much to ensure proper safety precautions were adhered to, without detriment to rate of fire;[30] this probably saved *Lion* at Jutland. It is documented in a signal from Beatty to Jellicoe, and one he sent to the Admiralty, that he believed that the cause of the battlecruiser losses was lax magazine safety.[31] This is further highlighted by a report from the Third Sea Lord agreeing that the explosions were "due to gun crews having ignored cordite safety regulations".[32] Now, having laid the blame at the door of lax magazine safety, Jellicoe signals the Admiralty, suggesting that rather than magazine safety the real cause was lack of sufficient armour on the turret roofs.[33] To this end Jellicoe suppressed any report that refuted his and Beatty's version of inadequate armour.

Reg obviously saw none of the action. He thought that the ship fired "about a dozen salvoes in all when the firing ceased".[34] He remained in the engine room, still at action stations, until about nine o'clock in the evening, when the Senior Engineer came down and ordered them to go to the ventilation fan flat above the engine room to get some sleep. It was apparent in the morning that the High Seas Fleet had effected an escape back to the safety of their naval base. So *Iron Duke* and the rest of the Grand

Fleet, many running low on coal, turned for home. Reg echoes many later commentators when he commented on the British reports of the battle,

> *The first report of the battle was a brief one giving our casualties and, if I remember rightly, very little about the enemies. This I think was a tactical error, and must have caused some misgivings amongst our friends abroad. However later when the casualties of both sides had been correctly assessed it seemed we had not done too badly.*[35]

Reg may be being somewhat optimistic in his assessment of the battle, but it was not the unmitigated disaster for the British that the Germans had reported immediately after reaching the safety of Wilhelmshaven. In the final analysis it is true to say that both Jellicoe and Beatty made mistakes, Jellicoe may have been too cautious, but had he not been it could have been catastrophic. He later admitted that the lack of training for night actions lost him several opportunities and he felt he did not employ his cruisers to best advantage. Beatty failed to pass on vital intelligence and allowed the lax cordite safety practices that resulted in the loss of three battlecruisers. Had the British shells been more effective, as they were in 1918, together with more armour, safer cordite handling procedures and better communications, the outcome could have been very different.

Now Reg and *Iron Duke* returned to the monotony of life in Scapa Flow. He continued with his private course of instruction, which he completed in October 1915, and by this time the Engineer Commander considered him fit for advancement to Acting ERA 4th Class, some nine months since he had left training as an ERA 5th Class. This meant an increase in pay. Reg mentioned that it nearly doubled, a considerable improvement, and an increase in responsibility and:

> *That I carried the rate of Acting Chief Petty Officer. This today has been altered to Petty Officer. I was now given more responsibility of my own, and allowed to keep watch in the Engine Room despite the fact that I had not yet received my Boiler Room Watchkeeping Certificate.*[36]

It is at this time that Admiral Jellicoe went to the Admiralty as First Sea Lord and Admiral Beatty was appointed as Commander-in-Chief of the Grand Fleet. This meant that *Iron Duke* was no longer the flagship and reverted to a private ship. With this some of the officers also left, amongst them Engineer Commander Moorshead, who was promoted to Engineer Captain a few months later. He was replaced by Engineer Commander Bill, so Reg had lost his mentor but he benefitted from Engineer Commander Moorshead's patronage.

Reg's journal is silent for some time until he mentions the catastrophic events of 9 July 1917, when HMS *Vanguard* exploded at her anchorage.

> *I was sleeping in my hammock in what was known as "Q" flat when I remember being awakened by the shutting of the watertight doors at the top of the approach ladders overhead. There seemed to be a lot of bustle but I was so tired that I dropped off to sleep again. When I awoke in the morning I asked what all the hustle and bustle had been about. My friend said in astonishment 'What don't you know, the "VANGUARD" blew up at midnight last night.' This news astounded me and I wondered why we had not all been turned out. I went on deck, and sure enough there was a blank space where the ship had been the previous day.*[37]

The cause of this disaster was never fully resolved but the most likely cause was believed to be an undiscovered fire in a coal bunker or tent fuel space, which smouldered for long enough for the heat to ignite the cordite in the nearby magazine. But from Reg's response he was not going to let anything interfere with his sleep, in the best possible tradition of Artificers.

The war at sea was now primarily concerned with the submarine threat which was, in part, countered by the long-overdue introduction of the convoy system, a system that had been tried and tested over a hundred years before in the Napoleonic Wars. This had little impact on Reg, though it was still necessary to take the Grand Fleet out to exercise to maintain its fighting efficiency. As always after such exercises it was necessary to coal ship, an evolution that involved all of the ship's company, as Reg noted:

> *This exercised the whole of the ship's company including the chaplain. All buckled too. The stokers off watch trimmed the bunkers. I had been allocated the job of looking after the collier when she came alongside. I had to inspect the winches for defects, not with a view to putting them right but to ensure no false claims were made by the company who owned the collier. If anything went wrong with the winches whilst coaling I called upon our Engine Room Staff to remedy the*

*fault. Unless it was within my capacity. After coaling was finished I went round
again to ensure all was well. Our own Ship's Crew manned the winches, and
in general did a very good job. In so far as I can recollect I never had cause to
quarrel with the Chief Engineer of the Collier. Each hour during coaling a hoist
of flags was made to show the amount of coal embarked during the last hour. As
far as I can remember the average was about 300 tons per hour. This rate slowed
up when the bunkers were nearly full but it represented a considerable effort.*[38]

Later in 1917 Reg was confirmed as an ERA 4th Class, having gained
all the relevant certificates to allow him to take charge of both boiler and
engine rooms. At this time his benefactor, Engineer Captain Moorshead,
returned to offer further aid in advancing his career. He was offered a post
on Captain Moorshead's staff. Captain Moorshead had recently taken up
the appointment as Squadron Engineer Officer of the Light Cruiser Force
and it seems he was keen for Reg to be part of his staff.

Also at this time Commander Bill approached Reg to gauge his
thoughts on taking a commission. Reg seemed a little apprehensive at first
but this was due to the fact that he still had to wait three years before he
was eligible to sit the examination and he was unsure what might happen in
that time if the war continued. This did not show any lack of ambition but
shows a pragmatic approach to the future. His ambition may also have been
tempered by the reaction of one of his mess mates, ERA 2nd Class Green,
whom Commander Moorshead wished to recommend for a commission
but who refused because as a married man with two children it would not
be viable financially to take that step. Reg met him some years later in HMS
Nelson. He asked Green if he regretted turning down this opportunity and
was told that he did not, however Reg noted that Green's reply was not
totally convincing.

It was now time for Reg to leave *Iron Duke* with some regret, but once
the war was over there would be much to contemplate. The first necessity
for the government and the Admiralty was to reduce costs and that would
involve both men and matériel and with it much disruption and upheaval;
there were many failures to understand the concerns of the lower deck by
both government and Admiralty, which would come to a climax in 1931 at
Invergordon.

Another Boy Artificer destined for high places joined HMS *Indus* in
1915. His name was J.E. Cooke and after his time in *Indus* he went to sea in

HMS *New Zealand*, the flagship of the Admiral of the Fleet, Lord Jellicoe, as an ERA 5th Class and while onboard was rated ERA 4th Class. The ship was sent on a tour of the Dominions so that Lord Jellicoe could plan and coordinate the naval policies and defences of the British Dominions, and she travelled to India, Australia, New Zealand and Canada. On her return to the UK she was paid off to reserve and scrapped in 1922. John served on several ships as an ERA 4th Class, HMS *Royal Arthur*, HMS *Pandora* and HMS *Athlestone* as an ERA 3rd Class before being promoted to Mate (E) in 1924. He was promoted to Lieutenant in 1925 and served in HMS *Hood*. He was promoted to Lieutenant Commander in 1933 and Commander in 1936. He had appointments ashore and afloat for the next few years and during the Second World War served as the Engineer Officer of HMS *Furious* and then in the same position in HMS *Anson*. In 1946 he was promoted to Captain and joined the staff of the Engineer-in-Chief as his assistant. In 1953 he was promoted to Rear Admiral and retired in 1957. A division in *Fisgard* was named after him in 1966.

Before leaving the First World War there remains one small mystery. HMS *Wallington* was an Auxiliary Patrol Base based at Immingham, where trawlers and patrol boats taken up by the Royal Navy for service in the North Sea were maintained. A discharge certificate for Wren Muriel Whitworth shows that she joined the Women's Royal Naval Service on 29 October 1918, a few weeks before the Armistice, and served until 15 March 1919. It seems strange that she should be accepted into the WRNS so close to the Armistice but the real mystery surrounds the entry for "Rating", which is stated as being "Artificer". This was some seventy-two years before equal opportunity gave girls the chance to enter the Royal Navy as Artificer Apprentices. How she was employed in *Wallington* as an Artificer is unknown and probably unknowable after all this time.[39]

As well as Artificers at sea, there were some who joined the Royal Naval divisions ashore and in the trenches. So these divisions were not made up entirely of seamen and Executive Officers but did include men from the Engineering Department and, while the numbers are not great, some were from the RNVR and some became Artificers. Later there was still a presence on the Western Front:

As we are coming up this year to remember the 100th Anniversary of the First World War I thought it worth taking a look at the part played by the Artificers of the Royal Navy. That's easy, you might say, as they were most likely amongst the ships company of every ship afloat. That's true but did you know that as well as fighting at sea the Royal Navy fought ashore?

The Royal Navy Division (RND) was formed in August 1914 from naval reserve forces when warships of the fleet were fully crewed. The tradition of naval personnel serving on land had been long established and a shortfall in infantry divisions in the Army led to the formation of the RND.

The RND had fought at Antwerp and Gallipoli and in 1916 it was transferred to the British Army as the 63rd (Royal Navy) Division and as an Army unit fought on the western front for the remainder of the war. Following the outbreak of war a Royal Marine Brigade of four infantry battalions was formed from men of the Royal Marine Light Infantry (RMLI) and Royal Marine Artillery (RMA) who were not required for sea service. Shortly afterwards it became apparent that there was still a large surplus of mobilised manpower in the Navy itself and on 17th August a decision was taken by Winston Churchill, then First Lord of the Admiralty, to form eight battalions in two Naval Brigades which would join with the Marine Brigade to produce a composite Royal Naval Division. In addition to those already serving as regulars or reservist a massive recruitment campaign was launched and posters were put up to enlist yet more men. Men between the ages of 18 and 38 with a chest measurement of 34" and a height of 5' 3 ½" could join for the princely sum of 1/3d per day!

The eight battalions were named after past naval commanders, Drake, Benbow, Hawke, Collingwood, Nelson, Howe, Hood and Anson. Training was slow; most resources being needed for the rapid expansion of the Army. Naval personnel were not issued with field equipment or Khaki uniforms, rifles were drawn from Royal Navy stockpiles and these were older "Charger Loading Lee Enfield" rather than the more modern "Short Magazine Lee Enfield" issued to the Army.

The RND remained under Admiralty control even though they were fighting alongside the Army and retained the great naval traditions even while on land. They continued to fly the White Ensign on the field of battle, used bells to signal time, used naval language such as "going ashore" and "coming on board", continued to use naval ranks rather than army equivalents and remained seated during the toast for the King's health. While senior ratings were transferred from regular service to provide a permanent established framework and some officers were provided by the Army, the recruits were almost entirely reservists or men who had volunteered at the outbreak of war.

Despite the fact that they were engineers the records show that as many as 14 artificers were transferred and recruited into the RND. Of the 14 artificers 13 were Engine Room and just one was an Electrical Artificer, the first of this branch being created on 13th May 1901. Three of the artificers were from the RNVR of the day.

Artificers known to have served in the RND:

Gerald STEPHEN, joined as an Ordinary
Seaman and became an ERA.
Percival Stanley WEBSTER, ERA 1st Class.
Robert TYLER ERA (RNVR).
Malcolm John MACAULAY, ERA 1st Class.
George GUNN, ERA.
Frederick Henry CHITTY, ERA.
John PORTER. EA, (RNVR)
Jim Horace OSBORNE, ERA 1st Class.
Cecil Claude TURNER, ERA.
Robert STEEL, ERA 1st Class.
Matthew BELL, ERA.
Cyril Arthur HUTT, ERA
Arthur BULLEN, joined as Able Seamen.
then became ERA.
Thomas William GASCOIGNE, joined as Ordinary
Seaman, became Able Seaman then ERA 2nd Class.[40]

But there were still some innovations that would affect ERAs. The primary one was the introduction of the Ordnance Artificer in 1919, by an Order in Council of 22 March 1920.[41] Up to this time any requirement for technical expertise on guns and turrets was provided by either Armourers or from ERAs seconded from the Engineering Department and given a short course at HMS *Excellent*, the gunnery school on Whale Island in Portsmouth. By the end of the war it had become clear that a more coherent structure was necessary and that dedicated Artificers was the way ahead, with the initial source being those ERAs who were already conversant with the technical aspects of guns, mountings and turrets, and also those Armourers who showed the requisite aptitude and skill to be able to carry out the duties of an Artificer.

At the same time as the introduction of the Ordnance Artificer, it was decided that as well as ERAs joining as Boy Artificers the same procedure should be extended to OAs and EAs and that the term Boy Artificer should be superseded by the new rate of Artificer Apprentice, a term that remained in use until 2010, and that the length of training should be extended from four years to four and a half years. Entry as before would be by competitive examinations, which were the same as those for entry as an Apprentice in the Royal Dockyards, set by the Civil Service Commission. The examinations could only be sat after a handwritten application by the candidate on the "Prescribed Form" had been received by the Commission. The examinations were held throughout the country, in London, Edinburgh, Belfast, Glasgow, Portsmouth, Devonport, Chatham, Leeds, Pembroke and Sheerness. There were three compulsory subjects, arithmetic, English, and geometry and algebra, and a choice of either geography or physics and chemistry. The results were published for each area in order of merit and it appears that there were many who did not achieve a sufficient standard.[42]

There would now follow a decade of turmoil and change, much of it driven by the financial constraints that were inevitable after the vast expense of the war. During the war there had been neither the will nor the need to change anything in the training of Boy Apprentices nor in the requirements for ERAs joining directly from industry. It was, however, inevitable that because of the huge numbers of engineers required some would be of a standard that fell well behind that required in peacetime, when it was possible to pick and choose the best engineers. The best could only be retrained by offering a remuneration and lifestyle superior to that in civilian industry.

chapter four

The Twenties and
the Geddes Axe

• • •

*He has filled them with wisdom of heart, to work all
manner of work of the engraver, and of the artificer.*[1]

I n 1853 the Board of Admiralty introduced a system of continuous
service, to supersede the existing method of signing on a commission by
commission basis.[2] With this came guaranteed rates of pay, with an Able
Seaman paid 1/7d a day, which was increased by 1d a day in 1912 and a
further 2d in 1917. There was also a move by many on the lower deck to
join the death benefit societies that were keen to represent their members'
interests.[3] In 1919, as a result of the Jerram Committee,[4] a bonus of 1/6d
was included and in 1920 pay for an Able Seaman was set at 4/0d a day,
and, despite many scares about pay cuts throughout the 1920s, the 1919
rate remained. Further problems with cuts meant that promotion was far
slower than it had been during the war. Carew observes that "The Navy in
the 1920's was no place to seek quick advancement".[5]

Immediately after the First World War there was a need for the
government to reduce the Armed Forces to save money and those that
remained were often employed on tasks involving strike work during
disputes with police, miners and dock and railway workers;[6] there were also

61

several cases of indiscipline in those ships fighting the Bolsheviks, which led to courts martial, and severe sentences, including the death penalty, were meted out to eighty-seven men.[7] Of course, there were many who considered this was not the work of the Navy but of the police and at a time when there was much social agitation it caused unrest and disquiet among the lower deck.

There was also the lobbying from the many lower deck death benefit societies for improvements in pay and conditions. But such lobbying caused disquiet in the Admiralty that these societies were becoming too radical and, in the opinion of Sir Charles Madden, Commander-in Chief of the Atlantic Fleet, they were tending towards trade unionism.[8] This view was supported by the Director of Naval Intelligence, who was of the view that "now the welfare system was established, every possible step should be taken to discourage the societies' further development".[9] The new Welfare Committee System was heralded by the Admiralty as the most effective way for the lower deck to air its grievances, while it was intended by the Admiralty that the death benefit societies would have no recognised role in the new system.

The new system proved just as ponderous and ineffective as many ratings expected, and many were frustrated and disillusioned with the new system. Much of this slow response was caused, whether intentionally or not, by the Admiralty keeping the Welfare Committee waiting as to which proposals had been accepted. There was much dissatisfaction when it was learnt that proposals that had been rejected could not be resubmitted. A delegation from the Welfare Committee, Chief Writers King and Lane, had a meeting with the First Sea Lord, Admiral Sir David Beatty,[10] but received no assurances that welfare representation would improve. Within a few days the Welfare Committee was disbanded.[11]

This was seen as the time for the Admiralty to press home its advantage and emasculate the death benefit societies for good. To this end Admiralty Fleet Order No. 3657[12] was issued. This recognised the "legitimate" activities of the societies but made it plain that any other activity would be a contravention of King's Regulations and would be dealt with appropriately. This, of course, pulled the rug from under the societies and as their role diminished membership went into sharp decline.[13] The Admiralty had won a great victory, but at a cost of resentment at the lack of recognition for lower deck representations, which would come back with a vengeance in 1931.

There was, however, one benefit society which remained above all the political machinations and that was William Barrett's RNEBS; this could be attributed to the higher pay and quicker promotion prospects of Artificers, but may be the likelihood that Artificers were happy to be in employment and relatively well paid and for the moment secure when in industry there was much unemployment and hardship.

That there was security of employment was not universal and the passing out class of Artificer Apprentices of December 1922 were discharged en bloc, without any compensation, services no longer required.[14] This must have been a devastating blow to these men who had endured four and a half years to find at the last hurdle that there was no future for them. There were also cost saving measures introduced, all training would be concentrated at *Fisgard* at Portsmouth and the other training establishments were closed. This was all part of a much larger cost saving exercise initiated by Lloyd George's post-war government and recommended by a Committee of National Expenditure chaired by Sir Eric Geddes. The recommendations covered all aspects of government spending and included a savage reduction in the number of officers in both the army and the Royal Navy. This reduction was always referred to as the "Geddes Axe" and caused much resentment.

It is into this volatile atmosphere that a young boy named John Gurr received a letter from the Admiralty to make his way to HMS *Fisgard* to enter the Royal Navy as an Artificer Apprentice. John came from a naval background, born in Gillingham in 1906, the son of a ship's Corporal who was killed during the First World War when his ship HMS *Cressy* was sunk, along with her sister ships *Aboukir* and *Hogue*, by a German submarine in the early days of the war. John was one of the successful candidates out of the some 2,000 applicants who sat the civil service examination the previous April, with the results published on 9 June 1922, as John wrote in his autobiography:

> *I was pleased when my Headmaster called me to his study to tell me I had been successful. I had been assisted by Nomination on account of my father, a Petty Officer (Naval Police), who had been killed when his ship HMS* Cressy *was torpedoed with her sister cruisers* Hogue *and* Aboukir *on September 22nd 1914.*[15]

Much of the early weeks and months in *Fisgard* would have differed little to the routine that Reg Bennett would have followed some twelve years earlier in HMS *Indus*. Indeed, the accommodation would have also been very familiar to Reg. The hulks of *Indus* differed little from *Fisgard*. There was the same kitting up, the same swimming test and the same parade training and physical exercise. Whereas Reg wrote of the Boys being organised by classes, John mentioned the separate divisions – Anson, Benbow, Grenville and Rodney – and their divisional colours and he commented on the keen rivalry this divisional system gave, not only to sporting fixtures but to even normal day-to-day events.

On Sundays there was the privilege of a lie-in until 0700 and egg and bacon for breakfast, but this was tempered by the necessity to prepare for a Sunday ritual:

> *Then we donned our No.1 uniforms ready for Divisions at nine and Captains Inspection after which the Junior Class was detailed to rig church in the gymnasium and unrig after the Service, which was always boisterously sung. At one o'clock we were all at liberty to go ashore if we wished – either by "Gosport Liner" (ferry boat) direct from the ship to Harbour Station Pier – Fare one penny, or by walking from the ship to Gosport and take the ferry from there to Harbour Station – Fare One Half-Penny – quite a money saver.*[16]

John's entry was only twenty-five strong, very much smaller than the average intake. This was another result of the government economies and the "Geddes Axe", the more normal intake being around sixty or seventy boys. John's entry was made up of sixteen ERAs, six OAs and three EAs. Of the ERAs, eleven were allocated as fitters and turners, two as boilermakers, two as coppersmiths and one as an engine smith. With the trades allocated, Christmas leave was granted and on his return his class was no longer at the bottom of the hierarchical ladder; in 1924 his class started their "Senior" years and had to sign on for twelve years' service.

John wrote little of his remaining years at *Fisgard* until his "passing out" in December 1926 and his subsequent time in the Naval Barracks in Portsmouth waiting for the draft to his first ship. There was some confusion as to which ship he was to join. First it was HMS *Revenge*, but in no time at all it was changed to HMS *Emperor of India* and he sailed down to Portland on the aircraft carrier HMS *Furious* to join her, travelling to his new ship on an old motor-launch, arriving at seven-thirty in the evening, in time for a late supper.[17] At the time of John's "passing out" there were more ramifications of the government's austerity drive. Despite assurances from politicians, among them Stanley Baldwin, that the 1919 rates of pay were permanent, cuts were still being discussed.[18] Finally an Admiralty Fleet Order was issued stating that men recruited after October 1925 would receive only 3/- a day, as opposed to the 1919 rate of 4/- a day for Able Seamen.[19] The fact that Admiral Sir David Beatty raised no objections to this swingeing cut is in stark contrast to his vigorous opposition to the Treasury's demand "for cuts in spending on new cruisers".[20]

It should have been obvious that having two levels of pay for the same rate was a recipe for disaster, but the Admiralty appeared blind to any such problems. One of the first troubles was that those on the 1925 rate could not afford the same mess bills as those on the 1919 rate: bills could be as much as 10/- a month and on foreign stations as much as 25/-[21] and those married men under twenty-five received no marriage allowance.[22] NAAFI revenue dropped and applications for relief from hardship to the Royal Naval Benevolent Society increased, putting a strain on that organisation's finances. A further strain on household budgets was the high cost of rental accommodation in naval home ports.[23] This could not be alleviated by living away from these areas as the cost of travel was also prohibitive: there was no way out.[24] That these hardships were known is indicated in a report by the Commodore of Portsmouth Barracks detailing the difficulties many young men with families faced.[25]

These cuts were not only for seamen ratings but across the board. New entry Artificer Apprentices also had their pay reduced and on top of that the cherished gilt buttons on their best suits were changed to black buttons. While in financial terms the reduction in Apprentices' pay was not significant, Apprentices had always been lowly paid until they had completed their training it was the loss of the gilt buttons that rankled most.

The Admiralty clearly believed that the divisional system, whereby ratings could, through their Divisional Officer, make verbal representation of grievances, was quite sufficient. That those who were not articulate enough to air their problems, and that in many cases the ratings saw the Divisional Officer as no friend but one who always found fault, did not inspire confidence in the system, as well as there being a disciplinary disincentive to make complaints whereby "the complainant risked punishment for bringing unfounded charges against his superior or making a vexatious complaint".[26]

There were other protests in the form of mass leave-breaking. One example is HMS *Revenge* in the Mediterranean Fleet in 1930; a previously happy ship was treated to harsh discipline by her new Captain, with not only leave-breaking but desertions the result of this breakdown in relations between Captain and lower deck. Even worse was to follow a few months later, when the crew of the submarine depot ship HMS *Lucia*, feeling harshly treated and seeing no other option, refused to turn to and stayed below in their mess decks.[27]

The consequent courts martial caused public uproar at the perceived injustice of the sentences and, as Carew points out, prior to the mutiny "a shipwright had raised a perfectly legitimate grievance with the first lieutenant but was punished for making a frivolous complaint".[28] There was little else the lower deck could do to raise concerns with treatment and conditions, all other avenues being effectively blocked.

Another young man who joined *Fisgard* at the time of the "Geddes Axe" was Don Cantellow, who made his way Portsmouth in January 1923. As he wrote of these early days,

> To be honest, I almost missed the boat! Told to report to Portsmouth Dockyard Main Gate I got off the train from Waterloo at the Town rather than the Harbour Station and was directed to Unicorn Gate. From there I had to trudge around the seemingly endless dockyard wall via several gates until I finally reached the Main Gate where I received a rocket from the P.O. in charge and no great enthusiasm from the rest of the new entrants! By the time we had walked to North Corner Jetty in the rain to catch a steam-pinnace to Hardway I was soaking wet, dead tired, very miserable and on the point of chucking it all in! However, I survived this first hurdle and in the early evening of 2nd January 1923, during the apprentices' Christmas leave period, I stepped aboard HMS Fisgard. This quartet of venerable hulks was destined to be my home for the next three and a half years, and I was soon sitting down to a meal with my new colleagues.
>
> I don't recall the details of this meal, I must have been ravenous for it wasn't long before I developed a very poor opinion of Fisgard food in general and the quite revolting cocoa, fishcakes and sponge pudding in particular, all of which seemed to feature so frequently on the menu. The notorious Geddes Axe had recently fallen on the Navy and our A class was only 24 strong, 14 ERAs, seven OAs and three EAs.

After supper we were issued with our kit and instructed to mark it in black ink using a wooden type. The uniform outfit was complete except for two suits and included two hammocks, two nightshirts, "Long-John" underwear, two black bow-ties, stiff white collars, boots and shoes, a "housewife" and boot brushes. We were then shown how to sling our hammocks and after making a passable job of this unfamiliar task we retired for the night in the A class section of the communal mess deck on the accommodation hulk formerly and somewhat aptly known as HMS Terrible.

Next morning after breakfast we were marched to Levy's Naval Tailors in Edinburgh Road to be measured for our No 1 double-breasted suit in a navy blue material (oddly called Tartan) and a single-breasted serge suit, both with brass buttons. On then to Pitt Street RN Baths to take the Swimming Test which strangely only lads from Naval ports failed. We then marched back to Fisgard for final settling-in before our solitude was ended by the return from leave of eight classes, all bigger than ours, and all but "J" class sharing the same mess deck with us!

I recall having to sing to both "H" class and the almighty "J" class (who had their own flat on another deck) as part of the initiation ceremony.

In those days only Chief Artificers and Masters-at-Arms wore three brass buttons on each sleeve and Artificers went from 5th Class (Leading-Hand rate) to 4th Class (CPO rate). In 1925 new regulations were introduced which affected pay and conditions. All CPOs became entitled to wear three brass buttons on each sleeve, Apprentices and 5th class Artificers lost their brass buttons and 4th Class Artificers lost their CPO status and became POs.

I spent three and a half years in the Fisgard hulks at Portsmouth and the final year of my apprenticeship at Chatham from where my class, by then reduced to 21 were the first class to pass-out as "J" class. The accommodation in RNB Chatham was pretty awful but the food was much better than in Fisgard.[29]

In 1924 another Apprentice joined who would a somewhat greater impact on the service than John Gurr. His name was Walter Frederick Boyt Lane. He was born on 7 February 1909 in humble surroundings in Copnor, in Portsmouth. There is no record of his time as an Apprentice, but he joined the Royal Navy Engineering College at Keyham in 1926 and during the war he was awarded the Distinguished Service Cross while serving as a Lieutenant Commander in HMS *Cossack* at the second Battle of Narvik in 1940, and was then mentioned in dispatches while serving as the Commander (E) in the battleship HMS *Warspite*. After the war he was Engineer-in-Chief at Bath and then Director of Marine Engineering at the Admiralty from 1958 to 1961. He retired as a Rear Admiral in 1961 and passed away in 1988. Lane Division in HMS *Fisgard* was named after him in September 1966.

There was a serious incident in November 1925 when the Selborne–Fisher scheme for officer training was suddenly abolished and the Officer Corps was split into twelve categories: Executive, Engineer, Medical, Dental, Accountant, Instructor, Chaplain, Shipwright, Ordnance, Electrical, Schoolmaster and Wardmaster. As Penn commented,

> *Thus the conception of the military and the civil officer, antiquated, outdated and hopelessly out of place in the Twentieth Century, was at last relegated to the pages of history. How much rancour, bitterness and argument, how many pages of fruitless discussion, how many harsh words, unkind and unjustifiable statements, how many insults and snubs might have been saved if this decision had been made fifty years before!*[30]

Despite these sentiments there were many engineers who branded the decision a "great betrayal" and there was much of the old dissension with letters in the press both for and against, but the biggest bone of contention was that the distinguishing colours were reintroduced and all officers wore the executive curl. Engineers continued to be classified as Lieutenant (E); nevertheless, they claimed betrayal, alleging the new purple to be more maroon than the former purple.

At the same time as John Gurr was leaving *Fisgard*, another Artificer Apprentice also joined the fleet as an ERA 5th Class. His name was Raymond Haydn Tribe and, while he was not at that time any more noteworthy than any other Apprentice, there was much in his future career that did make him stand out from his peers. He was commissioned before the Second World War and in a distinguished career rose to the rank of Rear Admiral, one of only fifteen ex-Artificers to reach flag rank. A division at HMS *Fisgard* was named after him in 1972.

In early 1927 a young Lieutenant joined *Fisgard*, having just returned from service on the China Station in HMS *Petersfield*. He was familiar with Apprentices, having joined as a Boy Artificer in 1911 and having served through the First World War as an ERA. So Reg Bennett was back in an environment he knew well. When he joined *Fisgard* it was at the time that the senior classes were on their way to Chatham and much in the establishment was in a state of flux. As was to happen in his next time involved with Apprentices, he did not have a high opinion of some of his superiors. He considered one incident considered worthy of inclusion in his journal:

> *I had been in the Establishment about three weeks before I had the opportunity of talking to the Engineer Commander. I had of course been formally introduced to him on arrival. On the second occasion he sent for me before noon. He delivered a homily to me about my conduct, almost in the terms of the vicar to the village idiot, and ended by saying if I did not suit "US" the imperial we! He would get rid of me. He had previously interrogated me as to my personal affairs, and hearing I was married with a child I suppose his words were meant as a threat, and that I should cower in my shoes. He was rather taken aback at the reply that he got. I immediately went over to the attack, and told him that if he felt like that he should apply for my relief right away. I had not asked for the job, didn't particularly relish it, and so would not greatly disturbed if he did ask for my replacement. He then blurted out that he had asked for me – a bad tactical error, and that he hoped that I would be happy there. To show his good faith and sociability he said that his wife would call on mine to see if there was anything that she could do for me. This made me open my eyes for he was the complete snob, and in his opinion a great condescension. I did not take it at more than face value. However if felt I had won the first round with this stupid ma, and felt I could handle him.*[31]

These are strong words indeed from a junior Lieutenant and reflect a man who knew where he was going and was confident of his ability and ambition. He mentioned in his journal that there was some domestic toing and froing between Reg and his wife and Commander Buckmaster and his wife, which eventually fizzled out to nothing, but could have had repercussions to a less astute man than Reg.

Because of Reg's perceived knowledge of diesel engines he was put in charge of the diesel generating plant as there was no Electrical Officer borne, an incredible omission in an Artificers' training establishment that included Electrical Artificer Apprentices. This turned out be something of a poisoned chalice as the steam generating plant had recently been condemned and prior to Reg's arrival a lack of diesel expertise had resulted in many power outages, which left the Establishment in the dark for hours on end. The man who had been employed to maintain the diesel plant was a retired CERA, but it was obvious that the task was beyond him and that the four machines required serious attention. Despite this and the unwanted attentions of Commander Buckmaster, who seemed to show a lack of engineering expertise at every turn, Reg managed to get all the diesel engines to a good state of repair and they operated without trouble for the remaining two years that Reg spent in *Fisgard*. Indeed, he was recognised as an "expert" on diesel engines:

> One of the Apprentices who was later my Senior Engineer in the "Formidable" told me that the apprentices had enshrouded me in the halo of glory in so far as Diesel Engines were concerned. Little did they know, yet I was always interested in this type of engine for they provided many interesting problems.[32]

Despite this diversion, Reg's main task was as a Divisional Officer to "Rodney" Division, which he thought could do with a fillip, it not being in the best of shape, particularly on the sporting field. In this endeavour Reg led from the front, taking part in the very next sporting fixture, a cross-country run, and in this he insisted that the Divisional Petty Officers discard their bicycles and run with Apprentices. One can only speculate how this was received by the Petty Officers. But this was insisted on under threat of being returned to barracks. All this had the desired effect and the junior Apprentices duly won the trophy and this set the tone for more sporting enterprise.

In his time as a Divisional Officer Reg was concerned at certain aspects of discipline amongst the Apprentices that he believed was due to the slackness of the Duty Petty Officers. The aspect that caused him most concern was the suspicion that there seemed to be little movement after Reveille and his suspicions were confirmed when he entered the Apprentices' mess deck to find all abed and no Duty Petty Officer. This resulted in a reprimand for the Petty Officers, who were unhappy that they would no longer be able to take their time over their early-morning cup of tea. It was a similar story with the leave books, which Reg believed were being manipulated to show all the Apprentices were on board when, in fact, some were still ashore. This manipulation could only be down to the Petty Officers, who had access, whereas the Apprentices did not. Reg believed this was again due to slackness on the part of the Petty Officers, though there was some suggestion of bribery. The outcome on this occasion was rather more serious and the Petty Officers involved were relieved of their divisional duties and "returned to Depot."[33]

During his time in *Fisgard* Reg does make much of the snobbery of many of his brother officers, particularly the Executives:

> *The Naval section was snobbish, and suburban in their outlook and the wife of an ex Lower Deck Officer was not well received in "pukka" circle, especially the wife of an Engineer Officer. We ignored this, welcomed those that accepted us, and felt sorry for those that who put on the "Dog" as the Americans had it in those days. Those were the days of calling cards and etiquette. We did not call socially on those from whom it was known that we should receive snub. This applied the Commodore of the Barracks and his wife. She used to segregate the Engineers and Paymasters from the Executive Branches. We did not call on them socially.[34]*

It would seem incredible to anyone today that such behaviour was normal, but it had long been a bone of contention amongst Engineers that they were still perceived as "engine drivers" and not socially worthy of a commission. There is the apocryphal story of two deck officers discussing engineers; one makes the observation, "I do not question their necessity, Abuthnot, merely their presence on the Upper Deck in daylight".[35] It is hard to contemplate such an attitude today and such sentiments have no place in modern society.

Despite the poor accommodation afforded by the hulks that made up *Fisgard* there were many Apprentices who looked back on these days of bad food, worse living conditions and harsh discipline with fond nostalgia, as Tommy Boustead, who joined Benbow Division in 1928, wrote:

> *The hulks were in the form of a square and numbered Fisgard 1, 3, 2 and 4 when viewed clockwise from aloft. Fisgard 1 was the ship's company accommodation, F2 was Workshops, F3 (the former HMS Terrible) was the apprentices accommodation etc and F4 was more workshops. The hulks were interconnected by covered walkways. Fisgard 2 was a mystery to us juniors for it seemed to be the sacred province of J Class who were destined to be, at Christmas 1928, the very last class to pass out from HMS Fisgard (Afloat). Some juniors may have left the path between F3 and F4 with some trepidation for I seem to recall the*

dentist was housed in F2 which was known as Crystal Palace as its upper works were extensively covered by glass. Fisgard 3 was connected to the Hardway shore by a long bridge and the water between the bridge and Fisgard 1 formed a boat pound for the cutters and whalers used for instruction and recreation. The water between the bridge and Fisgard 3 was used for swimming and water polo. What fun the environmentalists of today would have had if they had been around in the 20s – I don't recall any epidemics or other significant illnesses attributable to the life we led! I must confess however that I had the unique experience shortly after joining of being lowered in a cot into the hospital boat (no access for wheeled ambulances!) and being transported to RNH Haslar where I was hoisted ashore and my cot pulled up the rails into the hospital wherein I was hastily transferred to the Zmotics ward to spend some time in miserable isolation to recover from smallpox vaccination fever. This was clearly not attributable to the effluent from Fareham and Portchester which flowed past our enclave at least twice a day![36]

This gives some idea of the final layout of *Fisgard* and of what many terms of Apprentices considered quite normal and compared very favourably with what was awaiting them at Chatham. As Tommy noted, he "emerged on to the deck of another of the hulks which we learned was to be our living, recreational and educational home for four and a half years. In the event it was only two and a half years when we were transferred to RN Barracks Chatham. That's another story and certainly from my viewpoint a very sad one – from a good school to a penitentiary!"[37]

In 1928 it was becoming increasingly clear that the hulks that made up *Fisgard* were no longer fit for purpose, It was decided that the workshops were no longer suitable, but it must also have been the standard of accommodation that was the real driver for change; living conditions had changed hardly at all since the first Boy Artificers joined at Chatham in 1903. To this end there began a three-year period of phased movement to new accommodation at Chatham. It started with the move of Senior Apprentices to Royal Naval Barracks Chatham, where they were accommodated with junior stokers, where the food was appalling and their leave arrangements much restricted in comparison with the liberty of many junior ratings with less service time.

Another viewpoint is provided by Charles Lamdin, who joined *Fisgard* in Rodney Division in 1927 and he remembered the move to Chatham with less than grateful anticipation of new accommodation and better living conditions:

In 1852 the prison hulks afloat in Portsmouth harbour were declared unfit for accommodation and the convicts were moved ashore. Seventy-six years later, in 1928 the Admiralty decided that the Fisgard hulks were unsuitable for Artificer Apprentices and decided to convert the former Detention Quarters at Chatham into a shore base for the exclusive use of Boy Arts.

The movement of apprentices, which was phased over several years, began with the two most senior classes, (J and H) in 1928 and was followed a year later by the next two most senior classes (G&F). The "new" Fisgard Block at Chatham was not ready for occupation until January 1932 so in the meantime "senior" Boy Arts, with at least two and a half years service, were accommodated in two double rooms of Duncan Block in RNB Chatham (HMS Pembroke). Some of my reminisces of this unhappy interim period in the history of Fisgard are given here.[38]

He continues in the same vein, having little good to write about Chatham, He still looks back to *Fisgard,* lamenting its demise.

Over the years, HMS Fisgard at Portsmouth had developed many amenities, not least of which was a separate locker and living area away from the mess deck. There was no such luxury in Duncan Block, the mess deck doubling as a hammock sleeping area. Other facilities missed were the Dark Room, Hobbies Room and Recreation Room with billiard tables etc. There was no chapel for quiet reflection – in fact we were right back to basics!

The occupants of the other wing of Duncan Block were Stokers and other junior ratings who were generally only there for a short time compared to our long sojourn; they enjoyed rather more generous leave than us and seemed to think we were a crowd of "pansies". This did not endear them to us and our reaction, particularly early on made us far from popular with them and with the RNB Authorities.

Our life, compared with that in Fisgard at Portsmouth, was considerably changed. Immediately after a quick breakfast we fell in front of the Block, were quickly inspected and were then marched to our workplace, some 15–18 minutes away. This routine occurring daily regardless of the weather conditions. Although the food in Fisgard had not been particularly good, here in Chatham Barracks it was quite appalling. Occasionally, when you were employed in the Dockyard, you were able to take a packed lunch – two rolls with ham and either apple, orange or banana. This repast, washed down in St Mary Island Canteen with a large pint of "Goffer", and supplemented by a four ounce Duncan chocolate bar (cost 4d) was a real treat!

Eventually we were allocated a Rec Room on the far side of the Barracks, some 800 yards from our living quarters, near to a football ground and next to the Dental Surgery.[39]

From these memories from some of the Apprentices who were there at the time, the move seems poorly planned, poorly executed and with little consideration given to the young men it would affect most. There seems to have been little thought given to how the Apprentices would spend their leisure time, such as it was, or even to the most basic well-being of boys of this age, which certainly revolves around their stomachs and how well this organ was catered for by the quality and quantity of food available. While the senior Apprentices endured this less-than-ideal accommodation, the old Detention Quarters were being made ready for occupation by all Apprentices and by the end of 1931 the accommodation was ready.

Meanwhile, life onboard *Emperor of India* followed the pattern of naval routine in the inter-war period, a series of exercises, manoeuvres and courtesy visits to foreign ports to show the flag, and so it was for John Gurr, who recalled a visit to Vigo in north-west Spain. This was his first trip to foreign climes and he was somewhat disappointed with the town, which he thought was more of a village and "hilly and dirty and a couple of afternoon walks for us was quite enough to see what little there was to see and sample the Spanish wine".[40] What a disappointment this must have been for a young man abroad for the first time. Though he was much happier when the ship sailed from Vigo to conduct more exercises before anchoring off Gibraltar. As he noted, "Ah! This was better. Clean streets – or Street, as there was only the one – Main Street, and the weather was so much better, warm and sunny, after the grey and stormy days in the north Atlantic; *Emperor of India, Benbow,* the two aircraft-carriers and a couple of the cruisers had to anchor miles out in the bay which meant a very long boat-trip to get ashore".[41]

The ship continued around the western Mediterranean, including a visit to Malaga, where the ship had to anchor more than a mile offshore, which again meant a long boat trip to get ashore. This led to an interesting episode; the motor-launch had broken down and for whatever reason it was decided that Liberty Men would be taken ashore in the sailing-pinnace, not the best idea in ideal conditions, but with very light winds it took over two hours to reach the town and on the return the wind died completely. This left the boat at the mercy of the currents and it duly drifted into the night, with *Emperor of India* fading into the distance. Fortunately the sailing-pinnace still had oars onboard and with thirty Liberty Men toiling they managed, after two hours, to regain the safety of the ship.[42]

As well as these goodwill flag-showing trips to foreign ports, the ships also arranged sporting fixtures between each other. Football was always well supported but it seems that fleet regattas were particularly popular; it is not clear whether that is with the lower deck or the Captains, though it is not hard to imagine which. These regattas would generate intense rivalry, whether inter-department or inter-ship, and everyone was expected to take part in some capacity. Similarly, any sort of "Ship open to Visitors" was also expected to be supported by everyone. This included such activities as "Carnival Week" in Plymouth, home port to *Emperor of India*, something that John remembered well:

> *We were "Open" most afternoons and had even more visitors as the wives, mothers and fathers and children of the entire (almost) ship's company came on board, and on one day we held a Childrens' Party. What a day! They were everywhere and we all had to see that they came to no harm. The capstan was rigged as a roundabout; the barrels of "A" turret on the foc's'le were use to support swings; a long slide was rigged from the top of "Y" turret down to the quarterdeck, and the main derrick normally used for hoisting the steam picket-boats inboard – was used to lift a large "viewing platform" into the air to give the children a sea-gull's eye view of the ship and Plymouth Sound. Tables were brought up from messes and set below the guns of "Q" turret amidships laden with tea, bread and butter, jam and cakes for our young guests, and a wonderful time was had by all; The Week ended with a dance on board and a Search-light Display, and we steamed along to Torbay to entertain thousands of holiday-makers and the residents of Torquay and Paignton all keen to see "their Navy" as they climbed and clambered everywhere.[43]*

So life continued for John through 1928, with more exercises, visits and "spring" and "summer" cruises, more regattas and more visits to show the flag. This record of the period in Plymouth and Torbay with the ship "Open to visitors" gives a good indication of the day-to-day life onboard a Royal Navy warship and how the public perceived the Service and its sailors.

At the end of 1928, in response to an Admiralty fleet notice, John volunteered to join the cruiser HMS *Diomede*, which was just commissioning for service with the Royal New Zealand Navy, but, as is the case so often with such plum jobs, that was the last John heard of it and instead he stayed with *Emperor of India* until she unexpectedly returned to Plymouth to decommission prior to being scrapped. So instead of finding himself on the way to New Zealand he was instead sent to the newly built county class cruiser HMS *Shropshire* as part of the commissioning party. By now John had progressed to Acting ERA 4th Class and was confirmed in this rate on 19 February 1929,[44] a few months after he had had to bring forward his wedding day because of his new draft, and he married on 12 August 1929.

It was necessary to travel from Chatham by train to join the ship on the Clyde at Dalmiur. The train left at six in the morning and there were about 200 officers and men on the train, complete with packed lunch of "cheese- and corned-beef-sandwiches, a Rock cake and an apple and orange".[45] Sparse enough fare for a journey of over twelve hours. It was straight into work the following day, steam was raised and the engine room staff acquainted themselves with the machinery. With very little time the ship sailed for Chatham. It was now that the benefits of having oil-fired boilers was apparent: no longer the grind involving the whole ship's company, together with the filth, noise and discomfort of coaling ship.

As well as the ease of fuelling there was also the benefits of a new ship, with its greater creature comforts, compared by John: "she was clean and comfortable with lots of space and a high deck-head, more on the lines of a passenger liner".[46] It was in December that the ship was considered to be ready to join her squadron and they sailed into Grand Harbour, Valetta, in time for Christmas.

There had been dramatic developments during the 1920s, some not for the good, and these caused simmering resentment that would surface in the new decade. Training of Artificer Apprentices had moved from Portsmouth and *Fisgard* to less-than-ideal temporary accommodation at Chatham, Apprentices had lost the privilege of gilt buttons on their no.1 uniform and pay had been reduced for those who joined after 1925.

There was also the realignment of rate, with 4th Class Artificers no longer being Chief Petty Officers but instead having the substantive rate of Petty Officer. There was much to ponder, both for John Gurr and for the Royal Navy at large.

chapter five

The Thirties, Peace, Mutiny and the Storm Clouds of War

• • •

Old Tubal Cain was a man of might,
In the days when earth was young;
By the fierce red light of his furnace bright,
The strokes of his hammer rung:
And he lifted high his brawny hand
On the iron glowing clear,
Till the sparks rushed out in scarlet showers,
As he fashioned the sword and spear.[1]

As the new decade opened, life as an ERA at sea did not change. There continued the watch-keeping, maintenance and defect repair. The ships continued with their seasonal cruises, the exercises and visits to foreign ports, some lively, some not. But there were still problems on the lower deck with representations to the Admiralty and the lack of any mechanism to highlight grievances very much to the fore.

In the Mediterranean John was unfortunately taken ill with stomach pains, just before Christmas 1929, which required an operation in the Naval Hospital at Bighi, situated in the town of Kalkara, Malta. This indisposed John for some time and his ship sailed without him for the "spring cruise". It also somewhat curtailed his Christmas celebrations as he was not well enough to rejoin *Shropshire* until the end of January. Things continued with further exercises, port visits and inter-ship and -squadron sporting fixtures.

As can be imagined, when the Mediterranean Fleet returned to Malta there would be literally thousands of sailors ashore at any one time, many headed straight to the hedonistic delights of Stradda Stretta, always known to sailors as "The Gut", a street of virtually nothing but bars, with the occasional food establishment, which were usually best given a wide berth, in the interests of keeping a stable stomach. Another very popular recreation was the regular tombola sessions, the only form of gambling allowed in the Royal Navy, and for a shilling outlay it was possible to win what John refers to as "The BIG one", which on a Saturday night after pay day could be as much a £100, the amount a stoker could earn in a year.[2]

In August 1930 the First Lord of the Admiralty, A.V. Alexander, paid a visit to the ship and told the ship's company that they would soon be on their way to Australia in exchange for HMAS *Canberra*, which would spend a year exercising with the Mediterranean Fleet. John was very excited at the prospect but some on board were less enthusiastic. There were those who were approaching pension or completion of their engagements and those who, to John's amazement, did not want to go to Australia and so suitable replacements were trawled from the other ships of the Fleet. The short notice of this major alteration – they would be sailing from Malta on 15 October – to the ship's programme may seem astonishing to modern eyes but such actions were rather more commonplace when ship undertook two- and three-year foreign commissions. But, as John was only too aware, such delights were liable to disappear as swiftly as they had appeared and sure enough as the ship left dry dock in Malta the whole exciting voyage was cancelled: the Australian government could not afford to finance the cost of the exchange.

At the same time as John was looking forward to his time in Australia, in Chatham Reg Bennett, now a Lieutenant Commander, had arrived in readiness for the influx of Apprentices that would be coming from Portsmouth in the New Year. At this time the Commanding Officer was an Engineer Commander named "Tiny" Dalton; as Reg wrote, "Tiny" was anything but and cut an imposing figure when refereeing rugby matches, but he would be leaving at the end of the year, when an Engineer Captain would be appointed. Reg would be in charge of workshop training with four Lieutenants under him.

The senior officers in *Fisgard* did not impress Reg overly. The Captain, Engineer Captain Carlisle, he describes as:

An able administrator, and amiable in character, but with strong personal prejudices. I did not think much of his engineering, and in fact he left most of such problems on my plate. He was the first Engineer to command an Establishment outside the R.N. Engineering College, and no doubt had been told by the Engineer-in-Chief to make a success of it. He was somewhat hamstrung by being subordinate to the Commodore of the Barracks, Andrew Cunningham, we were administratively part of the Barracks. He had, however, direct connections with both the Commander-in Chief, and the Admiralty in certain matters. The Commodore of e Barracks was Cunningham and he kept his fingers out of our pie to a greater extent than most people expected. I felt that this arrangement made it necessary for Carlisle to tread warily.[3]

The Executive Commander, Guy Ottley, Reg describes as a pleasant and popular officer, liked by all. He had been one of the first officers to change from Executive to Engineer in November 1925 when the Selborne–Fisher scheme for officer training was suddenly abolished. Ottley spent much time in these early days preparing the organisation of the Apprentices and for whatever reason decided that the Establishment should be run on the entry system rather than the new divisional system. Reg had experience of the entry system from his own time as a Boy Artificer and had, indeed been a Divisional Officer to Artificer Apprentices during his time at *Fisgard* in 1927. He was quite sure then that the divisional system provided a better way of ensuring a more equitable experience for both junior and senior Apprentices, the juniors would not be at any disadvantage on the sporting field and the senior Apprentices could exercise their "powers of command" over their juniors, though this may have led and indeed did lead to abuses that were commonly called "sprogging", fagging by any other name, and a problem that would remain for many years.

One of the pressing matters was the appointment of a "Headmaster". Reg mentioned this in his journal:

The holder of the post in "Fisgard" was one Mathieson by name, and he had been Headmaster in the "Indus" when I joined in 1911, and was Headmaster in

"Fisgard" during my period there in 1927-29. I therefore knew him well, and, though a likeable man, was no great shakes at his job. Moreover he was very near retirement. It was therefore decided to retire him at that time, and replace him with a Head Schoolmaster in the R.N. Educational Service with the rank of Headmaster Lieutenant.[4]

Meanwhile in the Mediterranean John Gurr had suddenly found himself with a pierhead jump to HMS *Wren*, a "V and W"-class destroyer, which, as he mentioned, at 1,100 tons is a very different proposition to a 10,000-ton cruiser. The ERA's mess was the first obvious difference:

I climbed aboard – it was only about six-feet freeboard – and walked along the steel deck to the break of the fo'c'sle where, just inside the screen was a 2'6" diameter hatch with a vertical ladder leading down to the ERA's Mess, a compartment 16' long by 8' wide and 7' high, and a home for four – the Chief and three ERAs. Our kit was stowed in the seat lockers along the ships side where we sat at table for meals. Suitcases were kept in overhead racks and hammocks in a bin in the corner while in another corner a rack was provided for the crockery, cutlery, condiments, bread and other provisions. There was also a folding wash-basin stand, and one stoker had the task of looking after us and the Mess.[5]

This gives some idea of the living conditions onboard a small ship in the thirties. The mess must have been all but inaccessible in rough weather and almost uninhabitable if you were trapped there in the sort of weather John encountered shortly after joining, where it was preferable to sleep in the engine room. The CERA did make him go to the mess for something to eat, though his seasickness must have made eating something of an ordeal.

There was a silver lining to joining *Wren*, in that the ship had reached the end of her commission and was due to return to Devonport in April 1931, a year earlier than would have been the case had John stayed on *Shropshire*, and this allowed John to see his nine-month-old son for the first time He returned to barracks at Chatham after his leave to await his next ship. This was not long in coming and he joined HMS *Malcolm*, which was the leader of the Nore Reserve Flotilla, and this allowed John to go home when not required for duty. It was while he was in this job that John, now an ERA 3rd Class, had an unfortunate incident with some Artificer Apprentices from nearby *Fisgard*, who had been sent to help with the refitting of the underwater valves while HMS *Abdiel* was in dry dock. Without checking himself John allowed one of the Apprentices to "box up" a valve; naturally the only valve to leak on the subsequent flooding up was the one he had not personally checked, a salutary lesson that could have had a disastrous outcome had John not quickly rejointed the valve.

The new accommodation in Chatham was ready and the temporary use of Duncan Block, with its poor accommodation, lack of facilities and abysmal food, was finally a thing of the past, with one class, Rodney 1927, being the only class to have spent the whole of their two years in Duncan Block, The new accommodation consisted of three blocks surrounding a triangular parade ground. The blocks provided not only the living quarters for some 600 Apprentices but also a gymnasium, school rooms, library, sick bay and drill shed. There were also what Vic Blackman, Grenville 1933, describes as "subterranean facilities of laundry, rifle range, photographic dark room and 'Snips and Snobs' shops".[6] Quite an improvement to the facilities originally offered in the spartan Duncan Block when the first Apprentices arrived in Chatham.

There were also many extracurricular activities; this included what Vic described as a "creditable dance band"[7] that played at the popular "Green and White" dances held at the Gillingham Pavilion. There were also the inevitable sports teams to join and Apprentices were encouraged to take part in all manner of sport and there were many sporting triumphs. In 1931 Apprentices won the Nore Command Cross Country Championship and they were well represented in command and national boxing competitions. There was a strong presence in local football leagues, where the Apprentices' teams were always well to the fore. There was also a triumph in the annual rowing cutter race which had been dominated by Royal Marines and Royal Engineers, as Charles Lamdin wrote:

In the Summer of 1931 the Apprentices had the audacity to challenge the Royal Marines and Royal Engineers in their annual rowing cutter race. The great day arrived and the tow path around St Mary's Island swarmed with supporters of the three crews. The race, over two miles, started near Chatham Pier and went down river to Upton Reaches. It had been expected that the REs would win but in the event the Boy Arts crew won by 600 yards. From then on any lingering doubts about the manliness of the Boy Arts was dispelled and all the old animosities were buried. We had gained the respect of our neighbours in RNB.[8]

The simmering resentment felt by many junior ratings came to a head at Invergordon in September 1931. In a budget earlier in the year that would, it was hoped, address the financial black hole facing the country, income tax was increased and indirect taxes were also raised. In a bill that was passed separately, the pay of all those in the public sector, judges to policemen, government ministers to sailors, had their pay reduced on average by 10%. Unemployment benefit would be reduced by the same amount and contributions would be raised, with payments limited to twenty-six weeks. Confrontation, long simmering, would now come to the boil.

It was unfortunate that the Admiralty accepted, as their contribution to the economies, the implementation of the 1925 rates of pay for all. This brought in disproportionate cuts for those least able to afford them; Admirals saw their pay reduced by 7%, a Lieutenant Commander by 3.7%, but an Able Seaman on the 1919 rate of pay by 25% constituting a huge hole in the family budget. Together with the cuts in pay, there were to be changes in pension rights, something that would not immediately assist on cutting the deficit but did adversely affect the levels of pension for many, and these were seen as another betrayal.

The Atlantic Fleet at Invergordon was without its Commander-in-Chief, Sir Michael Hodges, who was ill, and command of the fleet was devolved to Rear Admiral Wilfred Tomkinson in HMS *Hood*; this would be his first independent command.[9] Now a catalogue of errors occurred, both in communications to the Admiral and to the lower deck: Tomkinson was only informed of the pay cuts hours before sailing for Invergordon, with no specific detail or instructions. A letter had been prepared, seeking to justify the pay cuts on the basis of the 1923 Anderson Committee report, now eight years out of date.[10] While this was signalled to foreign units, it was sent by surface mail to units in home waters; the letter addressed to Tomkinson directly was sent in error to HMS *Renown*, a ship he had left two months previously.[11] Worse still, the main copy had gone to HMS *Nelson*, but as Admiral Hodges was ill the letter was pigeonholed to await his return. So Tomkinson, while aware there were to be cuts, did not appreciate the scale on the most junior ratings. A further warning signal from the Admiralty did not arrive in *Hood* until Saturday, when the office was closed and, consequently, no action was taken.

By this time, not only had the news of the cuts spread around the fleet, both from daily newspapers and the BBC, but the severity of the cuts was apparent and there were a lot of very unhappy Able Seamen ready to go ashore. There were rumours that there would be a meeting, most likely in the naval canteen, and these rumours were reported to officers onboard several ships. HMS *Warspite*'s Master-at Arms reported this to the Patrol Officer and similar rumours were reported to the Commander of *Hood*,[12] who made the remarkable comment "Don't worry. We shall be all right on this ship!", [13]showing a complete lack of appreciation as to the depth of feeling amongst junior rates.

This incident was predominately a junior rate protest, though it must be said that many senior rates were most remiss in their actions by not reporting to their superiors the amount of unrest the pay cuts had generated. This also had little effect on Apprentices in Chatham apart from the sight of some ratings from HMS *Valiant*. As Charles Lamdin commented:

Whilst we were doing our passing-out test job, (the dreaded Locomotive end), the Invergordon Mutiny occurred. During our two weeks Passing-out Parade Course we shared the RNB Parade Ground with a group of seamen from HMS Valiant who had been involved in the Mutiny and were undergoing a six weeks intensive High Disciplinary Course. They certainly were put through the hoop![14]

It was in December 1931 that John Gurr was told to "Report to Drafting Office for Draft, I did – and was told I would be joining the battleship *Valiant* on December 29th 1931",[15] the same ship that had been at the heart of the Invergordon Mutiny and whose sailors had been "put through the hoop" in Chatham. Again, this was a seismic shift from *Wren* and *Malcolm*; the ERAs' mess had five CERAs and thirty-four ERAs. Further to the aftermath of the mutiny there were rumours that the ship would pay off, and this was indeed what happened, but John remained onboard while the old crew left and were replaced in the early days of January. With this came a change in daywork employment. In his new job in charge of the maintenance of the ships motor boats, John had an unfortunate accident, caused by the carelessness of two of his stokers, who, during the removal of the picket boat propeller shaft, just let go of it when they heard the pipe "Hands to Tea"; this resulted in the shaft falling onto John's hand, crushing three fingers of his left hand. This limited John's employment for some time and he was consequently put to work in the machine shop working as a turner. It was soon after that *Valiant* paid off and John returned to barracks. In another change of direction John was now sent to HMS *Scout*, one of a class of 900-ton destroyers built during the First World War and now somewhat venerable. This ship and two others, *Scimitar* and *Tempest*, formed the Reserve Flotilla, with only reduced complements, two ERAs and a CERA, which meant that the ERAs were in a two-watch system when the ship was at duty or stand-by.

The routine for these ships was fairly leisurely and consisted of such tasks as guard ship for the Royal Thames Yacht Club Regatta at Southend and attending a civic week at the Thames-side town of Erith. There were more serious issues such as when the ship was ordered to "Proceed with all despatch" to locate HMS *Stuart*, the destroyer leader, which had been in collision with a merchant ship in the North Sea off Great Yarmouth and required assistance to return to port at Sheerness.[16]

HMS *Fisgard* finally closed in December 1931. As the local paper said at the time,

> *Royal Naval Artificers serving the world over will hear with a pang of regret that, with the dismissal of the present classes of Artificer Apprentices to their Christmas Leave on December 23, HMS Fisgard will pass out of existence as a training ship. The closing of the Fisgard will be regretted too by the people of Gosport for the Association between the town and Fisgard has always been of the happiest.*[17]

The working day at *Fisgard* was not for the faint-hearted. "Call the Hands" was at 0600, followed by breakfast, and the working day started at 0730 at the "Factory". This involved a half-mile march there and the same back for their dinner at midday. Work in the "factory" started again at 1315 and continued until 1700, when the same half-mile march took them back for tea. This work at the "factory" was followed by three nights of the week by two hours of schooling from 1800 to 2000.

Reg Bennett commented that this long day was more than he was expected to endure when he was a Boy Artificer and it was decided that the day required modification, particularly for the younger Apprentices. As Reg recorded in his journal,

> *It was argued that they were no longer fresh and alert at the end of a long day. It was therefore decided to introduce daytime study from 10 a.m. to noon*

for the junior apprentices i.e. in their first two years, and for three days a week. This meant that there must be a modification in the teaching staff, from part time civilians to full time Naval Schoolmasters. This rearrangement of the instructional hours also meant that I had to modify the arrangements for the Trade Instructors, and as these were mostly civilians recruited from the Dockyard I had to walk warily as the Yard were discharging some men due to the Financial crisis through the Country was then passing [sic].[18]

He went on to mention that there was considerable pressure to increase daytime instruction, which he managed to thwart, though with little help from Commander Ottley, who "was no use or support to me in these matters".[19]

It seems that the other two Services showed an interest in the training at *Fisgard*. The Royal Engineers sent some officers at Easter and the Royal Air Force Apprentices Training Establishment also visited, though they showed far more interest than the Engineers, who only wanted to watch the rifle drill. It transpired that the RAF employed ex-naval Artificers as trade instructors. However, the RAF did not require the depth of skill taught at *Fisgard* but required only fitters capable of changing parts and troubleshooting.[20]

This meeting of Service culture did have an important outcome. It was apparent that now all Apprentices were in one place they had lost their cutting edge on the sports field and it was therefore decided to challenge the RAF Apprentices and they accepted. Reg formed the opinion from observing the RAF Apprentices that they came from a much wider background then the Artificer Apprentices, who seemed, predominately, to be recruited from the home ports and tended to be the sons of naval ratings or dockyard employees, and he wondered if there was insufficient publicity allied to the lack of encouragement in secondary schools to promote apprenticeships in the Royal Navy.

There remained problems with the training syllabus. While Electrical Apprentices were trained alongside ERAs at HMS *Vernon*, the headquarters of the Torpedo and Electrical Branch prevaricated as to what was to be taught and there was the added restraint of a lack of available funds, which meant that any training aids had to be procured from the scrap heap. Despite these constraints Reg wrote that the Electrical Apprentices and those ERAs who also received some electrical training – some 75% of them in fact – did receive more than adequate training under the direction of Lieutenant Gibson, who had served with Reg in HMS *Hermes* prior to joining *Fisgard*.

One innovation introduced by Reg was the introduction of comprehensive welding training, something that he considered to be of the greatest importance on remote stations and in times of war. To this end Reg produced a syllabus and he submitted this, together with a training plan and suitable test jobs and final test pieces. As he wrote,

> *The cost I estimated to be £5,000. This magnum opus had taken me six months much of my spare time, and quite a bit out of my personal pocket. It took about six weeks for the Admiralty to reply, and then it was to ask for more detail of the training, which in any case commenced in a small way. This was done, but it took me 18 months to get the matter through.*[21]

This innovation had a successful outcome, with the first passing out tests being of a very high standard, and Reg mentioned that he had first-hand experience during the war of the importance of his initiative.

The association with the RAF Apprentices at RAF Halton now bore fruit, with hockey, rugby and football played in the winter of 1932 and cricket in the summer of 1933. Reg gained some satisfaction in that the only game won was cricket and he had been the team trainer.

As Reg had noted during his time in *Fisgard* in 1927–1929, there was still considerable resentment against officers promoted from the lower deck and Reg mentioned that things had not improved. He recounted the prejudice he found for lower deck officers amongst his fellow Engineers:

> *As an example when I called on the Engineer Admiral on the staff of the C-in-C on joining the Staff of the Establishment, he asked if I was married. This was just after the Invergordon affair. I told him that I was and that I had two young children. He threw up his hands in horror and said "Well there you are" as much as to say that such things are irresponsible. I said I did not understand what he was getting at, and he said I was too young to be married. I disagreed, and pointed that the only certain thing about my future was that of continuing in my present rank, Lieutenant Commander and retiring at 45, or at best being promoted to Commander and retiring at 50. I was now 36 years of age so had I postponed marriage I should have found myself encumbered with heavy expenses*

*[sic] of a growing family as I was about to retire. He had no answer to that, and
I don't think he had thought about it in that connection, or had he? He had two
daughters of marriageable age who had not yet found a partner. No one knows
what colours a man's vision.*[22]

Time was to show how misguided the Admiral was and how well Reg did
in his later naval career. He also thought that Captain Carlisle showed some
prejudice, particularly when it came to the selection of Apprentices to go
on to RNEC Keyham as Midshipmen (E). It was normal for one a year to
go down this path but Carlisle cast a veto occasionally. Reg seemed to think
that this may be because his son had just failed to gain entry to Keyham.
But his prejudice was tactfully circumvented to allow the recommended
Apprentices the chance at commissioned status.

By this time Reg's time at *Fisgard* was nearing its end and he asked as
to his next appointment and, after Captain Carlisle visited the Admiralty,
the result was an appointment to the destroyer HMS *Active*; though she
was relatively new her Engineer would normally have been a Warrant
Officer. This, of course, Reg took as a slight and expressed his anger perhaps
rather too forcibly, threatening to resign. It did, however, have the desired
outcome and his appointment was changed to HMS *Acheron*, which was
of the same class as *Active* but had what Reg described as "advanced
experimental machinery",[23] though as the ship suffered from "mechanical
problems", even in her first year of service and which continued to plague
her throughout her life, one wonders whether the "advanced experimental
machinery" was too advanced and too experimental. Just before Reg left
Acheron he achieved his ambition and was promoted to Commander on
30 June 1935.

John Gurr, meanwhile, was awaiting his next draft, having been told
by various friends and colleagues that he was bound for the China Station
and that, of course, the one draft he would not get was HMS *Dragon*, a
D-class cruiser from the First World War, which was due to deploy to the
West Indies. Still waiting for his "definite" China draft, John saw his name
detailed for *Dragon*, such are the vagaries of the Service. So now John found
himself one of twenty engine room ratings waiting to take over from the
crew returning from the West Indies. Having taken over the ship, John was
ready to say farewell to his family and the ship sailed on 21 September 1932
to join the 8th Cruiser Squadron at Bermuda.

This commission started with a bang when they were ordered to assist the Survey Vessel HMS *Challenger*, which that had run aground off the coast of Labrador but fortuitously managed to refloat before *Dragon* arrived.[24] As can happen all too frequently in the West Indies, a hurricane had caused devastation on some of the islands and the inhabitants required assistance. To this end *Dragon* landed some much-needed stores on the small island of Acklin and then steamed on to Cayman Brac, where it was too deep to anchor so the ship steamed up and down, continually distilling fresh water for the islanders, this water being landed in a large canvas container that was normally used as a recreational plunge pool rigged on the upper deck. All the while the ship itself was short of water and the temperatures below decks were almost unbearable, so the ship's company was glad to leave and sail for Kingston, Jamaica, for some respite.

The ship continued to visit islands in the West Indies and had the occasional trip further afield, with visits to Tampa and, having transited the Panama Canal in company with Noël Coward, who entertained the ship's company, San Diego, California. The ship continued up the West Coast to Esquimalt, their first port of call in Canada. There continued further visits in Canada and the USA before the ship returned to the West Indies. This seems to be an almost idyllic peacetime existence that would have been the envy of many sailors not as fortunate as John. It was while in the eastern provinces of Canada that the ship was involved in a serious incident, which John recalled:

> We passed Quebec on Sunday evening, August 12th and went alongside in Montreal at 9 o'clock next morning after being involved in a serious accident.
>
> A Pilot was on board to conduct us up-river and as the ship approached her berth she had to turn to starboard to enter the Basin. I was at my normal station for entering and leaving harbour when – "Full Astern" was ordered at the same time as severe jolting was felt on the starboard shaft and the ship's side.
>
> As we had turned to enter the Basin the strong ebb tide carried our stern towards the port side of the 600 ton tanker Maplebranch, berthed at the entrance to the Basin, and our starboard propeller-blades cut a huge hole in her bottom, causing her to sink and rest on the bed of the river. Fortunately there were no casualties although damage was considerable. Divers found that one blade of our starboard propeller was completely missing; a second had lost two-thirds of its surface area and a third blade had folded over on itself. Our own

divers smoothed the ragged edges and the best was hoped for in the knowledge that there was a spare kept in Bermuda Dockyard.[25]

This damage was obviously beyond the expertise of even the ERAs on board but does not seem to have detracted from the visit programme, which continued unabated. But after the spare propeller was fitted in the floating dock in Bermuda it was decided that a new shaft was essential and as ever the rumour mill churned up various destinations for the new shaft to be fitted, Norfolk, Virginia, was the closest, followed by Halifax, the Clyde, and it was welcome news to everybody on board when the ship's home port of Chatham won the lottery.

All good things must come to an end and on 20 November 1934 the ship returned to Chatham, having been away for two years and two months. John's son had been two when he left and his daughter only six months old. Twelve days' leave was, of course, welcome but would seem to modern eyes to be poor recompense for two years' absence. The ship was docked down in Chatham and a new propeller shaft was fitted; this took until early January 1935, when John was rated ERA 2nd Class and the ship was ready to go to sea for trials prior to returning to her station in the West Indies. There were visits to Galveston in Texas, Cuba and Miami. But this return to the West Indies was only to complete the commission and by 15 August 1935 the ship had returned to Chatham and been paid off. This time John was able to enjoy forty days' foreign service leave.

While John was spending his time at sea, a young boy called Ron Claverley was on his way to HMS *Pembroke* for a medical prior to joining *Fisgard*. Ron, when in his ninety-eighth year, remembered it well:

Soon I received a summons to report to the Naval Barracks, H.M.S. Pembroke for a medical test. To my dismay [and my father's] I failed with swollen tonsils. That was puzzling because we thought they had already been removed. Dad marched me off to see the Medical Officer in the R.M.B. I had another unacceptable complaint, and the M.O. told me to drink a pint of barley water the night before my next medical and I would pass. My tonsils were removed in Maidstone hospital.

I joined H.M.S. Fisgard, the home of Artificer Apprentices, on Tuesday the 25th of August 1935. On that day my childhood ended. After finishing off a Destroyer I was building with my meccano set, I set off from home with a small suitcase and a change of clothing. Full of excitement, I went to join Royal Navy, the finest Navy in the world. When I got there I was told to go home I was too early "Come back about four o'clock, you can leave your suitcase here", the Petty Officer said. Often in the years to come I thought I should have kept on going. I duly returned, let in, and given a tea of bread, butter and jam with a big mug of tea to drink. Some of my class had already arrived and soon the main bulk arrived from Portsmouth and Plymouth. Only 8 of us were from the local area. By the time the last arrived, we were 91 in total, most of who were sons of Navy men or Marines.

On joining we were given a pay and bed number, mine being 243 and 72. When I went to bed on that first night, I realised that for the first time in my life I was on my own; I had to look after myself, no one else would, the other boys would be looking after their own welfare, and I could not contact my parents, and even if I did they couldn't help; I had signed the next 15 years of my life away. I belonged to the Royal Navy, body and soul.

However I wasn't completely inexperienced, my young life of constantly changing schools and environments had honed my primeval instinct of self preservation to a fine degree. I decided until I found out what my new life was all about I would keep a low profile and observe.

On the second day we were given and dressed in green P.T. kit, and told from now on we were Grenville Division and our divisional colour green. Other divisions were Benbow [blue], Rodney [red], and Anson [amber], all named after famous admirals.

Our descriptions were taken and entered on our service documents. Mine read: – Stature: 5ft 7 inches. Chest: 32.1/2 inches. Hair: dark brown. Eyes: blue. Complexion: fresh. Marks, Wounds, and Scars: numerous scars left knee. 1 inch scar on chin. numerous moles on back of calf. The navy got all this for nothing. What a bargain!

We were 15 years old, children really, and the Navy took over the roll as foster parents, and it took its responsibility seriously. It was stern and patriarchal, but to ease us into Navy ways we had a Chief Petty Officer with years of experience, like for instance, "You will do as you are told my lad, or else"!

We went to the clothing store to be kitted out and I must confess when I wore my uniform for the first time I felt pretty good. I, me, Ron Calverley E.A.A. Mx51806 had joined the Navy to see the world, and what did I see? I saw the sea. At least that's what the old song said. There was another song we learnt later on, sang to the tune of a well known Salvation Army hymn:

This my story; this is my song,

We've been in commission too b...y long, Roll on the Nelson, the Rodney,

the Hood

This three funnelled b...d, is no b...y good

Another version: Roll on the Nelson, the Rodney, Renown,

This long funnelled b...d is getting me down.

There was one disappointment. Our No I uniforms were made to measure and we weren't allowed ashore until we had them. I waited 6 weeks for mine so the local girls had to wait before they could see this uniformed Adonis. That reminds me, there was an expression, "He's got his feet under the table". It alluded somewhat enviously, to the apprentice who had found a girl friend, taken home to see her mother and given free home cooked meals. I never succeeded in achieving that status, but I had "near misses."

The first 14 days were spent on the parade ground learning how to march, salute, do rifle drill and obey orders with alacrity. I enjoyed it while it lasted; I liked playing soldiers having been brought up in a military atmosphere.

The class had to pass a swimming test. We had to swim two lengths of the swimming pool and keep afloat for two minutes. It sounds easy enough, but not when fully dressed in a duck suit. It was a seaman's uniform made of material like canvas. P.T. instructors stood on the side of the pool with long poles. If an apprentice tried to swim to the side too soon he was pushed back in, and if he appeared to be drowning he was fished out. Actually it is not as bad as it sounds, the instructors were all heart. At the end we all looked like drowned rats.

With the preliminaries over it was time to get on with the main training course. The biggest trauma happened when we first entered the workshops. There was a vice for each boy with a bolt of steel in it about 3 inches in diameter and 3,1/2 inches long. There were tool boxes by each vice with a boy's name stencilled on the lid. Inside were a 1&3/4lb hammer, flat and cross cut cold chisels and numerous files. One boy was so small he had to stand on his tool box to reach his vice.

Our task was to convert the steel bolt into a hexagonal block, this meant chiselling away the surplus material. The racket was deafening with 91 boys hammering away with enthusiasm. It only took the first day to produce a multitude of blisters on our soft schoolboy hands, and every the time the chisel slipped our hands were lacerated on the sharp chiselled surface. Eventually the task was finished and the hexagon stamped with the boy's number, carefully oiled and stored away, to be produced at a future date, for use in another test job. The second test was more complicated. Each boy was given a bolt of cast iron about 3 inches long and 3.1/2 inches diameter, with an eccentric hole cast in it. The test was to change the external diameter into a hexagonal shape and then fit the original block into the latter. We had to finish the job within a given time, and of course all dimensions to a 1000th part of an inch.

By the time we, the latest A class had finished the first 6 months at Fisgard we were bonded as a division and the next four years did not seem so formidable. We had learnt a thing or two and not so "green". We had passed our first 6 month exams and were to become B class enabling us to enjoy a mid week evening shore leave. Friendships were formed with other classmates, one of whom was a boy Ivor Key who came from the Isle of Wight.

Before I go on any further with my story a word of explanation wouldn't be amiss.

There were three types of apprentices: Engine Room Artificers, Electrical Artificers, and Ordnance Artificers.

There were a certain number of places allocated for each type and before joining we had to let the Admiralty know our order of preference. I chose E.A. for my first preference and I was lucky enough to get it, and as it turned out in later years it was the best thing I could I have chosen.

All apprentices had to undergo four and a half years training in Chatham Dockyard to qualify as Artificers 5th Class. Then they diverted; the E.R.A's joining the fleet for more practical training; the O.A's went to Whale Island, the R.N. Gunnery School in Portsmouth, for further instruction, and last but not least the E.A's went to H.M.S. Vernon in Portsmouth for 6months, and there, they learned the intricacies of ships electrical systems [gunnery control], torpedoes, mines and depth charges. So as an E.A. from the day I joined to the day I put foot on board ship 5 years would lapse.

There were nine classes of apprentices, A. B. C. D. E. F. G. H. and J. On passing exams every 6 months you moved up a class. If, however you failed you were put back a class and failing twice meant discharge. A to D were junior and E. to J, senior apprentices. Pay day occurred once a fortnight, starting with 4 shillings and finishing with eighteen on reaching J class. We were always rich the first week and poor the next. Our dirty laundry was collected regularly by an outside laundry every week, the Navy paying for it to be done. We were responsible for the up keep of our kit. We had a small clothing allowance held by the Paymaster. Each time an item of was bought, the cost was deducted from the allowance and anything left over was given to us when we went on seasonal *leave. The most I received was £3, but it still made me feel like a millionaire. Looking after our kit was always a priority. Now and then we had to lay out our kit for inspection to make sure it was in good condition. and if not, it had to make good at our expense, and probably given a few kit musters as punishment. Seasonal leave I thought was generous; 14 days Christmas and Easter; 21 days for Summer and at school half term a long week end…*

I hope I am not boring you but the next four and a half years were a significant part of my life and my memoirs, and it would be remiss of me not to tell you about them.

Fisgard my new home was built of red brick and consisted of three large buildings enclosing a parade ground capable of accommodating 700 apprentices on parade.

One building of two floors [including the ground floor] housed our school class rooms, J class recreation room, a gymnasium with a stage at one end, and a sick bay. The other buildings had an extra floor. One building housed the senior apprentice's dormitories and recreation room [J class was privileged to have their own dormitory on the ground floor] and the other building housed the junior dormitories and recreation room. Also for general use for all apprentices, the galley, a dining hall, NAAFI shop and library, and in the basement the Chapel, a hobbies room, ironing and drying room, and last of all a shoe shop.

The entrance to Fisgard was via a main gate and guard room, and across the road from the gate was the Naval barracks way below us as we were built on a hill. The road was known to all and sundry as The Khyber Pass.

The four main dormitories accommodated two classes, one at each end, where through swing doors there were ablution rooms, toilets, towel racks, a cloak room and double stairs leading to the parade below. Each dormitory slept about 170 – 180 boys. The dormitories were divided down the middle by a 5ft high partition, with gaps to allow access to each side. Beds were arranged with their heads against the partition, and at the foot of each bed was an old fashioned seamans' chest, with three deep drawers, two above one, without locks, standing about 2 ft high.

On both sides of the dormitories were great big sash windows and under the windows and running the whole length were more beds and chests. Between that row and the beds against the partition, ran another row of beds. It all sounds rather crowded, but in fact there was plenty of room. Apprentices were allowed to place one suitcase on the top of their chest, but it had to be navy issue so that they were all the same.

The beds had two blankets in the summer and three in the winter. No sheets were supplied not even for the mattress. The blankets were rough navy blankets, with two black stripes on each, and when not in use they had to be folded in such a way that the stripes were vertical and in line. They were then placed at the head of the bed with the pillow on top.

To go to bed the method adopted by most boys: – Spread a blanket on the bed and lay on it; pull the edges over yourself so that you were cocooned; place the other blanket over yourself and tuck the edges under. When that was done the next trick:-raise your feet so that the ends of the blankets hung, then lower them with the blankets now under, and you were as snug as a bug in a rug.

Nature did not control the seasons, the Navy did. On the 1st of May summer began and on 1st of October winter began So on the 1st of May you had two blankets and on the 1st of October three blankets.

Smoking was forbidden in the dormitories. Junior apprentices were not allowed to smoke anywhere. To throw down a cigarette end or match was an offence, and if caught punishable. Receptacles were placed at strategic places so there was no excuse. On reaching the age of 18 you could buy 1lb of duty free cigarette tobacco every month for one shilling and threepence.

All raincoats, overcoats and towels had to be kept in the cloakrooms. The dormitories were evacuated from 7.30 a.m. to about 4 p.m. during which time some old Navy pensioners swept the floors, cleaned the toilets and showers. Any item left lying around and not stowed away was confiscated and put in the "Scran Bag". In our case, a large cupboard, where everything was just chucked in. The fee for retrieving it was 3 pence an item, but we boys could retrieve it for bar of Navy soap, much cheaper. The system wasn't peculiar to Fisgard, it was used throughout the Navy, and sometimes the scranbag was the nearest port hole. Needless to say on the whole Fisgard was spotless. Strict discipline made sure it was.

Although we lived in barracks, shipboard language was used all the time. "In" was on board, "Out" was ashore, "Late" was adrift, and we, the "Ship's Company". To go ashore a "liberty boat" had to be "caught" at a specified time. This involved lining up on the parade ground to be inspected by the officer of the day. Liberty men had to be properly dressed and spotless. It was nerve racking until he got to the end of the line and passed you fit to go ashore. Then your identity card had to be handed in to the guardroom and collected on your return. Missing the liberty boat by seconds meant staying on board until the next one, even though you were on dry land and could walk through the main gate. If you were late on return you were "adrift" and punishment inevitably follow. I remember a notice being put up by the main gate for everyone to read before going on seasonal leave stating that trains or 'buses running late would not be accepted as an excuse for being adrift.

I think this is an appropriate time in this saga to tell the story of my shoes. On joining, we were kitted out including a pair of Naval pattern shoes. They were more like boots with the tops cut off. Nobody liked them and were nicknamed "pusser's crabs". When enough money was saved the boys bought a smarter pair ashore, or from Fisgard's shoe shop. If they were bought from the shoe shop they were acceptable, but bought ashore meant more care had to be taken in your choice, style and pattern was important.

I was waiting in line to be inspected before going ashore, when the duty officer looked at my shoes and said, "Where did you buy you those shoes"? I replied "In the shoe shop, Sir". This was a lie because I had bought them ashore; I didn't think he would bother to check. They were confiscated and permission to go shore refused and I thought when "they" found out I would get at least 7 days 8a punishment. So that was that, and I waited for the inevitable punishment, and then I received a letter from my father saying he had received a pair of shoes with a letter of explanation from the Captain's secretary. My father could not believe it and saved them for my next leave.

Apparently when shown, the shoe shop manager confirmed I had bought the shoes from his shop, so two of us had lied. He sent word he would like to see me and I apologised and thanked him for his support. It wouldn't have done sales much good if he hadn't supported me. The Fisgard motto was "Singuli in Solidium" which loosely interpreted meant "One for all and, and all for one", and my friends would have thought twice about buying any shoes from him. I suppose the authorities had no choice they were not going to let me wear them again so they were sent home.

Mid week evening shore leave was linked to our school terms, similar to civilian technical colleges. During term time one evening's leave was available; in non term time two evenings, the exception being A class who were not allowed any mid week leave for six months, until they became B class.

The first liberty boat mid week was about 5 pm. and 12.30 pm on Saturdays and Sundays. This was because we worked a 5 1/2 day week and on Sunday mornings we paraded for inspection before marching off to church in the R.N. barracks. We were not allowed to wear civilian clothes, and consequently had to be on our best behaviour when ashore. The 8 "locals" at times were allowed to stay over on Saturday night with their parents. I lost the privilege after a few months when my father left the Marines and moved to London, and incidentally brother Arthur at twelve years of age started his sixth school. It must be a record. We had to return from leave and be back on board by 9.pm and be in bed by 9.30, for the Officer the Day's rounds. He checked that no one was missing, everything was neat and tidy, and the windows were set correctly and all the same. Windows were always open on the leeward side. In winter the top half was down and in the summer all the way down.

It was hard luck if you found yourself on special duty when it was your turn to go ashore. When on duty we were the "Fire and Fatigue party" and involved a bit of tiding up, and putting out an imaginary fire. We had to pull out a small pumping engine with huge wheels, run out the hose and connect it to a hydrant, usually getting wet through in the process, and having a good laugh [not those who got wet].

In the evenings there wasn't a lot to do apart from studying of which I wasn't a devotee. In retrospect if I had stuck to my books I might have become an Admiral.

Each recreation room had a billiards table, table tennis table, dart board, piano, and radio. The gymnasium provided room for indoor sports such as fencing, boxing, deck hockey, basket ball. Sometimes it was used as a concert hall, the boys providing their own entertainment and music.

The R.N. barracks had a snooker hall with many tables available, so there was a good chance of getting a game. It also had a cinema, 2d being the entrance fee. Tobacco was very cheap, and most naval ratings smoked; stepping into the cinema was like stepping into a thick fog. It wasn't unusual for a boy with only a halfpenny in his pocket to go round the dormitory playing "double or quits" to get enough money to visit the Cinema.

From Fisgard to the barracks we crossed over the Khyber Pass, entered a side gate and descended 70 steps. I mentioned those steps because during a P.T. lesson we were made to run up and down them until we were exhausted, as a punishment for being stroppy.

We had four meals a day, but don't start licking your lips; the food at Fisgard left something to be desired. I can honestly say that all the time I was in Fisgard I felt hungry. In fact I was so thin if I stood sideways you wouldn't be able to see me. Eggs were fried at 5a.m. and by the time we got them they were like rubber. We called them "rubber heels;" herrings in tomato sauce were called "train smash." Other nicknames have long been forgotten. Brown sugar was plentiful, *and I often made myself a sandwich with it. Tomato or brown sauce sandwiches were O.K. as well.*

At breakfast, apart from the main meal, we were given two rolls and a knob of butter. Nobody ate them at breakfast. It was common practice to take them to work to eat mid-morning at "stand easy". They were life savers, and if the weather was freezing each boy was given an enamelled mug of hot chocolate to drink with them. Once during my time at Fisgard we were given turkey for dinner in one of the Navy Weeks and no doubt to impress the visitors. [26]

There are very few recollections of life in *Fisgard* for this period, particularly when the Apprentice is still with us. It is worth quoting Ron at length:

Which reminds me, every Navy Week one of our classes gave a gymnastic display in the Dockyard arena.

Our work and training were out carried in special workshops on St Mary's Island, the far side of Chatham Dockyard. To get there, we marched from Fisgard, through the R.N. barracks into the dockyard, passing on our left, H.M.S. Cardiff, a light cruiser, and on our right, H.M.S. Marshal Soult, a monitor. The Cardiff lead the defeated German Grand Fleet into Scapa Flow at the end of W.W.1. The Marshal Soult was also a relic of W.W.1. It carried enormous 15 inch guns and she partly submerged off the Belgian coast to bombard the Germans inland. Both were Reserve ships and never left their moorings during the time we were at Fisgard. On we marched over a cantilever bridge on to St Mary's Island. We were always ordered to break step on the bridge as the resonance of our marching feet could damage it [and us].

One and a half to two miles separated Fisgard and our workshops and took us about 20 minutes to cover the distance. We marched from Fisgard to the workshops and then back for dinner, then again to the workshops before returning for tea. Feeling tired and hungry we trudged the last journey, and when the Commodore of the R.N.B. saw us he likened it to the "Retreat from Moscow." Transport was never provided, regardless of weather conditions, we marched.

We had our own volunteer band and members were given an extra day to add to their summer leave, so I volunteered. I couldn't play any musical instruments as such, nevertheless after a few lessons [2] I was allowed to play the drum in time for Navy Week, and I found myself in the near side front rank playing a Kettle drum in front of admiring crowds of people. I was put off by some young pretty girls laughing and giggling as they started to march beside me. Suddenly my left drum stick developed a mind of its own and jumped out of my hand into the air. I caught it on the way down hoping it had not been noticed but my musical career was doomed. I wasn't encouraged to play much afterwards [in fact, never].

I liked most of the time in the workshops. Our instructors were civilians and quite a few ex-Chief Artificers, all highly skilled in their craft. As the months went by the tasks given to us became more difficult and interesting. At the end of every six months we were given a test job. It had to be completed under a certain time or lose marks. We had drawings to work to, with 1000th part of an inch tolerances.

The first eighteen months were spent on bench fitting, all by hand, the only machine tool allowed was pillar or bench drill. As the months went by and my skill developed I became proud of what I was doing. A few months earlier the only tools I handled were a screwdriver and a spanner, and to shape pieces of metal into a design with 1000th part of an inch tolerances, I would have thought impossible. The other boys were the same, applying themselves diligently to the tasks given to us. The thought of being put back a class if you failed might have had some input. We also spent 4 weeks in the Engine Smithing Shop learning to forge, harden and temper tools ready for grinding. To complete our stay, we had to forge a wheel spanner. The Navy seemed fond of wheel spanners. I remember an exam question asking how I would make one.

On entering the Shop we were told a hoary old story about two apprentices [which no one believed]. One apprentice put his hand on an anvil and the other swung a sledge hammer. The boy with his hand on the anvil thought the other would not swing the hammer and the boy with the hammer thought the other would remove his hand. Oh dear, oh dear. Alas! [Only it wasn't his hand but another part of his anatomy]

T he next part of our training, when we became senior apprentices, involved the use of machine tools such as 4, 6, 8, and 12 inch lathes, mills, grinders, and shapers. One apprentice, Ivor Key while operating a lathe lost a bit off the top of his little finger, and the joke was that the lathe was examined to see if it had been damaged. However when it came to Test jobs we weren't allowed to use the latter three machines, presumably because on a warship, there wouldn't be any. Only Repair ships would have them.

The E.A.'s took time off from the machine shops to spend 4 weeks with dockyard workers in their Electrical Engineering workshop, to learn armature winding and other skills. I enjoyed my 4 weeks, the atmosphere being more relaxed, and most importantly of all, on giving one of the civilians two pence he would return next day with a ready to eat small rabbit pie. It was also a good opportunity to get a good toolbox made by a dockyard carpenter, for a few coppers.

E.A.'s for their final year, separated from the main stream, and went to a different workshop to learn to work to one 10,000 the part of an inch tolerances. In retrospect all it needed was more time and patience. We made some very nice tools, which we were allowed to keep. Mine are rusting on the bottom of the sea.

One job involved shaping four pieces of steel that when assembled became an interlocking one inch cube. I took it on leave and showed my father, and he showed it to his company's Chief Engineer. He ran a micrometer over it and wouldn't believe it was handmade. My instructor told me that mine and Ivor Key's cubes were exhibited at the Edinburgh Engineering Exhibition. We did not receive any recognition, it was expected of us.

I was given a small piece of wood from H.M.S. Victory, and told to make a gavel. A little piece was left over which I placed in the handle of a screw top screwdriver. I thought that wherever I went I would have a piece of the Victory with me. However fortunately, we did not stay together or else I too would be at the bottom of the ocean.

I can remember my last Test job, as if it were only yesterday. It was designed to test the skills we had learnt in the last four years.

The daily routine as far I can remember started at 6.30.a.m., breakfast 7-7.15a.m., dinner at noon, tea 4-4.30p.m., school 5-7p.m. [in school term], supper about 7-7.30 pm and like all good boys safely tucked up in bed by 9.30.p.m. The senior apprentice's routine differed from the juniors to allow staggered meal times because the dining hall could not accommodate 700 boys together.

I know that as soon as my head touched the pillow I went to sleep, to be rudely awakened at 6.30.a.m. with the Tannoy screaming out "Wakey wakey, Rise and shine, Rise and shine! You've had your time! You've had your time! Get out get out! Rise and shine!" Followed by music so loud it was enough to wake the dead, a favourite being The Post Horn Gallop.

Our main sports were rugby, football, cricket and hockey. The classes were big enough to form teams to play against each other. Those boys good enough went on to represent Fisgard against other Navy and civilian teams. I went ashore once to play 5 a side hockey, which was great fun, besides getting ashore for a little while.

One afternoon, instead of going to the playing fields we stayed in Fisgard, and changed into our P.T. gear, and our Divisional Officer ordered us to line up in two ranks. "About turn" he said to the front rank and facing us were our boxing opponents for the afternoon. It did not matter if there were differences in size or weight. The afternoon was a bit of a fiasco; it was a case of "Don't you hit me hard, and I won't hit you hard".

The D.O. appointed himself the referee, and stopped one fight because "There isn't enough blood" He said in a jocular tone of voice. To liven things up one pair had to fight with a pillow case over their heads but the fight was stopped when one of boxers thumped the D.O. To hit an officer was tantamount to committing suicide. "I am sorry Sir, I couldn't see what I was doing; I had a pillow case over my head." The D.O. had a sense of humour and the culprit got away with it. I asked him afterwards if it was deliberate, "Of course," he said, "I just looked down saw the tips of a pair of black shoes and hit out."

Apprentice Tim Mahoney developed a lump on his shoulder when injured playing rugby. He was referred to the R.N. Hospital in Gillingham and to our astonishment he was operated on and invalided from the Navy within a few days. I met him again years later in Portsmouth and we chummed up for a while. We travelled to Australia House in London just before I left the Navy, with the objective of emigrating. We were both accepted as potential good Aussies; he finished up in Tasmania, and I, in Godalming.

Every winter each class had to run a marathon. We were taken in Navy Lorries and dumped miles out in the country, and told to get back under a certain time. Even though the weather might be absolutely foul we still had to run. Actually it was good fun, nevertheless about a dozen of us [myself included] decided to get back late as a mild form of protest, or just being stroppy.

When we arrived we found ourselves locked out. We were let in one by one and our names taken. Instead of going ashore the weekend, we were marched to the workshops in the dockyard and spent Saturday and Sunday afternoons making Whitworth spanners. They were made in double quick time to avoid a repeat the next weekend. That wasn't the end of the episode, oh no! the whole class was made to run the marathon again.

On the second run we all got back in time except two, Cliff Lee and me. Cliff was in such a bad way he could hardly walk, so I stayed with him. The next day he had his appendix removed in the R.N. Hospital. As for me, I was let off. I met Cliff again briefly in Australia and years later in the Spotted Cow, but after a few meetings he died.

When I was 17 years old I spent about 14 days in the R.N. Hospital. A blister on my left hand had turned septic, and it went from bad to worse. It became swollen and blown up like a balloon. My fingers were splayed rigid and looked like sausages. I had reported "sick" days before, but sent back to work. I reported "sick" again and this time rushed to hospital, and being under 18 years old a telegram was sent to my father asking permission to operate. I was in such agony, all I could say – "take it off, take it off"! And I really meant it. The surgeon operated on me in the ward almost as soon as I arrived. When I woke up the relief from pain was incredible, and the surrounding bed was in a mess.

The sister told me when they cut into my hand the pressure was so high that blood and other matter squirted like a fountain. An hour later I tucked into a supper of sausage and mash with gusto. I was so hungry I could have eaten anything that didn't move.

I enjoyed my stay in hospital; my hand had to be drained every day, but the food was a lot better than Fisgard food. The Ward Sister made me work. Another patient in the ward had a bad right hand and no doubt she concluded that two patients with a good left and right hand between them was as good a person with two good hands, so we were given little jobs like dusting and cleaning cutlery.

To control 600 intelligent teenagers, who could not accept blind obedience, may have been a problem, but not for the Navy. On joining we all had to sign papers confirming we would serve 12 years, from the age of 18, so the first 3 didn't count. After we had all signed we mustered on the parade ground to have the "Articles of War" read to us. They consisted mainly about crime and punishment, quite a few ending "punishable by death". To us 15 years old, it was part of the glamour of being in the Royal Navy. We didn't know any better, for the ensuing four and a half years would be a regime of strict discipline. However we soon learned to live with it, the trick being, not necessarily to be a good boy but not to get caught and we were very good at it. No boy ever told on another, as I have said before our motto was "Singuli in Solidium".

The punishments available were stoppage of leave, 8a, 10a and extremely rare, cells. In my four years at Fisgard there was only one case of cells being awarded. A couple of boys decided to go absent for three weeks in the hope they would be discharged on their return. Were they surprised! The usual punishments were a dose of 8a, or 10 a. The number of days awarded depended on the severity of the crime, or the state of the Commander's liver that day. 8a and 10a punishment demanded that you paraded at 8pm dressed in P.T. kit with a rifle. You were then given 30 minutes of physical hardship, running with the rifle bouncing on your shoulder with only a shirt for protection or held *at arm's length, or above the head. A favourite was to hop on your haunches holding the rifle in front, which meant without care you were guaranteed to fall over. The ordeal wasn't over for the boys on 10a punishment. They were not allowed to sleep in their beds, and had to roll up their blankets and sleep on the floor of the gymnasium. They had to sit down in the dining hall on a separate table, to ensure only the regulation food was eaten, and the two rolls and butter denied them.*

The apprentices had their own self imposed code of conduct and behaviour. I remember the humiliation one boy suffered by being scrubbed by his classmates because he hadn't bothered to bath for a long time, and another boy being chastised for laughing at a classmate being beating up in the boxing ring.

Ask a Fisgardian his worst term and without hesitation he would reply "A" class. In the apprentices hierarchy "J" class were the elite and "A" class were at the bottom of the heap, and treated as such until the next "A" class joined 6 months later. Although it was illegal "A" boys were expected to fag for "J" boys on demand. I managed to avoid the ignominy.

At the end of August 1939 the apprentices had returned from their annual leave, and our class were about to start the new and final term as J class, with 6 months before us of intense study in preparation for our final examinations before leaving Fisgard for good. However fate played its hand, we were going to leave in the next 48 hours.

We were mustered on the parade ground and to our, and I must say, delighted surprise told that the Admiralty had decided we were sufficiently trained to be rated 5th class artificers.

We had joined Fisgard as children and now 4 years later we marched through the main gate and down the Khyber Pass for the last time. We were happy young men, assured, confident, self reliant, perhaps a bit older than our years, toughened by our experience and ready for anything, and off we went to our various depots. There were sixteen 5th class E.A.s, and we arrived at H.M.S. Vernon on the 2nd of September. War was declared the next morning.[27]

Ron has a few words on what his time in *Fisgard* meant to him and it is indicative of the esprit de corps that being an Artificer engendered in Apprentices throughout the years:

Before I go any further with my memoirs I must write a few more lines about Fisgard. On that day in August 1935 I joined an intensely communal society

*and lived cheek by jowl with other boys of my own age for four years, and in a
kind of way it proved itself supportive.*

*In today's terms life at Fisgard was harsh. In exchange for a good academic
education and the best craft apprenticeship in the country I endured long working
hours, inadequate food, restrictive liberty, strict discipline, and very poor pay.*

*I have never regretted my life in Fisgard. It has proved invaluable for me
in and out of the Royal Navy. It was the most extraordinary experience. Most
ex-apprentices, and I certainly, remember it with pride and affection.*[28]

By October John was once more on the move, this time down to Portland
to join the destroyer HMS *Vivien* but this time in Portland was short-
lived as the ship was ordered to Chatham, where the ship was paid off on
28 October and then recommissioned with a new crew immediately, with
only John of the old crew remaining. This seems a recipe for inefficiency as
no one seemed to know what was going on or what they were supposed to
be doing on a strange ship. However, they soon found themselves back at
Portland working up the new crew. Even this was short-lived as in no time
the ship was back at Chatham and into dry dock for a refit prior to sailing
for the Mediterranean following Italy's invasion of Abyssinia. Christmas/
draft leave was granted and the ship was due to sail on 27 December. As is
the way of the Service, sailing was postponed and postponed again, until on
11 January everything changed again and the ship, with nothing in the way
of explanation, paid off and the ship's company turned to barracks.

Once again the cycle of change began and John was drafted to HMS
Scout. This was John's second time on board *Scout* and the ship was still
in the Emergency Flotilla. On 20 January King George V died and the
Emergency Flotilla was employed escorting foreign royalty and heads of
state across the Channel and North Sea. Following this the routine reverted
to taking Boy Seamen from HMS *Ganges* to sea to acquaint them with
what life at sea was like and possibly encourage some of them as to the
superiority of the Engineering branch.

By May of 1937 it was decided that *Scout* was in need of a refit to
prepare her for service on the China Station and to this end there was
much checking of stores and spares, John finding some wrapped and dated
25 December 1916. Despite the engineer asking John to stay on for the
China deployment, but not wishing to volunteer, he declined, ready to take
whatever draft came his way. And so by July 1937 John's name appeared on

a draft list for the advance party for HMS *Ajax*, which was to recommission with a Chatham crew prior to deploying out to the West Indies, even the Drafting Commander, with whom John had served in *Valiant* and *Dragon*, considered him lucky to be returning to that part of the world.

Away from John there was activating in the training arena of Artificers. It had become clear that the facilities at Chatham were not sufficient to meet the Navy's increasing demand for Artificers. A parallel establishment was set up in Rosyth on HMS *Caledonia*, a former Cunard White Star ocean liner that was commissioned as a training ship on 23 April 1937. As John Carver, who joined Duncan Division in 1938, remembered:

> *She had started life as the "Bismarck" – pride of the Nord-America line and was destined to carry Wilhelm II (Kaiser Bill) on a triumphant tour of the globe after he had won the '14–'18 war. Events failed to materialise and she was allocated to Great Britain as part of the reparation and became SS Majestic in the White Star Line, and then the Cunard Line, on the North Atlantic run. The Admiralty acquired her in about 1936 and fitted her out as an accommodation/training ship to be based in Rosyth and gave her a Scottish name to encourage recruitment north of the border. She was the largest ship in the RN at that time and was home to fifteen hundred Seamen Boys, five hundred Artificer Apprentices and about a hundred Ship's Company.[29]*

The first class consists of sixty-two electrical and engine room apprentices, who joined as Grenville Division, as one of the earliest entrants, George Penny recalled:

> *He planned my journey from Totnes to Rosyth ensuring that I should arrive on board before this time. Consequently I arrived at Inverkeithing station at 0600 on the 17th August 1937 and took a taxi to HMS Caledonia. Someone woke up the two Divisional Petty Officers, Garscadden and Kemp, and the former, seeing my rosy cheeks and bucolic air, turned me over to Kemp with a bad tempered remark about the Navy "now recruiting Farmer Georges straight from the wilds of Dartmoor." Thus was the origin of "George" by which I was thereafter known!*
>
> *Being the first apprentice to arrive I was given the Ship's Book Number 1 and my Official Number was DMX55012. This led to me also being the first to suffer "6 cuts" (caning) on a warrant of Captain Atwell-Lake. My memory of this occasion is vivid to me because after a group of us had been caught smoking,*

dear old Garscadden expostulated angrily to our Divisional Officer that "as the other miscreants (Ernie Perkins and Bob Hyett) had greater official numbers than I did, this made me the senior hand of the place wherein we were found." Hence my punishment should be doubled![30]

This was indeed a baptism of fire into the Royal Navy and *Caledonia*. As well as these new recruits there were also some Apprentices sent up from Chatham; these consisted of half a class of both Anson and Rodney Divisions. These boys would clearly have the upper hand over the newly joined boys of Grenville Division and there was sure to be some sprogging carried out in the traditions of Artificer Apprentices. In January 1938 Benbow Division was formed and in August Duncan Division, thus breaking with the tradition of only having four divisions. As well as this there were two divisions of direct and special entry Apprentices.

Horace Polhill travelled up to Rosyth on 17 August 1937 and remembered travelling through the Dockyard, probably his first sight of a naval dockyard:

Along with about a dozen ex-schoolboys I arrived at Inverkeithing Station at 1815 hours on Tuesday 17th August 1937. A RN bus awaited our arrival and as we travelled along Admiralty Road, Rosyth, a piper was playing a lament as we headed towards the dockyard. Speculation grew that it was a local custom, a welcoming sound introducing us to Scotland!

Our journey through the dockyard revealed an area of utter desolation – rusting unused railway lines, rabbits scuttling everywhere. Passing the main dry docks was the sight of the upturned hulks of the German battle cruisers, Moltke, Grosser Kurfust *and* Frederich der Grosse, *sunk at Scapa Flow after World War I. All three were being broken up for scrap by Metal Industries. Beyond the dry dock, moored in the adjacent large basin, loomed a huge liner alongside an enormous cantilever crane. This was HMS* Caledonia *and would be our home until the outbreak of World War II. It was commissioned into the Royal Navy on St George's Day 1937 and was the largest ship ever to fly the White Ensign. Formerly it was the German passenger liner "Bismarck" and then the Cunard/White Star liner "Majestic" of 56,000 tons.[31]*

The composition of the divisions included, as mentioned earlier, some Apprentices from the Mechanical Training Establishment, *Fisgard* Block, at Chatham. Some of these Apprentices were less than happy about being sent north of the border or being taken out of Chatham, as Dennis Stiff wrote:

> *As Anson '36, we were not too thrilled to be drafted over the "border" so soon in our "calling" and the bleak panorama of Rosyth dockyard on a late summer evening in 1937 was not too thrilling either. I don't know if it is generally known but Anson '36 were the last class to sign "indentures" to serve apprenticeships at Chatham. This subsequently caused the Admiralty a spot of bother when starting training at Caledonia. In 1936-37 the Admiralty decided to commission Caledonia as a training-centre in the north, recruiting the Seamen Boys from that area. To start apprentice training, a line was drawn across England from Bath to London and apprentices in Rodney '37 and Anson '36 who lived north of this line would be sent to Rosyth – this produced about twenty names! To make the number up, except those from the Chatham area, names were drawn at random from these classes. The complement now contained many from Portsmouth and Devonport. It should be remembered that pre-war there were no "travel warrants" issued when we went on leave, so we had to pay our own fare which was, I think, a quarter of the standard rate, provided one was in uniform (paybook/identity documents did not come into use until the spring of 1940).*[32]

Whether it was the change of location or bracing Scottish weather, there seems to have been an influx of Apprentices who were destined for great things. Among the boys who joined *Caledonia* in 1938 were Ronald Albert Harcus, born on 25 October 1921 in Mile End, London. He had joined *Fisgard* in August 1937 and so was among the first to be sent north to *Caledonia*. He saw service in the Mediterranean in HMS *Nigeria* and was selected for promotion, being commissioned as a Sub-Lieutenant in 1943. At one stage in his career as a Commander he served in *Caledonia* as the Executive Officer and as a Captain served as the Fleet Marine Engineer Officer. He was promoted to Rear Admiral in January 1974 and retired in 1976, He died on 21 August 1991.

Another Apprentice during 1937 was Michael Harold Griffin, born on 28 January 1921 in Devonport. He also travelled up to *Caledonia* from Chatham and went to sea in 1940, serving on HMS *Devonshire* in the South Atlantic when she was responsible for sinking the German raider *Atlantis*.

He was commissioned in 1941 and after training at the Royal Naval College at Greenwich he subsequently joined HMS *Kent* in the North Atlantic. He joined the Submarine Service and served on several submarines during the war. As a Captain he was the Commanding Officer of HMS *St Vincent*, the Boy Seamen's training establishment in Gosport, until it closed in February 1969. He was promoted to Rear Admiral on 7 January 1972 and retired in 1977. Admiral Griffin died on 14 July 1995. A division at *Fisgard* was named after Admiral Griffin in May 1973.

To continue this fertile period for Apprentices who reached flag rank, we have Derek Garland "Spike" Spickernell, born on 1 June 1921 in Portsmouth. He did have the added advantage that his father was a naval Commander. Notwithstanding this he joined *Fisgard* in 1937, joined the cadet training cruiser HMS *Vindictive* as an Engineering Cadet in January 1939 and attended the Royal Naval Engineering College at Keyham. He served in surface ships throughout the war and joined the Submarine Service just prior to the end of the war. He was promoted to Commander in 1953 and Captain in 1962. He was promoted to Rear Admiral in 1971 and retired in 1975, his last appointment being Director General Quality Assurance. He died on 14 May 2009. Another division added in May 1973 was named after Admiral Spickernell.

Having dealt with these future worthies it is time to return to the more mundane everyday life at *Caledonia*. Having Boy Seamen in the same establishment was very novel, as Horace Polhill observed:

> Caledonia *was also a training ship for Boy Seamen and it was the first time in history that they shared their training alongside apprentices. By mid 1938 the ship "housed" about two thousand Boy Seamen and over four hundred apprentices. This included about a hundred Special Entry apprentices who had joined us as Hawke and Drake Divisions at the end of 1937 and January 1938, and January 1938 after serving the first part of their apprenticeships in civilian industry. During our first year, one of the main activities in the dockyard was the maintenance of the breech mechanisms and barrels of many gun barrels of various calibres. These were laid out on cradles in rows covering the large area between the parade ground perimeter and the steps leading to the new factory. This activity we observed with great curiosity as we passed the area on our way to daily workshop instruction. Little did we realize at the time the importance of this work; shortly afterwards the gun barrels disappeared for service in the rapidly expanding Fleet.*

The Special Entry Apprentices had previous experience and were also some years older than the new entry Apprentices, typical of these older boys was George Wallis:

> *I had done three years of my apprenticeship training in Gibraltar dockyard and they signed me up at the Naval Base there in December 1937. They gave me a liner passage home, which took four days' travel from the 27th December, arriving at Tilbury Docks, London, on the 31st December. I spent two days in London and arrived at* Caledonia *on the 3rd January 1938.*
>
> *The "Special Entry Artificer Apprentices" were started in 1937 to build up the fleet as the threat of war was in the wind. Hawke Division was the first, and was started in September 1937. Drake Division started in January 1938, Blake followed, then Duncan. As each division passed out, new ones joined throughout the war.*[33]

As with *Fisgard*, certain Apprentices were given extra responsibilities and authority and were rated as Chief and Petty Officer Apprentices, but it seems that, for whatever reason, these older, more experienced direct entry boys were generally overlooked for this position, known as "Hook Boys", and this caused some resentment amongst these boys, as George recorded:

> *We joined in January 1938 as "senior apprentices", all over the age of nineteen. We had no Hook Boys in our division so they put this little squirt in charge of us. We called him "The Weasel" and he was collecting station-cards from all the division. I was one of several who were put on a charge through him.*
>
> *We had to fall in as a division on the jetty to march to Bay 1 in Rosyth dockyard where we worked. The Weasel was in charge of us as we marched. One day we arrived at Bay 1 and before he dismissed us he said a very nasty thing about our division, then dismissed us. The whole division pounced on him and tore him to pieces. He looked like a "scran bag" when we had finished and he had to find his clothes. We all reported him and he was told never to go near Drake Division, which he made sure he did not! The next day we had one Chief Hook and four Petty Officer Hooks made up from apprentices in our division and no one else came near us. The division The Weasel came from was Anson, which was a good crowd ruined by this one person, however the whole division suffered when we moved from King's Road School to the new hutments. We moved by seniority; Hawke first, then Drake, then Anson. The ground outside was all muddy and the*

Anson huts were the third from the road and so they wanted to walk through our huts to avoid the mud. Everyone except *for Anson was allowed to go through our hut. All because of this one idiot!*[34]

So it seems that "Apprentice Power" did have some momentum. This also highlights the folly of allowing a callow youth power over older young men. One of the problems that the direct entry and new entry Apprentices had to overcome was the slinging of a hammock, no instructions provided. Luckily for many on their first night the hammock was already slung and ready for occupation, though it would still take some practice and much wrestling to sling them on subsequent nights. Another problem appears to be the infestation of rats that plagued the establishment and this tested their nascent engineering skills to provide a solution, as Derek Hughes, who joined Duncan Division as a new entry in 1938, recalled:

I remember the rat-trap that someone in Grenville or Rodney made. It had the usual spring loaded U-piece that slams down on the rat, but to clinch matters, in order to reach the bait, the rat had to step on a piece of copper sheet connected to one wire of the 220 Volt main. The other wire was connected, via a 60 Watt bulb and, I think, a bell circuit, to the Upiece. Death was swift – violent – certain. On the other hand, the beast's passing did not go unnoticed which is the fate of many in this harsh world.[35]

As had been the policy, since Artificers, both Boy and Apprentice, had been introduced there was much store placed in sport and the Apprentices prided themselves on the prowess of their sports teams. There was also a swimming pool at *Caledonia*, situated some decks down, which did offer a viewing gallery from her days as a passenger liner. So no one escaped the obligatory swimming test. This consisted of completing four lengths of the poll, about 100 yards, wearing a "duck suit" made of canvas and then treading water for three minutes. Those that failed were classed "backward swimmers" and had to complete remedial swimming lessons until they passed.

The Royal Navy regained its own air service in 1937, when the Fleet Air Arm of the Royal Air Force (covering carrier-borne aircraft but not the seaplanes and maritime reconnaissance aircraft of Coastal Command) was returned to Admiralty control under the Fifth Sea Lord and renamed the Naval Air Branch and by May 1939 the Admiralty had resumed full control over naval aviation. In 1952, the service returned to its pre-1937 name of the Fleet Air Arm.

This raised the problem of who would carry out the maintenance of the aircraft, and the existing system of training was opened up to Aircraft Artificers. But the first fifty of the Aircraft Apprentices joined the Naval Barracks at Portsmouth, HMS *Victory*, on 23 August 1938 and carried out a joining routine, including kitting up, medicals, basic drill and relevant lectures on the Royal Navy. On 15 September 1938 they travelled north to complete their training at RAF Halton with the RAF Apprentices. The naval Apprentices were divided equally between airframe and engine specialisation. Their discipline and administration were in the hands of naval officers and senior rates but training followed the RAF curriculum. There was naturally much rivalry between the two Services, which manifested itself primarily on the sports field. These Apprentices retained the existing divisional names and it was Rodney 1 Division who first received part of their training in *Caledonia*, joined later by the boys in Benbow 1 Division.

All this is remembered in a after dinner speech given by Mike Simpson (Keppel 44) at a Halton Apprentices dinner on 18 April 2008:

> *Thank you for the great honour of inviting me to be your guest tonight. You are the founders who launched the Aircraft Artificer branch of which I am proud to be part. Others transferred across from the RAF, but you are the pedigree ones who were totally committed from the outset, when you first joined the navy as Naval Air Apprentices.*
>
> *In 1938, after a long battle, the Fleet Air arm was transferred from the RAF to the Royal Navy. A Pyrrhic victory one might say, as it left the navy to fight a war with some outdated aircraft and no maintenance infrastructure. However, after training and depending on artificers to support the fleet for the previous 35 years, the navy decided to base its new aircraft maintenance structure round the proven artificer system.*
>
> *Accordingly, on the 23rd August 1938, fifty 15 year olds, who had passed the entry exam for the other naval apprenticeships, were assembled at the RN Barracks Portsmouth, for despatch to RAF Halton to be trained as Aircraft Artificers. Six monthly entries followed, many of whom are represented here tonight. As the founders of our branch, you deserve and have the respect of all the Aircraft Artificers who followed you. Starting from nothing in 1938, the Fleet Air Arm by 1945 had become a powerful and efficient element of the Royal Navy.*

This was due to two main factors; well trained naval aircrew flying American aircraft and the evolution of an effective maintenance system to support them, of which the Aircraft Artificer formed the core.

You trained my generation, first in the classroom, and then as young artificers in the hangar. Being exapprentices, we became senior rates almost immediately, so you probably also tried to teach us maturity in the mess. Doubtless you will recall that some of us took longer to achieve this than others. But the layers of what we learned from you, we passed on to the next generation and they continued to do the same. Since the war, our breed has been further tested in Korea, the Falklands, both Gulf wars and at this very moment in Iraq and Afghanistan, and not found wanting. You can therefore be proud of what you started.

My entry was the last to go to Newcastle-under-Lyme, and one of the first to go to Arbroath. So it was as an apprentice that I first met your generation, as they were the majority of our instructors. Arbroath brings back some vivid youthful memories of instructors. Bob Shilling, a brilliant engines lecturer in the morning but different in the afternoon. Taff Rowlands, aircraft metal repairs, on how not to drill through main spars. AA Tunks who taught tanks. Ted Whitley, on components, recently from the Holm Sound, an aircraft repair ship in the fleet train of the British Pacific Fleet. Ted gave us a glimpse of what we had missed. More wartime experiences from another instructor, who will remain anonymous, on how he and some other PO Air Fitters dosed the water system of the WREN's quarters in Alexandria with a substance called Spanish fly, and his vivid account of the social consequences. We really did believe everything you told us.

My own Keppel Division joined during the war, but we were not released until 1948, when the Fleet Air Arm was about to enter the jet age. To play our part, we were equipped with snail brand spanners, some hammers and chisels and the ability to recite Griffon mag timing by heart. As a young 5th class I was actually given that job, and all I could remember was, "insulate the primary winding with a piece of oiled silk". Nobody had ever heard of this, and I was told to use tickler paper. Four years later I was lucky enough to get promoted. I say lucky, because things are very different now, A few years ago, although retired, I was involved in the indoctrination of new entry Artificer Apprentices in Raleigh, and I was astonished to learn, that within two years, 40% of apprentices were likely to be extracted for Engineer Officer training at Southampton University. This took me back to 1952, when naval apprentice entries were running at well over 2000 a year, but under 10, from all categories, after eight years, became Upper Yardmen [E], going on to join their Dartmouth equivalents. In broad terms this means that a few years ago an apprentice had eighty times the chance to obtain a full commission than we did and in a quarter of the time.

This promotes some thought. The educational standards of these apprentices were the same, relative to their contemporaries, just as ours were at the time. In equivalent terms, one had to be about School Certificate standard to qualify for a naval apprenticeship. So what has changed? The answer is simply political and social attitudes. After two years training, under close supervision, the Navy can judge suitability for commissioned rank with accuracy. Much more accurately, I would think, than judging suitability on a morning's attempts to cross a bottomless chasm using a few planks. However, we are old enough to know the differences between then and now, and the very real bottomless chasm which existed in our time. This prevented the Navy from exploiting its own natural source of talent.

So what happened to me? In 1952, after the first hurdles, which included passing some exams, one knew that the only way to finally grasp this precious opportunity was to accept the reality of having to bullshit the selection board, basically by telling them what they wanted to hear. Amongst other things, this meant saying that in the PO's mess we only read the Times and the Telegraph. If successful, the final stage was upper yardman training at Hawke, located at the bottom of the hill at Dartmouth. Surviving the next four months, before actually being promoted, was a nerve racking test of devious skill, and not all survived. Looking back, one can see that at the time, Hawke epitomised the clash between the rigid social principles of the pre-war navy, and the reality of what was actually happening in the rest of the country. We were seen as an analogue of this dilemma, and Hawke's task was to upgrade us socially, to prepare us for a new lifestyle of which it was assumed we knew nothing. Hawke was a centre of muddled thinking, which appeared unable to acknowledge the difference between naval tribal rote and what was to us, normal behaviour. For example, being taught to say "in a ship" and not "on a ship" was regarded as being in the same category as having to be told to always say "thank you" after any kindness [both of these examples were listed in a handout]. This was a flawed assumption which implied that we had previously learned little about social behaviour, either at home or during our apprenticeship. There were no second chances at Hawke. If one didn't shape up, it was back to barracks with kitbag and hammock *within the hour. I still have my handout giving written examples of the officer like qualities that we had to achieve. Whilst some of this makes ridiculous and funny reading now, it wasn't funny at the time. It was deadly serious. Here are some examples: Do not say "shove off out of it" say "excuse me". Never address a senior rate as "Chief" always use "Chief Petty Officer". Shave every morning. Never wear vest and pants under your pyjamas. Brush your hair sideways and not back [for some us this brought an unexpected benefit in later life]. Never wear your cap in the mess. Never wear a pencil behind your ear. Make sure your hands are clean. When in pursuit of something do not exclaim "there the bastard goes" say "tally ho"… and so on. There were constant lectures. Our mentor was an arrogant young gunnery officer who appeared to dislike us as much as we disliked him. In one of his lectures about naval branches he was asked if he ever wanted to be a naval aviator. "No", he replied acidly, "if I had wanted to fly I would have joined the RAF". "But sir", said someone," as a gunnery officer, why didn't you join the Royal Artillery?" An innocent but high risk remark. In another lecture on the status of wives in wardroom life he announced that wives were expected to conform to similar standards, or else, he said in clipped tones, "You are not going to be able to cut the mustard". "But sir", came the plea from an RAN upper yardman in a worried Australian accent, "does that mean that my wife will have to cut the sandwiches?"*

We also had a mock ball to test our capability. We were a little surprised at this, with at least eight years dance hall experience behind us. Ladies were supplied from the wives of Dartmouth staff officers. One of my entry, well known for his excess of testosterone, drew a very senior officer's wife, who although rather old at about 35, was nevertheless very beautiful. In one slow and very close dance she suddenly stopped and within earshot exclaimed querulously, "Upper yardman Hickson?" "Sorry Maam", came the distressed reply, "but I can't help it". The course came to an end and in September 1952 and I was promoted Sub Lieutenant [E], eight years after joining as an Apprentice. I was lucky to have a long career afterwards, and during this time our paths must have crossed. I can recall three specific instances when this actually happened:-

In early 1952 as an AA4 in 771 Squadron, I was stuck at Milltown with a clapped out U/S target towing Mosquito, together with the Squadron CO, who wanted to fly us both back to Ford for the weekend, regardless. Under pressure, I did an unauthorised repair, but had the sense to seek advice from Lossiemouth's inspection department. Along came AA3 Spain who took one look at it and ruled, "It's OK if you are going to bomb the Tirpitz". I have always remembered and used that phrase. It was also a reminder that your generation had been involved in a real war. Thanks Alan!

In 1959 I was the AEO of 848 Squadron, a Whirlwind 22 Squadron based at Hal Far. At the same time Horse Hamon was AEO of 824 Squadron, a Whirlwind 7 squadron embarked in Albion. His unreliable 7's had been grounded again and so Horse had to borrow one of my 22's to provide Albion's planeguard. The one I lent him had been giving high autorotation revs which had been adjusted several times. The fault was found by 824. The large nut holding the rotor head on was unlocked and was gradually unscrewing, thereby fining off the blade pitch. 824 discretely fixed it, no incident signals, no witch-hunt, no mention anywhere, except in a "Dear Mike" letter from Horse, leaving me to deal with the miscreants. Thanks Horse!

In 1966 I became the new AEO of 800, a Buccaneer squadron based in Lossiemouth, destined for Eagle. I was not happy with various things that I had found, and I needed help to sort things out. Our Cdr [E] was well known for over-reaction and panic, but I had no alternative but to consult his Inspection Officer, Norman Dunne [his younger brother Bob had been an apprentice with me]. Norman gave some me some profound advice which worked, but nothing was ever said to CDR [E]. Thanks Norman! One last tale, to let you know that the naval spirit with which you grew up, lives on. In 1982 I was Commodore of the Barracks up the road. The Falklands event had just started and we were very busy, particularly having to fill manpower gaps in the Fleet which was sailing in 3 days, during the Easter leave period. Clearing lower deck helped, but we had a useful pool of about 100 16 year old Junior Stokers, long overdue in joining their first ship.

This was because the training pipeline had continued to produce them, after John Nott suddenly tied up four frigates. As a result, their numbers built up in the barracks, where we kept them segregated and occupied under boys' service conditions. However, as a concession, they were allowed normal ratings' leave the night before they left. On that night, the Officer of the Watch reported that a journalist from the Morning Star [used to be the Daily Worker] was outside the main gate interviewing ratings. This was on public ground and although we knew that the Star was not on our side, we could do nothing. To keep an eye on things, the PO of the Watch was told to stand in plain clothes next to this rather attractive female journalist and just listen. He reported that later that night, a Junior Stoker, nicely pissed, came rolling up Queen Street, just like many other sailors on their way to war had done before him. She stopped him *and asked if he was sailing south tomorrow with the fleet. "Yes", he said proudly. Then came the political question, "And why do you think you are going?" The youngster stopped and looked at her, chip halfway to his mouth, amazed at such a stupid question. "Ma'am, I'm going south to beat the s…t out of them". There were no more questions. So you can assume the navy you were in as young men still contains the same spirit. Thanks again for the honour of inviting me to dine with you tonight, in what I am told is the final fling of the Halton Brats. Good luck to all of you.*[36]

There is a small aside to this, there was the peculiar aberration that was neither one thing nor the other, which was procured to fill the gap before Aircraft Artificers were ready to join the fleet and this body of men, machinist, toolmakers, sheet metal workers and other skilled craftsmen were recruited from industry as "hostilities only" and given the rate of Engine Room Artificer (Air), which must have given rise to much scratching of heads and probably some ribald comments from existing ERAs.

It was decided after the "Munich Crisis" in 1938 that, the need for berths in Rosyth Dockyard being at a premium and there being the possibility that space would be need to repair ships damaged in the event of war, *Caledonia* should vacate her berth alongside and move out of her berth alongside and anchor in the Forth. This required the use of the capstan and as this had not been used for many years it required some TLC, as Dennis Stiff remembered:

The Admiralty then decided that damaged warships would need to be repaired and Caledonia was taking up valuable space in the basin. She would have to be moved and would anchor in the Forth. This would mean dropping the hook (anchor) and to do this, the ship's capstan had to be in working order. Two ERAs and two stokers from the Ship's Company won this task and six "highly skilled" apprentices from Anson Division were detailed to give the team the benefit of their vast experience. We duly presented ourselves to the Chief in the "Capstan Engine Flat", somewhere in the bows of the ship, and were allocated our jobs. Real engineering stuff at last – our previous experience had been packing steam cocks and glands with red or blue asbestos. Here was not a neat and shiny Ward–Leonard Capstan System, but a triple expansion steam engine driving a worm and worm wheel. The worm was about 12" in diameter and the wheel about 4', the centre-shaft driving the bollard was also about 12" in diameter. The engine was connected to the drive through a dog clutch and the whole shaft and gear system, apart from the actual gearing, had been liberally treated with some sort of orange paint. In the course of time this had set to the usual hardness found only on engine room (and delicate electrical) equipment.

Our job was to lift the cylinder heads of the engine and clean and lubricate the linings of the cylinders. This required removing the cladding around the cylinders and rigging a Weston purchase to lift the cylinder heads. The cladding consisted of glass fibre with an asbestos jacket covering it, and not being familiar with this rather prickly stuff we quickly learned to treat it with respect. The rest of the team wrestled with the clutch, removing the paint and then trying to get it to work. Various lubricants were poured over the parts along with the scientific applications of our hammers but nothing moved. We had numerous visits from the Engineer Officers on the ship's staff as the Captain was getting somewhat worried about how he would anchor the ship, and how he would pick the anchor up again. So to hurry things along, the Senior Engineer suggested a 14lb. sledgehammer, "and give it a little tap here and there." This was of no avail so on his next visit, after a demonstration he said, "we must warm it up a bit and give it another tap." To do this, two one-gallon blowlamps were brought to bear and much pumping and application of the pricker was needed (gas and oxyacetylene were much too modern for everyday use at that time). The heat was applied and the sledges swung but the clutch remained stuck. While this was going on, the bores of the cylinders were examined and lubricated and the engine was disconnected from the worm and turned over. The cylinder heads were secured and the cladding replaced. The engine was now deemed to be ready for steam.[37]

Fortunately the need for steam, which would have caused even more problems as, of course, the boilers had not been used for equally as long as all the other equipment and systems, became academic with the return of Neville Chamberlain from Germany with his note promising "Peace in our time". This was not to last long and with the declaration of war on 3 September 1939 there was much that would change.

As with the beginning of the First World War, everything started in total chaos. *Fisgard* at Chatham closed, with the senior "J" Class missing the last six months of training to be sent straight to sea. Classes A, C, E and G moved to church halls in Devonport, while B, D, F and H were first sent to HMS *Argus* in Portsmouth and subsequently to HMS *Frobisher* and settled eventually in wooden huts in the Naval Barracks. The Apprentices in *Caledonia* were moved off their former Cunard White Star ocean liner and billeted in Kings Road School in Rosyth, while a more permanent home was built for them to the north of the Dockyard. Finally in December 1939 because of the urgent need for trained Artificers to man the rapidly expanding fleet the apprenticeship was reduced in length to four years.

The accommodation in Devonport, the Ebenezer and St Mark's church halls was proving less than ideal so in October 1939 they were moved to the *Marshall Ney*, an old monitor which formed part of the Devonport Mechanical Training Establishment and finally in February 1940 they were settled in at Stoke Damerel High for School for Girls; the girls, perhaps to the Apprentices great disappointment, had already been evacuated.

The move to Kings Road School appears to have been fairly painless, as Horace Polhill who had been amongst the first to arrive at *Caledonia* remembered:

The outbreak of World War II on 3rd September 1939 caused a move from the ship to King's Road School Rosyth and a dramatic change to daily life. Immediately following the declaration of war, lockers were removed from the ship and as many as possible installed in the classrooms and corridors. Hammocks were stripped down to provide camp beds and considerable amounts of stores were transported to fill all the nooks and crannies not taken up for accommodation. A completely new feeding system was quickly established to cope with the school's limited cooking facilities. The whole move was accomplished in a few days and resulted in the daily marching routine to and from the factory being considerably extended. The mid-day meal was provided at the factory and usually consisted of a bag containing a Scotch mutton pie, cheese roll and an apple. The main cooked meal of the day was provided on return to King's Road School. When "evening class" instruction was scheduled, this was around 1930 hours, which helped in the staggering of the load in the makeshift galley. To ease the pangs of hunger on "school nights" tea, bread and jam, with the occasional slice of cake, were on hand when workshop routines ended.[38]

What is not mentioned is what happened to the pupils of the school, though it is likely because of the proximity of the school to the Dockyard that the school children were evacuated to a safer environment.

As well as the upheaval in Rosyth it was decided that those Apprentices in Chatham were too vulnerable to enemy action and were moved into temporary accommodation in Portsmouth and Devonport, though why these naval bases should have been any safer is not explained.

At the declaration of war John Gurr, by now a CERA 2nd Class, was still serving in HMS *Ajax* in the South Atlantic and had an early brush with the German merchant vessel *Olinda*, which professed to have no knowledge of the outbreak of war, despite being in the process of painting out her name. Not having the personnel to man a prize crew the *Olinda* was sunk with 4" gunfire. On Sunday, 3 December, the ship met HMNZS *Achilles* and the following day HMS *Exeter*; this was all in response to the report that the British ship *Doric Star* had been sunk by a "pocket battleship". It was expected that this ship would make for Rio or the River Plate and the Commodore expected to intercept them by about Wednesday, 13 December, as John wrote,

How Prophetic!

At Dawn action stations on the 13th as on many other mornings there was no sign of any other ship so at 0600 we reverted to our 2nd degree of readiness status and those of us not actually on watch returned to our hammocks for another hour's rest, but twenty minutes later the Klaxons sounded for Urgent Action! We jump-ed from our hammocks to hastily pull trousers over pyjamas, grab overalls, gas mask, torch, anti-flash and inflatable lifebelt and dash to our stations again. As we ran along the deck my neighbour, Spud Slater, said, "It's the Scheer! She's ten yards astern of us" I thought perhaps the morning was foggy and that the enemy had suddenly loomed out and was in danger of ramming us! But Spud ad apparently returned to sleep very quickly and was dreaming when the Klaxons blared, the morning actually being clear and sunny. Our three ships had been fanned out to cover as much ocean as possible with Ajax at the centre, Exeter far out to starboard and Achilles to port, and as it was Exeter who had sighted the masthead of the German apparently at exactly the same time as the enemy spotted her for she opened fire with her 11" guns at a range of 12½ miles – her third salvo hitting Exeter and causing a lot of damage. Exeter continued to close the range so that her own 8" guns could be more effective. We had all worked up to full speed and Ajax began firing at half-past six, my station – until (normally) eight o'clock – was "B" Magazine Flooding and the guns had only been firing for ten minutes when the hoist from the Shell-room was put out of action and the ammunition for "B" turret had to be carried up by hand – more than a hundredweight each shell – and trundled through the mess-deck.

"A" turret was working O.K. and the rate of fire was so fast that it sounded more like a Machine-gun. A Wireless rating passing through my station at 7.15 told me "Exeter is out of action and our main mast has been shot away, carrying the aerial with it. One seaman has been killed and several have been wounded"[39]

Shortly after this the *Scheer* turned away from the engagement and attempted to make her escape. It was during this chase that *Ajax* managed thirty-six and a half knots, her fastest ever. The badly damaged *Exeter* eventually reached Port Stanley in the Falkland Islands to effect repairs, while the remaining ships shadowed *Sheer* until she entered the River Plate and took refuge in Uruguayan territorial waters.

It was now time to assess the damage and make good whatever was possible. The OAs took apart the damaged parts of the turrets and the ERAs machined the relevant parts for the OAs to replace. There was also considerable damage to wiring and electrical cabling that the EAs spliced, replaced or repaired. Without the training and expertise of all the Artificers the ship would have remained in a parlous state. This is a fine reflection on the quality of training and the dedication of these highly skilled men and shows how important these Artificers were to maintaining the fighting efficiency of the Royal Navy.

chapter six

On the Move,
The Second World War

• • •

To Tubal Cain came many a one,
As he wrought by his roaring fire;
And each one prayed for a strong steel blade,
As the crown of his desire;
And he made them weapons sharp and strong,
Till they shouted loud for glee;
And they gave him gifts of pearls and gold,
And spoils of the forest free.
And they sang—"Hurrah for Tubal Cain,
Who hath given us strength anew!
Hurrah for the smith, hurrah for the fire,
And hurrah for the metal true!"[1]

Having finished 1939 with advancement to EA 5th Class six months
early, Ron Calverley was now at HMS *Vernon* for his more advanced
training. During this time his classmate Ivor Keys invited him to his parents'
house on the Isle of Wight; it was here he first met Pat, Ivor's younger sister,
who was to figure largely in Ron's future. By April 1940, Ron, Ivor and the
other aspiring EAs 5th Class were ready to go to sea and do "something

useful", Ron believed his war was not very exciting but his story paints a very different picture.

He was first drafted to HMS *Effingham*, a 6" gun light fleet cruiser of some vintage, having been laid down in Portsmouth in 1917 but not completed till 1925. She displaced 9,550 tons and having spent some time in reserve had undergone repairs and an armaments upgrade in Devonport. Ron remembered struggling up the gangway with his kitbag, suitcase and toolbox, a week before his twentieth birthday:

I found the Chief E.A., and met the three other members of the staff who were a lot senior to me. Six months ago at Fisgard I was at the top of the heap, and now I found myself at the bottom again, not that I am complaining, it was ever thus. The E.A's workshop was very small and something out of Dickens, and to my astonishment the lathe was so old it had to be worked with a treadle like a sewing machine. I found out later the gunnery fire control was so antiquated that it wasn't taught at the Vernon.

When it came to sleeping, the only place I could find to sling my hammock was above the lathe, and when at sea every time the ship rolled my bum hit the lathe headstock. However I had the best set of tools of all the staff, and I resolved to win the war. I wondered if I would ever get to love this ship, but fate had decided that I wouldn't get the chance.

Someone must have told the Captain I was on board, for we sailed the next day, steaming through the English Channel into the North Sea. The wind vane at the mast head was spinning like mad, but wasn't transmitting so I was sent up to fix it. The ship had been fitted with anti aircraft guns which made her a bit top heavy and she rolled more than usual. The sea was very rough indeed and one minute I was looking down over the port side and the next over the starboard side, and I quite enjoyed the experience. I couldn't help thinking that yesterday I was safely on dry land in the Vernon workshop, and now, less than 24 hours later I am up the mast head of old cruiser making it's way through rough seas in the English Channel and rolling about like a drunken sailor ashore on a Saturday night. I thought someone must be having a good laugh and I suspected my new colleagues down in the warmth of their workshop. I may have done them an injustice because after a while the next senior one to me came up to see how I was getting on.

Something wasn't right with our gunnery control system and on board were staff from the Vernon and civilian dockyard engineers trying fix it. Presumably they did, because when we got to Scapa Flow they disembarked. I thought Scapa Flow was the most desolate on place on earth. I saw several warships at anchor, until looking closer I could see they were dummies, a few large merchant ships disguised with convincing turrets and smoke stacks to look like the real thing. It was here where the German Grand Fleet scuttled itself after their surrender in 1918. More recently the Royal Oak at anchor had been sunk by a German submarine with an appalling loss of life one of whom was an ex class mate. Alan Chick had been top of our entrance exam, he left Fisgard in September and was killed before Christmas; he was to be first of many before the war finished.

Meanwhile I was trying to get used to my new life and shipmates. The ship's company were a mixture of Regulars [like me] Reservists and Pensioner Reservists. I celebrated my 20th birthday by myself, but I could now have 3d a day extra on my pay or a daily tot of rum. I chose the latter; it helped to keep the cold out and not only that but after a tot of rum the food looked a bit more palatable.

I learned we had a portable cinema on board and I volunteered to operate it, as I thought it would be interesting and something to do other than work when the opportunity occurred. The forecastle was the only place to set it up. It was very cramped and only a few of the lads could be accommodated at a time. The screen was about 5 x 4 ft, and the projector was sat on a table. The lads sat around the screen as it was a "see through". We had only a few films and when we left Scapa Flow it ended any future performances.

We stayed at Scapa for only 48 hours, but there was a mail collection, and I had time to get a letter off to my mother to let her know the name of my ship, I knew she would tell my father and Arthur, and I also knew Ivor would tell his family, as I was drafted before him.

We left Scapa and headed out across the North Sea and into the Atlantic, finishing up near Harstad a Norwegian town, 200 miles inside the Arctic Circle. The seas were rough, grey, cold and miserable as we ploughed on. Not far into the Aortic circle we encountered a blizzard and winds of gale force. The sea broke over our bows and severed our Degauss cable.

The Germans had invented an under sea magnetic mine, and when a ship passed over it, the magnetic field activated the mine's detonator to explode the mine and thus sinking the ship. To overcome this, the R.N. used the Degauss system, which neutralised the ships magnetic field by running an energised multi-cored cable round the edge of the ship's deck.

The conditions could not have been worse, and I was sent to the bows to look at the damage, followed by the Chief E.A. It was hopeless and beyond the ship's repair. We were told to return, but I could hardly move, the only protection I had from the weather was an oilskin. A couple of men escorted me back to my warm mess, and removed the frozen oilskin. I was so cold I just stood still and let them get on with it.

It was weird entering the Norwegian fjords. We were now in the 24 hr daylight zone, and distances illusionary until I got used to them. The cliffs and mountains seem to tower above us and my ship seemed puny by comparison; what appeared to be little boxes at the foot of the mountains were in fact houses.

We were anchored off shore from Harstad which was some distance away. After a few days the German Luftwaffe found us and amused themselves trying to sink us. They never succeeded, but their efforts caused problems. We always seemed to be at action stations, with our new anti aircraft guns blazing away. We were a sitting duck and philosophically accepted it was only a matter of time before our luck changed and we were hit, but ironically it wasn't by a bomb. Regular meals were far and few between, and the Chief Cook and his staff did a sterling job producing prodigious quantities of sandwiches.

My action station was in the forward repair party, whose job if we were hit, was to get the damage functioning again, similarly there was a repair party aft. Once at action stations the ship gave a huge shudder and a jerk causing everything loose to fall to the deck. A bomber had dropped a stick of bombs some yards from our port side.

I, with many others gave up slinging a hammock for a night's sleep. There wasn't any night only day light, and we were called to action stations on and off all the time, so we slept when and where we could, usually flat on the deck with our cap as a pillow. To undress completely was a luxury and a waste of time.

I often thought about Patricia and wondered if and when I would see her again. Like me, she just had a birthday [her eighteenth], and I was a bit concerned in case she was snapped up by one of the Servicemen flooding the Island. Although we were the best of friends, we were not what you would call in 2006 an item.[2]

This gives a graphic description of life onboard a warship in the Norway campaign. The ship embarked some French Foreign Legionnaires to transport to Narvik and one of them spoke to Ron. It turned out he was a Scotsman and he thought the idea of going to war in a ship was not for him as the idea that a hole in the ship could send it to the bottom did not appeal to him, any more than Ron considered the Foreign Legion the best place to be.

After Narvik the ship returned to Harstad for some minor repairs before once again setting out to capture Bodo, this time with soldiers from a Welsh regiment who were packed in below like sardines. On the way to Bodo Ron took the opportunity to go on the upper deck for a look at the beautiful Norwegian scenery, however while he was there disaster struck:

We were approaching Bodo through channels surrounded by islands and mountains, and I took the opportunity to go on deck before "action stations" was sounded for a bit of fresh air and a look at the scenery, which although beautiful and awesome, always looked cold, hard, menacing, and something of which to steer clear.

I was standing by the guard rail on the lower after deck, when suddenly there was a loud noise. The ship lifted and tilted over before settling down again, and for a few moments I thought the ship's superstructure was coming down on top of me. We had sustained serious damage hitting an uncharted reef and when it had been assessed the order was given to abandon ship. All the power had failed and the ship's boats could not be launched and efforts were being made to manhandle them.

Our escorting destroyers were closing in to help; our first priority being to disembark our Army guests. I was freezing, and I found a seal skin hat, and a coat that almost reached down to my ankles left behind by the Army; my Naval uniform was no protection against the cold [the seal skin hat is now in the possession of the Royal Marine Museum's curator. If you want to know how it got there, then ask my nephew Richard].

I had lost everything except the clothes I stood in, but what upset me most was the loss of my tools. I had spent many hours, indeed weeks and months of my youth making them. I was sorely tempted to try a rescue, but common sense prevailed. Like everyone else on board my situation was at least a bit precarious and my immediate prospects uncertain, and on second thoughts they were probably under water. Later I found a centre punch and a shilling in my pocket; since then I have used the former and spent the latter.

I returned to the guard rail on the lower after deck, to wait my turn to be rescued. I watched the destroyer Matabelle slowly, carefully and almost delicately draw alongside. Members of her crew lined her guard rail with arms outstretched ready to grab us. We were sinking and when our deck levelled with the Destroyer's and our guard rails about 2 ft apart a large sailor grabbed my hands and yanked me onto his deck, ripping the inside of my trousers in the process. I said "Thanks mate" and after he put me down I examined myself to see if I was still in one piece.

We survivors on board the Matabelle were packed below decks and it was our turn to be "sardines in a tin". We were now blind to the situation "up top" but I was told the Effingham was finally torpedoed to hasten its departure. It was a miracle there were no casualties, largely due to the Naval ratings being self disciplined, calm and without panic. We were also lucky the Luftwaffe did not find us; if they had it would have been a massacre as we were helpless in the water. It was the 17th of May 1940, and 5 weeks since I had left Portsmouth. In those 5 weeks I had my 20th birthday, started my rum ration, been frozen stiff, bombed, shot at, seen a bit of action, shipwrecked, saved, and lost my ship. I said to nobody in particular "This war is getting a bit personal."

The Matabelle had damaged a propeller on the same reef and when we made off she vibrated along. Eventually she hove to and when we came on deck I could see we were in another fjord, a few hundred yards across. On the other side a small Polish ship was moored. We were put in an open boat to make our own way to her. Half way across a German plane appeared flying very low, and in those circumstances I can assure you that the mind works quickly. We had already been told that life expectancy in those waters was about 4 minutes, and if the German pilot had machine gunned us there was nowhere to run or hide. But he didn't; the war was still young and perhaps there was a little bit of chivalry left. However I did see his bombs leave the plane, and watched them fall harmlessly into the sea. They made quite a splash.

The electrical staff were all safe and sound aboard the Polish ship, when our Divisional Officer came in and said a volunteer was required to stay behind in Norway and join a demolition party. The other members of the staff were married or about to get married so I was the only one unattached and single, and there was a silence after the excuses until I offered my services. I wasn't being brave or heroic. I was young and life was just one big adventure, and this was merely another one on offer. When the volunteers were mustered my name wasn't called; when our D.O. was informed, he, a man much older and wiser than myself said "Forget it". So I wasn't at best going to be a prisoner of war after all. My colleagues afterwards were very solicitous towards me. I was to be reminded about it again some years later.

We sailed for home and eventually disembarked at Greenock in Scotland and got on a train for Portsmouth. We travelled through the night, maintaining a blackout with the blinds pulled down; we kept on stopping on the journey, and at one stop a lot of ladies offered us mugs of tea and buns which were most welcome.[3]

This is hardly a war with little excitement: there is enough to last most people a lifetime. As with many Artificers, Ron particularly mourns the loss of his tool kit, particularly when it has been supplemented with "special" tools and adaptors. Eventually they returned to Portsmouth and as can be imagined in the variety of rigs and borrowed clothing they looked more like pirates than naval ratings. Having had their lost kit replaced, apart from their no. 1 uniform, which they had to procure themselves, they were sent on fourteen days' survivors' leave, the least they deserved, which Ron spent between the Isle of Wight, renewing his friendship with Pat, and home with his family. On his return to *Vernon* Ron was ready for a new draft, which was not long in coming:

On the 4th of June 1940 I was back in the Vernon waiting for another ship. Meanwhile I managed to visit Pat a few times. On the 28th of June I got a draft to H.M.S. Condor, a ship I had never heard of, and when I asked where it was and how did I get to it, the answer surprised me. "You will travel by train to Arbroath in Scotland; it's a Naval Air Station". Four of us travelled together, the other three were all 1st class E.A.s, and a lot older than me, so being only 5th class I was very much their junior, not only in experience but in age. We changed trains at Edinburgh, and went for a stroll along Princes Street to stretch our legs and get some fresh air; we had been crammed tight with other troops in a railway compartment all night. As we walked along a girl rushed up and touched my collar for luck [an old superstition]. And so the Norwegian experience was behind me, and what lingers most in my memory is the cold, the wind, the wetness and the greyness of everything. Perhaps next time I would be sent somewhere warmer [I wish]!

It wasn't unusual for survivors to be given a shore job for a few weeks before getting another ship and I thought I was in that category. I had 10 years to serve before re-engagement, and I expected at least 8 of them would be on board ship. I did not realise it at the time how a stroke of a pen by a Chief Writer in a drafting office had not only changed my career, but also my life and improved my survival prospects as the war pursued its course.[4]

Thus started a new relationship with the Fleet Air Arm. At this time HMS *Condor* was not complete but Ron's accommodation was good, he had a cabin to himself and he thought the food much better than the normal pussers' fare. The workshops were also incomplete and they had to make do with temporary workshops. Being on an air station was strange having been used to being surrounded by warships but Ron soon settled in and made friends with some of the aircrew, who arranged for him to go on a flight in a Swordfish, a nerve-racking experience that cooled his enthusiasm for flying, but he had nothing but admiration for those who flew in the "Stringbags".

> *It was September 1940, and due for promotion to 4th class, a Petty Officer's rating. I saw the Captain; promotion was granted and back dated 3 months. I was puzzled why, and I found, unbeknown to me, I was given 3 months accelerated advancement when I left Fisgard. Again for some unknown reason I lost it on the Vernon. Then the Captain restored it. My promotion dated from the 31st May 1940, so at 20 years and 6 weeks old I must have been the youngest Petty Officer in the Navy.*[5]

Ron remembered the night duties for the EAs came round every five days and some could be quite interesting:

> *The Electrical Artificers had to take turns at night duty which occurred every 5 days. It meant that if anything occurred during the night within our normal sphere of activity the duty E.A. was expected to deal with it. One night when I was on duty a magnetic mine dropped near the Wren's quarters. Fortunately it did not explode, and the Wrens were evacuated to another area. I thought "just my luck, I will have to deal with it", but before I could get my screwdriver the Captain sent for an Army Bomb Disposal Unit. Just as well, I would have blown myself and the station sky high. When daylight came it cheered up the sailors "no end" to see the Wrens in their night clothing walking back to their quarters.*
>
> *Other nights, when night flying was practised my job before night fell was to lay out an illuminated dummy runway, and stay with it until the exercise was finished, whilst the pilots in a Swordfish practised night deck landings. It was a precarious activity. One morning we went to pick up the equipment and the men. We found one of them an R.A.F man dead. An aircraft on takeoff had veered off and it's under carriage had hit him on the head. We stood clear after that, except the "bat man" officer who had to stand on the edge of the runway to guide the aircraft down. He was very good at ducking!*

Another night when I was on duty, the field telephone system had broken down, and It was my job to repair it. The telephone cable line had broken, and as I had originally routed the line, I was best placed to find the break and it couldn't wait for morning daylight. It was during the time we were expecting to be invaded by the Germans. My plan was to find which part of the line had broken, and to do that, I needed to find the middle, cut it, rig up a field telephone and try putting a call through each half, thus narrowing the search. I am relating this story because I had an extraordinary piece of luck, and as I write about it I can hardly believe it happened. So let me try and "paint you a picture".

The Black Watch were on guard and trigger happy, so I had to be very careful about showing a light. The line was 1/2 a mile long and as explained on the previous page ran on the periphery of the airfield, so under normal circumstances it wouldn't be easy to find. The weather was absolutely atrocious. It was a dark and stormy night, and the rain came down in torrents, and I could hardly see a hand in front of my face. Off I went in the pouring rain, stepping carefully and feeling my way like a blind man through long almost knee high grass, scrub and bushes. As I proceeded, I realised what I wanted to do was impossible, it would have to wait for the morning. On the other hand I didn't want to go back to the Control Tower reporting failure, so I carried on with my search, and when I thought I was about half way I groped around for the line, found it, picked it up to cut, and low and behold I picked it up where the break was. In the morning my colleagues wanted to know how I had found the break. I didn't tell them; "Sheer guile" I said.[6]

After Christmas leave, a few days of which Ron spent with Pat on the Isle of Wight, Ron was informed he was going to an RAF station to learn how to operate and maintain a link trainer:

The Link Trainer is an aircraft cockpit simulator, complete with controls and instruments, and it behaved like the real thing. The "pilot" sat in the cockpit and had his performance monitored on a separate instrument in front of an instructor. I used to maintain and service it once a week and I was on call if anything went wrong. I often used it for fun and to improve my flying technique, and if it stalled the only way to recover was to continue the dive into the spin at full speed, and pull the nose up. At least that's the action taken in a Link Trainer. Perhaps one day someone will lend me a plane to see if it is the same with the real thing.[7]

By this time Ron had been ashore for nine months and was concerned that he was missing out on the shipboard experience he would require for future promotion, however there were more important issues to be resolved and top of the list was Ron's forthcoming wedding to Pat. This seems to have come about without the normal courtship; when Ron asked Pat she apparently replied that "it's not a bad idea", and so the wedding was planned for 31 July 1941 and after the wedding Pat and Ron would set up home in Arbroath. However, the wedding was blighted by the tragic news that Ivor was "Missing – presumed drowned" after HMS *Manchester* was sunk in the Mediterranean. It seemed likely that the wedding would be postponed but in the event:

> I thought and understood the wedding would be cancelled, but Pat's parents wanted the wedding to go on quietly. July the 31st, 1941, was Pat's day, and everyone put on a brave face and tried to be cheerful. When I saw her in her wedding dress walking down the aisle she looked so young and beautiful, I thought "Why me"? One of the guests said to me afterwards "You looked like the cat what got the cream". And I replied "Well I did, didn't I"?
>
> At the wedding breakfast, there was such a contrast of mixed emotions that nobody could make a speech. I tried and managed a few words then sat down. Arthur my best man could not speak either [he was only 17].
>
> I had a weeks leave left, and Pat and I spent two days in London, and left for Arbroath, and a few days later I went back on board making arrangements to live ashore. Pat was only 19, and she took to married life like a duck takes to water. She was hundreds of miles away from home in a strange place; in lodgings that left something to be desired, with food rationing to cope with, and her husband away all day and often at night as well. We were young and very happy and as long as we were together nothing else mattered.[8]

Ron expected to be drafted to sea at any moment; he had been ashore now for fourteen months and Ron was hoping that perhaps the Portsmouth Drafting Office had forgotten him. It was at this time that Pat's father was taken seriously ill and was not expected to recover. Pat, of course was needed at home and Ron requested to travel down to the Isle of Wight with her. The Commander initially refused but relented by bringing Ron's Easter leave forward. After Pat's father passed away, her mother came back with them to Arbroath. This would have been very convenient if Ron was drafted and, as is the way, a draft was not long in arriving, as Ron remembered:

In April I received a draft to Sierra Leone on the west coast of Africa, known throughout the navy as the white man's grave. I was kitted out with tropical uniform including a white helmet, and sent to H.M.S. Waxwing a drafting depot to wait for the rest of the draftees to assemble. Pat, accompanied by her mother returned to the I.of.W. And I thought how lucky we were to have been together. I would always miss her as she had become very much a part of me, and would be so for the rest of my life.

When we left Waxwing we were 29 in total, including 6 Petty Officers. I was the only Artificer and the most senior, so I found myself responsible for the Draft [I forgot to mention that on 5 of February 1943, I had been re-rated as an Air Artificer [L].LFX637999 and established as a full time Fleet Air Arm rating]. We were to take passage on H.M.S. Archer, a light fleet Escort Carrier, berthed in Greenock on the Clyde, and to get there we had to change at Glasgow. There were others of her type, one of them H.M.S. Datcher mysteriously blew up in the Clyde with a terrible loss of life. The Archer stank of aircraft fuel and at the time I wondered if we were at risk. The Tannoy kept blaring out "Out pipes, Out pipes" [stop smoking].

I had been advised that one of the men, a Glaswegian had been in trouble ever since he joined the Navy, and he might desert when we got to Glasgow. I detailed a couple of lads to keep a discreet eye on him. We had to wait over an hour for our connection, and he approached me for permission to visit his home. I thought if he wanted to desert he wouldn't have asked me, and on the other hand if I refused him he would go anyway. So I gave him permission, and to my relief he returned in time. If he hadn't, I would have been asked some very awkward questions. It later emerged he was illiterate, and it most probably contributed towards his attitude. However there is a happy ending to this little story; one of the Petty Officers was a school teacher in civilian life, and in his spare time gave him a one-to-one education. I have told you this because, having read my memoirs so far you might have got the impression that the Navy didn't care. Well to be honest sometimes their care might be misconstrued as a bit draconian, but as the saying goes – "It never did me any harm."

When I boarded the Archer I was asked much to my consternation "What have you got that white helmet for? We are going to Iceland", and sure enough when we left the Clyde instead of turning south we turned north.[9]

131

So who can possibly say the Royal Navy has no sense of humour? It is also worth noting the casual way that Ron mentioned the change of category, from EA to Aircraft Artificer, the first "dual trade" AAs having only been introduced in January 1943. On passage to Iceland the ship was caught up in a violent storm and the twelve Swordfish aircraft carried onboard *Archer* bound for Ron's destination in Iceland could not be flown off until the storm abated.

No time was lost when we got ashore [with some relief]. We loaded onto three Lorries driven by Royal Marines, and off we went on a journey that was interesting to say the least. The roads were very narrow compacted lava dust, and it wasn't long before we were covered from head to foot in it. We eventually arrived at a place called Kaldadarnes, some miles south of Reykjavik. To get there, we had to go down a very steep winding mounting road, and the Marines drove like maniacs. If it was their intention to scare us, all I can say is, they succeeded.

Kaldadarnes was a small R.A.F. air station with one runway, but no longer operational. It was manned by many R.A.F. non-flying personnel. When we arrived, our Swordfish were parked in a large hanger and the pilots had returned to the Archer. The Swordfish were on "standby" and it was our responsibility to maintain them in a fit flying condition for immediate use if required.

All the buildings were built with corrugated iron painted green. Nissan huts served as living accommodation and ours was bare except for the beds and a large stove in the middle. We soon started to make improvements in our hut to make life bit more comfortable. We had no idea how long our stay would be. Wood was obtained and the R.A.F. lent us some carpentry tools and soon we had shelves and cupboards for clothes. We also cadged some white wash and lightened the interior. It wasn't quite like home from home, but it was an improvement. It was a case of "God helps them who helps themselves," and that is what we did. The huts were built on brick piles and it was a favourite R.A.F. pastime to throw smoke bombs under the hut and watch the rats run out. They were smaller than U.K. rats and brownish in colour.

Kalderdarnes isn't even mentioned on the map of Iceland. It was completely isolated, and apart from the British and a few American visitors without signs of civilization. There was one made up road out of the station and the gate was manned by R.A.F. policemen, otherwise the place was inaccessible. The air station was on a plain at the bottom of a mountain range that had Mount Heckla a slumbering volcano. Many years after I left Iceland it erupted. On one side of the station ran an exceedingly cold fast running mountain river. One of the Petty Officers became adept at catching salmon, which we cooked on the hut stove. The rest of the station was hemmed in by marshes and water pools. The marshes were a bird watcher's paradise, but our only interest was wading out searching for duck eggs, which were beaten up in a tot of whisky and drank raw.

We arrived in May 1943, and at the end of the month I was promoted to Chief Petty Officer's rate at the age of 23 years and 6 weeks. What I lacked in age I made up in seniority, and the R.A.F. involved me in a couple of their daily routines. Every morning I marched a mixture of R.A.F. personnel and Naval ratings to the ceremony of raising the flag. I had to take turns to visit the men's mess hall when they were having lunch and at each table I would ask "Any complaints"? The airmen never complained, but I knew what would happen when I got to my lads table; they were waiting for me. "Any complaints"? I said with bated breath, and I received a chorus. It was a novelty for them. It wasn't naval policy to ask ratings or anyone else if there were any complaints. Oh no! It just wouldn't do![10]

While the accommodation was adequate, Ron remembered the food being very good and not subject to any rationing, as was the case at home. Similarly, clothing was also unrationed and Ron took the opportunity to do some shopping in Reykjavik for Pat. There seems to have been little do and Ron complains of being under employed, to such an extent that he grew a beard, though there was the opportunity for some sightseeing, but the junior ratings were less than happy, the environment being cold, wet and gloomy and the natives definitely not friendly. But once again things were about to change:

It was like being in limbo waiting for something to happen, and at the end of October it did, but not what we expected. We were told to return to the F.A.A. Base, H.M.S. Daedalus at Lee-on-Solent, and to take passage on the Aircraft Carrier H.M.S. Pretoria Castle, a converted P&O Liner. She was moored in a fjord somewhere north of Reykjavik on the east coast of Iceland.

We loaded onto the three Lorries driven by the same Marines who transported us six months ago. Then I made a mistake, the weather was atrocious with a blizzard blowing in our faces. I decided to go in the front lorry with the others following behind. With visibility very poor we set off; it did not deter the Marine driver; he belted along. When we arrived at the Pretoria Castle I was one lorry short, which caused some anxiety, but after two hours it arrived safely, with the excuse it had broken down. I suspected it had stopped somewhere for refreshments. If anyone knew where to get some it would be the Marine. So we said goodbye to Iceland with no regrets. I thought the whole experience for a Naval rating a bit weird, and I hoped my next foreign draft would be somewhere warmer [it was to be one of the hottest and stickiest places in the world]. The Arctic Circle did not appeal to me, so we said goodbye to Iceland with no regrets. I thought the whole experience for a Naval rating a bit weird, and I hoped my next foreign draft would be somewhere warmer [it was to be one of the hottest and stickiest places in the world]. After a much smoother voyage home Ron landed at Greenock and then, getting a band of men together, they set off by train to Portsmouth. With ten days' leave Ron sped off to the Isle of Wight to see Pat and have a grand reunion. While Ron had been away, Ivor's toolbox had arrived. It had taken two years to travel back to the UK and, as has been noted elsewhere, tools were the lifeblood of Artificers:

> *He (Ivor) was killed on the 24th of July 1941, so its journey from the Manchester to Ryde had taken two years. It had been held up in a dockyard somewhere, probably in Gibraltar. It was a strange feeling looking at his tools, which were the same as the ones I had lost, except his name and not mine, was etched on them. The poignancy and irony were not lost on me. It was almost as if Ivor was saying to me "Never mind Ron, have mine." In April 1940, we two young men set out for whatever lay ahead, and now in 1943, I was the sole survivor with Ivor's tools. It could easily have been the other way round; we were both due for a ship at the same time. The Manchester, like the Effingham is a rusting hulk on the bottom of the sea.*[11]

Ron returned to *Daedalus* expecting a draft to another ship but spent several weeks doing odd jobs before going on a training course. This course would normally have been held at HMS *Vernon* in Portsmouth but after a bomb had landed in the base, killing a hundred in a single night, the main part of the establishment was evacuated to Roedean school in Brighton (HMS *Vernon* (R)), where bell pushes on the dormitory bulkhead were purportedly labelled "Ring for Mistress". This was followed by a course in Newcastle-under-Lyme, where Ron learnt about bombs and machine guns, this coming about after AA (L)s were made responsible for aircraft ordnance.

In February 1945 Ron was drafted to HMS *Deersound*, a refrigerator ship that sailed between UK and New Zealand converted into a repair ship. To reach the ship, which was in the Pacific, Ron took passage in HMS *Stirling Castle*, a P&O liner converted into a troop ship. Apart from a brief visit to Australia and an even briefer stop in New Zealand, Ron did not set foot ashore again until the end of the war in the Far East. With the advent of the "Kamikaze" planes, a signalling system for friendly aircraft was required and, as Ron remembered:

A signalling system was urgently required, so that our aircraft when approaching their Carriers to land could quickly identify themselves, before being mistaken for a Kami Kazi plane and shot down. The problem landed right on my plate so I set about developing and manufacturing a system and for the first time my bit of Ordnance training came in useful. The system got as far as a "bread board" demonstration, when the Americans dropped the Atomic Bomb, and the project was also dropped. The Japanese war officially ended on 15th August 1945. A lot has been said and written about whether or not the bomb should have been used, and mostly by people who weren't fighting in the Pacific [armchair strategists and pacifists]. We all knew that when the mainland invasion of Japan began a million or so casualties [including Japanese] would occur. Like the rest of the ship's company, and the Allied Forces I was delighted and thankful that the war was over. On the 14th of August I had no idea when I would return home again; on the 15th I knew my homecoming was only a few months away and I would be in one piece. Ambition achieved! However I was optimistic, my return to the U.K. was going to be unnecessarily delayed.[12]

Once the war was over the ship docked in Hong Kong and Ron was finally able to set foot ashore. But four years of Japanese occupation had left its mark and Ron felt distinctly "unclean" after his first run ashore, standing in the shower fully dressed until he felt better.

Things still did not run smoothly and Ron found himself ashore, though not where he wanted to be:

The Navy wanted to give a present made by the Deersound to Madame Chiang Kai-Shek, the wife of the Chinese Nationalist leader. I thought of the beautiful artefacts I had seen in the Hong Kong Pagoda, and I suddenly felt embarrassed. Our efforts would be like comparing a sledge hammer to a diamond. I looked at the materials that was available to me, and decided that the best thing to make was double desk top ink stand.

I never finished it, the Deersound *received orders to return to the U.K. and what was a happy ship despite war time conditions became a happier ship, and then the blow fell. My Boss came to see me and said that despite everything he had done to stop it, I was wanted on shore to do a special job. I left my ship on the 13th of Jan 1946, or rather it left me. There were worst places than Australia on which to be marooned, but I was too disappointed to appreciate it. I thought the special job might go some way to compensate me. I left my overcoat behind. Of course I hadn't worn it during the commission and the head cockroach took advantage of this and said to his mates "I have found the perfect place to lay eggs and have a good time." When I took the coat off the peg I found a ribbon of thick dense cockroaches under the collar, so my overcoat got back to the U.K before me.*

After many weeks doing very little, a draft finally arrived that would allow Ron to go home:

After many weeks, on the 6th of June 1946 I got what I wanted, a draft for home, and to take passage on H.M.S. Glory a Fleet Aircraft Carrier. It was on board the Glory that General Imamura surrendered 139,000 Japanese troops. I had to report to the Royal Australian Naval base in Sydney where I was told "You're too late mate she has already sailed". Apparently the Glory was bound for Adelaide to "show the flag," and to give thanks for Australian hospitality by being host to the local population for a couple weeks. The Aussie Navy took charge and I was put on an overnight train to Melbourne, where I was their guest for a day, before catching another train for Adelaide. This was done with such speed, alacrity, and efficiency by the Aussies I was beginning to think they were in a haste to get rid of me.

We ploughed through the Indian Ocean arriving at Colombo without mishap. I stayed at a naval transit camp for a few days, where we were warned "Watch out, there are scorpions in the toilets"! The short stay gave me the opportunity to visit the town where the sounds, smells and sights differed from Hong Kong. A fortune teller pestered me to tell my fortune. He said I was going to be a very rich man. I didn't believe him then, and I certainly don't now.

I joined a large Naval party and travelled across country by train to Trincomalee to embark on H.M.S. Queen, a converted Light Fleet Carrier. The train journey is one to remember. The carriages could have done with a scrub, and they rattled, rolled, jerked and jumped for miles through jungle with screeching monkeys and other peculiar noises keeping us awake as we travelled through the night. The seats were made with wooden slats to suit Asian bums and not the lean bums of British sailors. The heat was intense and the windows had to be kept open, an invitation for all sorts of insects to fly in. Our white uniforms seemed to attract them. They took one look at us with our light skins and white uniforms and thought it must be some sort of Asian festival and pounced. One chap at the end of our carriage gave a yell; something had flown in and had settled on his neck. Each carriage had a toilet, a hole in the floor, and although I could, I will not describe them. It is sufficient to say they were unusable, especially if you were a bit squeamish.

It was good and a relief to get back on board a British warship, with clean drinking water, showers, flush toilets and lousy food. I couldn't get under a shower quick enough to wash away the last remnants of a short Ceylonese adventure.

Our first sight of England was the south coast of the Isle of Wight. The sun was shining and the air and visibility so clear that the white cliffs of Freshwater Bay and the green of the Downs could be clearly seen. Nobody clapped, cheered or spoke and with our own thoughts we silently absorbed the scene as we approached closer and closer. My thoughts were dominated by a pretty and warm hearted girl who lived on the Island. We entered the Solent, passing through the Forts with the familiar sight of Ryde pier on the left, and the Southsea W.W.1 memorial on our right reflecting the sun. We could not enter Portsmouth Dockyard until the next day, which was disappointing, so we anchored in the Solent. It was early September 1946 and I had left the Deersound 8 months ago and travelled 10,000 miles to get here.

We docked the next morning. We were home and I stepped ashore in good old England. Unbeknown to me Pat had been waiting near the telescope on Ryde Esplanade to see our arrival, and when asked by two passers – by what she was looking at she replied "My husband is aboard that ship." They said "Ooh"!

I left the ship and went to Daedalus at Lee-on-Solent to store my gear and collect 21 days leave. Before leaving I went to the Mail Office to see if there was any re-directed mail for me. I was surprised to find an O.H.M.S. letter addressed to Air Artificer R Calverley B.E.M. The letter has since been lost but I can still remember what it said

On the advice of the Lords of the Admiralty
The King has been graciously pleased to
award you the British Empire Medal for
Distinguished service in the Far East theatre of operations.[13]

So Ron's long and arduous war ended, with enough excitement for most and with recognition of his sterling service. Ron served out the remainder of his twelve-year engagement and left the service, believing as many before and after that a life in the Royal Navy is not conducive to a settled and happy home life. Ron is now (2018) in his ninety-ninth year and looking forward to completing his century.

Meanwhile, the new accommodation for those Apprentices in Rosyth would be ready by the end of the Autumn Term and it was decided that, despite there still being some remedial work to complete that the boys would move from Kings Road School prior to Christmas leave, as Dennis Stiff recalled:

The arrangements at King's Road School continued until the new establishment became just barely habitable. The buildings were there but the interconnecting pathways and open cable and pipework trenches required some elementary knowledge of astro-navigation to negotiate these hazards in the blackout. Any apprentice who was wise enough to acquire an electric torch became a convoy leader to lead the way to the outlying huts.[14]

During that winter of 1940 working in the Factory when it was very cold, which was most of the time, as many remember, was not pleasant: heating was provided by fans blowing over steam coils. These steam coils were supplied from the boiler house, which often ran low on coke and could not maintain the demand for steam. The instructors were quickly issued with "Valor" paraffin stoves but such luxuries were not for the Apprentices. They kept warm by doubling around the Factory floor for five minutes every hour or so; no waste of resources there.

As is the wont of naval officers over the years, "cleanliness is next to godliness" and it appears the Captain was determined that the new establishment would uphold this axiom. To ensure that his exacting standards were maintained by the Apprentices the Captain carried out rounds of the accommodation at very regular intervals, Dennis Stiff remembered this all too well:

After leaving King's Road School, Grenville Division occupied C Block's two end dormitories nearest the parade ground. Soon, Captain's Rounds became a regular routine and necessitated a high standard of neatness with only Service articles allowed on display. During one visit to the upper dormitory, the Grockle's (Captain) curiosity was aroused by a local area map pinned to the inside of the door. Neither the accompanying Divisional Officer nor the Divisional Petty Officer could explain why the occupants' names appeared on the flags pinned onto the map. In due course the dormitory Hook Boy was required to spill the beans, the map actually indicated the whereabouts of the current girlfriends, in an effort to stop poaching within the division! It also helped to solve a transport problem. Not everyone owned a cycle, and crossbar lifts were very much in demand for some of the desperate return trips from the environs of Dunfermline. Grockle was not impressed and ordered a total ban on adornment of doors and walls. The apprentice who failed to take down the map for Grockle's rounds was very unpopular because of the loss of this essential facility.[15]

The "Grockle", as he was affectionately known, was Captain E.W. Hardy, who had recently been promoted to Captain, having been in command of *Caledonia* before the move ashore.

While all the Apprentices knew the establishment as *Caledonia*, this was in fact a misnomer, as Ian Rogers, who joined Collingwood Division in 1940 wrote:

We knew it as HMS Caledonia, although that was not its real name until after the war. Officially it was the MTE (Mechanical Training Establishment), or later the RNATE (Royal Naval Artificer Training Establishment). The establishment building programme had been interrupted by the outbreak of the war. The main factory was complete and the gymnasium and swimming bath complex were nearing completion, but the remainder of the establishment was erected in a hurry, on a temporary basis. These "temporary" huts lasted in fact for twenty-five years before new accommodation blocks were built, and the remainder of the "temporary" buildings lasted for over forty-five years until the establishment closed. The apprentice accommodation in 1940 was in three blocks, A, B, and C. These were allocated simply by seniority, the juniors being in C Block, the furthest away from the mess halls and recreation rooms, and the seniors in A Block nearest to them. Each block had eight dormitories, two per division leading off a central corridor. Owing to the lie of the land the southern four dormitories in each block were slightly higher than the other four. There were steps up and down to them from the central corridor. Thus we had those "top" and "bottom" dormitories mentioned earlier. Leading off the corridor there were also lavatories, wash-places, and showers. There were also "boot rooms" which were used and "towel rooms" which were not (except for "rounds"). The showers were bare concrete – no tiles – and a bit rough on the feet. Elsewhere there was the inevitable green lino on the floors and cream walls. The beds lined the walls of the dormitories with a clear space down the centre leading to a door at the far end opening out on to the grounds. The beds were staggered, one with its head by the wall and its neighbour with its head to the centre of the hut. Between each pair of beds was a twin steel locker for two people. Each half locker had a shelf, a small drawer and a large drawer in which we stowed all our personal possessions. The walls were lined with a fairly flimsy board, but the huts were centrally heated in winter by means of overhead rows of small-bore pipes, often used for swinging from! The windows had blackout curtains, which had to be carefully drawn so as not to show any light. The interior lighting was meagre and after "Lights Out", tiny blue lamps were left on in strategic positions to relieve the complete blackness.[16]

So the accommodation and furniture could well be described as "spartan" but there would be little appetite for the Admiralty to be anything but frugal in this time of war. There was also the lack of appreciation of any health and safety, with the buildings having asbestos roofs and outer walls and strawboard inner walls and ceilings. Central heating, such as it was, was supplied by steam pipes running just below the ceiling. Conditions in the depths of a Scottish winter must have been challenging indeed.

Meanwhile, at Torpoint, just across the Tamar from Devonport, work was continuing with new accommodation for Apprentices and by October 1940 the accommodation was ready for occupation:

The four accommodation blocks at Torpoint, each of seven huts, were named after the famous engineers Newcommen and Parsons (on the west or senior side) and Trevithick and Watt on the east or junior side. Each block contained an Ablution/Heads/Drying Room complex reached from the huts by an open-sided covered way. The huts were brick built with an unpainted breeze block lining, a concrete bitumen-coated floor and a corrugated asbestos roof. Apprentices slept in two tier beds separated by two wooden chests of drawers and used their hammock as a counterpane. In winter those who were not near to the stove laid their greatcoats on their beds under their hammocks to keep warm.[17]

While the accommodation was, by this time, adequate, there remained much to be done. The workshops were not fully fitted out and the whole site remained very much a "building site" and the paths and roadways were very rudimentary. This meant a problem with almost constantly muddy boots. The establishment was not as yet commissioned but remained the Royal Naval Artificers Training Establishment.

It was necessary to ensure that this new establishment was put on a sound war footing, so air raid shelters were constructed in positions convenient for the accommodation, buildings were painted with camouflage paint and blackout curtains were fitted to all the windows. To ensure adequate firefighting facilities "static water tanks" were constructed around the establishment; these tanks were utilised in later years to baptise birthday boys, unfortunate for those with birthdays in the winter, when it required the ice breaking before immersion. Because of the perceived chance of chemical attack a decontamination station was also constructed.

The construction of these air raid shelters was well timed as there was an air raid in December 1940 where a bomb blew a hole in the perimeter fence. Fortunately no one was hurt and there was no significant damage, though it did result in the road between *Fisgard* and *Raleigh* being widened. There were further air raids and as Paul Bass, who joined Hawke Division in 1941, remembered:

During an air raid in 1941 bombs fell on Raleigh *and* Fisgard. *We were in above ground shelters and the blast wave was enough to shake our trousers. We discovered later that the workshop had been hit and extensively damaged. Any hopes that we had that we would not be able to continue making the double hexagon test job were soon dashed as alternative facilities were found! I remember the oil tanks at Torpoint had also been hit and were burning.*[18]

While these raids were most inconvenient, it is likely that the establishment was not the intended target and the bombs were meant for the fuel tanks at Thanckes, though the raid in April 1941 resulted in 60% of the lathes being moved to the parade ground while the fabric of the Factory was repaired. It is to be hoped that the lathes were suitably protected from the elements.

Paul remembered, "Our Captain was P R 'Tiny' Dalton, a large man who was keen on boxing and so we all had to do it as well. Otherwise the main exercise was cross country walking or, occasionally, running."[19] Surely too much of a coincidence not to be the same "Tiny" Dolton Reg Bennett met at *Fisgard* when it was at Chatham, in 1931. Paul recalled that:

> For the first year we were paid 9d a day and by the time they had made deductions for tools and laundry we had 4 shillings a fortnight to spend. The main treat was to have tea at the YMCA in Union Street in Plymouth for a few pence. We had to be back in Fisgard soon after that. We all lived in Nissan huts in double bunks with a single stove in the centre. During cold weather we stoked up the fire until the chimney pipe was red hot, but those at the outer ends hardly felt any benefit from it. There was an open covered way between our hut and the bathroom. In my first few months there the chap in the next bunk to me was diagnosed with TB and died soon after. We all had to be tested, but there were no further cases, fortunately.[20]

Paul Bass was awarded a cadetship at the end of 1942 and was trained as a Marine Engineer at RNEC Keyham and Manadon. He served on HM Ships *Cambrian*, *Mauritius*, *Premier* and *Rodney* and completed the Gunnery Engineering Long Course at HMS *Excellent*. As a Lieutenant Commander he served as the Engineer Officer in HMS *Ulysses*, involved in the H-bomb testing at Christmas Island. After time in HMS *Vernon* he was promoted to Commander and was successively WEO of HMS *Lion* and HMS *Tiger*, where he acted as Liaison Officer for Ian Smith's Rhodesian Delegation in the "Tiger Talks". He was promoted to Captain in 1969 and was the first Captain Weapons Trials. As Director of Naval Manning and Training (Engineering) he was heavily involved with Engineering Branch development. He was promoted to Rear Admiral on 7 January 1979 and was appointed as Flag Officer Portsmouth and Port Admiral Portsmouth. A division was named after him at Fisgard Squadron in HMS *Raleigh*.

As a result of the heightened expectation of an imminent German invasion, as well as the Torpoint Home Guard anti-invasion platoons were formed within *Fisgard* in February 1941. These consisted of four machine-gun sections; the armament was of First World War vintage, old Lewis guns and rifle sections with insufficient rifles. These were supplemented by metal knobkerries referred to as "Dalton Knockers".

It is clear that the wartime environment had a deleterious effect on some of the Apprentices in *Caledonia*, as Ian Rogers wrote:

> We were into our D class Doubles when tragedy struck. One evening, one of our division, "Blondie" Griggs, had been down to supper, gone back to the "top" dormitory, loaded his rifle and somehow shot half his head off. This is somewhat difficult to do with a rifle and has to be a very deliberate act. An unfortunate apprentice following shortly afterwards found him with blood and brains over the floor. Blondie had been a popular classmate and always had a cheeky grin on his face. His death shocked us all. Why did he do it aged only sixteen? We will never know. Afterwards someone recalled that he had looked at Blondie's steel hexagon test job and passed a remark that it looked a bit of a mess. Blondie had replied, "Never mind. It won't be marked". There was an inquiry and the Range Officer (Lt Knocker) was in trouble. Apparently it was his responsibility to check that all the live rounds and empty cartridges were counted at the end of a shoot. This had obviously not been done the last time we had been on the range because Blondie had pocketed a round. An immediate result of this was that our rifles were removed from our dormitories and kept in the armoury from then on. Blondie was given a full military funeral and I was one of those on the ropes pulling the gun-carriage to the cemetery. I'm sorry to say that there were some irreverent remarks passed among the gun-carriage crew but perhaps Blondie would have appreciated that. He liked a joke.[21]

This must have been most upsetting for those who knew "Blondie" and there would have been no "counselling" in those days. Though it seems even after this dark episode there were those who could lighten the mood with irreverence.

There were precautions taken at *Caledonia*, similar to those taken at *Fisgard*, with the senior Apprentices manning the anti-aircraft guns, something Ian Rogers remembered well:

> In "defence" duties we graduated from firewatching to a Bofors 40mm.gun! There were two of these and we were drilled by an Army Sergeant of Artillery. I was No.4, the loading and firing number. My crew had BPH Walker as DC (Detachment Commander) and big "Paddy" Cunningham as No.1 (in-charge

gun). Hugh Cunningham, C.B.E. came out of the Navy when thirty, and then served about thirty years with the Northern Ireland Prison Service. He worked his way up through the grades from prison officer to Governor, and was the governor of some of the toughest jails of Northern Ireland, finishing his time as the Governor of Crumlin Road prison in Belfast. Others in our gun crew were Harry Woollains from Plymouth as No.2 (trainer) and lofty Bill Dennis as No.3 (layer). Harry later served in submarines but he developed very poor eyesight and I lost track of him. Bill Dennis was probably the tallest apprentice ever and towered over the average man. He became a Lt Commander in the Navy. I was No.4 and Nos.5 and 6 (ammunition numbers) were "Tub" Russell and Alan Deller. A later crew change saw "Tub" Russell as DC and Les Pack as No.1, both Portsmouth men. "Bruno" Owens from Cullompton and "Job" Munday from Maidstone took over as ammunition numbers. I later served with Job in a submarine. Les Pack died in a plane crash in about 1950. We trained furiously but the air raids were over as far as Rosyth was concerned. We aimed to get the gun off its wheels and onto its supports in one minute flat, and we also learned how to change barrels in double quick time. When manning the gun, as No.4, I had to jump onto the firing platform, grasp the loading handle and shout, "Held," the reason for which I have completely forgotten. We sometimes went to the firing range at Ferny Ness on the coast east of Edinburgh to fire at sleeves towed by aircraft. Those pilots must have been brave! I had to load the clips of shells and fire the gun. I clearly remember the first time I trod on the firing pedal to actually fire the gun. I expected a bang but not that loud. It nearly made me jump off the platform![22]

John Gurr and HMS *Ajax* arrived back home in January 1940 and found out that together with *Exeter* the ships' companies were to be honoured with a lunch at the Guildhall in London. John and seven other Chief Petty Officers went ahead to act as markers for the main body who would be marching to Horse Guards Parade; there King George VI inspected them and presented medals and orders awarded as a result of action off the River Plate. John recalled that there were thousands lining the streets as the ships' companies marched "via Trafalgar Square, Northumberland Avenue, Embankment, Queen Victoria Street, Queen Street and King Street to Guildhall".[23] On arrival at the Guildhall they were all met by the Lord Mayor, Sir William Cowan, who welcomed them and led them into the Banqueting Hall, where they were joined by some of the Merchant Navy

Captains who had been prisoners onboard *Graf Spee*. After a splendid lunch, and with every man now the proud possessor of a cigarette case embossed with the City of London crest, they set off by train to Plymouth.

It was not long before the *Ajax* was at sea again escorting a convoy south. It was now August and John came off watch one morning with swollen feet and a pain in the groin. He seems to have misunderstood the doctor's instructions and continued with his normal watch-keeping only to find himself relieved of his watch; he should have been "turned in" in the sick bay. He was consequently sent home on the hospital ship *Oxfordshire* and from there, after a couple of days in bed, was sent to the depot ship *Edinburgh Castle*. He then joined the armed merchant cruiser *Carnarvon Castle*, which would reunite him with the *Ajax*. Though nothing in wartime is that simple; after arriving in Cape Town John was sent over to the naval base at Sinonstown.

No sooner had he arrived than he was told to return to Cape Town. From there he was directed to the motor-vessel *Durban Castle*, the largest motor-vessel in the world at the time. He remembered his accommodation was "palatial", with a lounge, bedroom, bathroom, dressing room and a shower room, rounded off with his own personal steward: luxury indeed. In convoy with a large number of ships the *Durban Castle* sailed towards the Red Sea. Here the few naval personnel onboard were landed to catch a train to Alexandria, a journey of about twelve hours. Naturally, on arrival at Alexandria no one was expecting him and he had no travel documents, which meant he was the last to be dealt with. He eventually reached the *Ajax* at ten-thirty that evening. After action in the Mediterranean there was one sad note John recorded: his cousin Lieutenant H.J. Slaughter, an observer in the Fleet Air Arm, was lost when his plane was shot down during the raid on the Italian naval base at Taranto.

Action was rather lively in the Mediterranean at that time, with the Germans invading Greece and the *Ajax* employed ferrying troops or taking evacuees off, escorting convoys and generally trying to keep the German and Italian air forces at bay. Naturally there was much that was done on the spur of the moment, the situation in the Mediterranean was very fluid and the ship had to sail at a moment's notice, whatever the state of the machinery. Such a time was the invasion of Crete, where four ships had already been sunk. The Commander-in-Chief, Admiral Sir Andrew Cunningham, had visited the *Ajax* and his message to the ship's company was that Crete must be held. John remembered this time as:

It had been a terrible two weeks in which hundreds of men had been killed or injured and many good ships sunk or damaged.[24]

In November the ship embarked many tons of ammunition and a large quantity of torpedoes and sailed at twenty-eight knots to Malta. Here they were employed harrying the German fuel convoys to North Africa, but it also gave an opportunity for the ship to be dry docked, considering the air raids Malta had to endure it was clearly not the safest place to dock. But the damage that had been sustained in the near-continuous attacks from German and Italian planes made it imperative that the damage to the main engines be repaired. It was only thirty hours in dry dock but even then there were neither the facilities nor spares to conduct a complete repair and the outcome after a trial was "*Ajax* is unfit for operational duties and her speed should be limited to 22 knots".[25] As well as the bad news from Pearl Harbour came the shocking blow of the loss of HMS *Prince of Wales* and HMS *Repulse* by the Japanese off the east coast of Malaya.

John spent all of December in Malta, his first time back on the island since 1931. Things now were very different: much of Valetta around the dockyard was in ruins and this was the case for most of the island. The ERA's Club in Floriana was damaged and a shell of the pre-war club that had been such a haven for John and his fellow ERAs. Even around Christmas there were unrelenting air raids, though for some inexplicable reason Christmas Day saw a lull in the bombing.

By the end of December the ship was back in Alexandria and spent time there and at Suez, where things were somewhat quieter than Malta, giving the engineers the time to fit the newly arrived parts for the engines, which were successfully fitted and trialled to ensure a satisfactory repair. And then, at last, there was news of a return home. The ship passed through the Suez Canal and made her way down the Red Sea, with the temperature on deck and in the machinery spaces rising inexorably. They crossed the Equator on 8 March 1942 and had a brief stop in Mombasa for fuel. By 13 March they were in Durban, where there was a welcome break and the chance to do some sightseeing out to the Valley of a Thousand Hills. They sailed on to Cape Town and then Freetown, which was reached on 4 April. They had been expecting to arrive at Chatham on 16 April, but, such are the vagaries of the Service, this was changed to Greenock. In total contrast to the Mediterranean and South Africa, Greenock was cold and wet and uninviting, but it was home. John left the ship on 16 June 1942, when she paid off, after four years and ten months on board.[26]

John once again suffered from ill health; an unexplained weight loss resulted in his medical category being downgraded and he was employed in the depot workshops This was followed by a course on Packard engines as fitted to motor torpedo boats and on completion of the course he was sent to Lowestoft to maintain MTBs at HMS *Mantis*. He was often called upon to go to sea on these boats after there had been repairs and on several occasions the ship he was on came under attack; on one occasion the ship came under attack by German aircraft and the second in command was badly wounded by cannon fire.

It seems that John's poor health continued to dog him and in mid-February 1943 he was admitted to hospital in Chatham and had an operation, the nature of which he does not specify. After a brief convalescence he returned to the depot to find a draft to the repair ship HMS *Maidstone* awaited him. This was cancelled owing to his continued downgraded medical status. John spent the next few months repairing and refitting various ships in the dockyard and it was not until 27 August that he was reassessed as Category "B". This resulted in a draft to the repair ship HMS *Greenwich* on an unspecified foreign location, then seven days' "draft leave". After a period of what he describes as "non-operational" duties, which seems to have been the escorting of prisoners. John found himself onboard the Cunard liner *Queen Mary*, bound for Canada, for onwards transit to *Greenwich* in Reykjavik. While there John appears to have had some sort of relapse and was once more admitted to hospital. John described what happened next:

> In the hospital the next morning the Ward Doctor tapped my chest and listened with his stethoscope for a while, then departed to return later with two colleagues and all three took turns to tap, prod and poke. They then went into a huddle against the screen around my bed – "Mutter – mutter" – until one came over to me and asked, "How do you feel?" I said "Fine! I'm here because my daughter has German Measles". There was another consultation then – O.K. You can discharge to Depot at 1 pm.[27]

By 18 May 1944 John was on his way to the Clyde to join HMS *Euryalus* as the Senior CERA and there followed an intense period of working up the ship. There followed an event that is typical of how naval humour overcomes

147

the actual events. The issue of tropical clothing immediately sparked the news that the ship was bound for Murmansk or Spitzbergen. The truth was rather more prosaic: the destination was Trincomalee in Ceylon.

While John Gurr was serving in the *Ajax*, Reg Bennett had joined the aircraft carrier HMS *Formidable* as the Commander (E) and served at the Battle of Cape Matapan and for his efforts in the battle he was 'Mentioned in Dispatches'". Later in 1941 *Formidable* was badly damaged by German dive bombers and this entailed repairs being carried out in Alexandria; for his resourcefulness and initiative in the repairs to *Formidable* Reg was appointed to be an Officer of the British Empire in the 1943 New Year's Honours List. On 30 June 1944 he was promoted to Captain and served for the next six years on loan service to the Royal Canadian Navy in Newfoundland, as the Chief Engineer at Sheerness and as the Engineer Manager in Malta. He was promoted to Rear Admiral on 8 November 1950. He was appointed Commander of the British Empire in the Queen's Birthday Honours list of 1952. Admiral Bennett retired in 1954 and a division in *Fisgard* was named after him in 1966. He died in 1976.

While many will be familiar with the prisoner of war camp in Colditz Castle, there may be only a few who know about the Artificer connection with the camp and the daring escapes made by them during the war:

HMS/M Shark *was a Royal Navy S-class submarine which was launched on 31 May 1934 and fought in the Second World War. Shark is one of 12 boats named in the song "Twelve Little S-Boats". She was surfaced whilst on patrol off Skudesnes, southwest Norway on 5 July 1940, when a seaplane was sighted astern. As the submarine submerged, she was bombed, the explosions causing considerable damage. Without steering gear and the hydroplanes jammed hard to rise, the submarine's bow broached the surface, where she continued to be bombed.* Shark *began to sink by the stern and all high-pressure air was used to return her to the surface. Once on the surface she attempted to get underway steering on main engines, but was sighted yet again, and attacked. The submarine then tried to fight off the aircraft, succeeding in shooting down a Dornier Do 17. The No.4 ballast tank was holed, and with more aircraft arriving she had no option but to capitulate. At about 0400 hours the next day three German minesweeping trawlers M-1803, M1806 and M-1807 arrived to take* Shark *under tow but she began to sink stern first about 25 nautical miles (46 km) west-south-west of Egersund, Norway.*

The boat's captain, Lieutenant Commander Peter Buckley, was involved in planning a number of escape attempts from POW camp. ERA W. E. "Wally" Hammond also made a number of escape attempts before being sent to Oflag IV-C at Colditz Castle on 17 September 1942 with ERA Don "Tubby" Lister from the captured submarine HMS Seal. During their short stay at Colditz, Wally Hammond made a silent working punch to remove rivets from window bars. They made a successful escape with ERA Johnson by campaigning for a transfer from Colditz, arguing that they were not officers. They were transferred to Lamsdorf prison camp (Stalag VIIIB) on 27 October 1942 but escaped from a Breslau work party, and reached England via Switzerland in 1943. The photograph shows W.E. Hammond and D. Lister in Switzerland after escaping from their prisoner of war camp at Lamsdorf. Armed with forged identity papers, money and civilian clothing, Hammond and Lister volunteered to wash up the Sunday soup cauldrons in the wash house and slipped out of the camp through a nearby garden. They travelled by train to join the Colditz escape route at Dresden, showing German cigarettes as they passed through the police checks. Going via Nuremburg they continued to Ulm, accepting a drink from a German soldier along the way. Finally they ended up in Switzerland where they later held a great Christmas party with other escapees. Tubby Lister's submarine was HMS Seal, she was damaged by aircraft on May 4 1940, she was subsequently surrendered and towed to Frederickshaven and underwent temporary repairs to make her seaworthy, she was then towed to Kiel. Admiral Carls believed Seal was a war-winning asset and insisted that she be made operational, despite the probability that three superior new German U-boats could be built for the same cost. The equipment and armour were completely incompatible and it would not be possible to obtain spares. Nevertheless, repair was undertaken and in the spring of 1941 she was commissioned into the Kriegsmarine as U-B under the command of Fregattenkapitän Bruno Mahn. Mahn, at 52 years old, was the oldest German submarine commander on duty in World War II. She was used as a propaganda exhibit and training boat, but it took until late 1942 for Krupp to fabricate the whole mechanical system. Practice runs revealed so many snags and the financial costs were so unrealistic, that by the middle of 1943 she was paid off, stripped and abandoned in a corner of Kiel dockyard. Later she was hit and sunk in the same Allied air raid that sank the German heavy cruiser Admiral Hipper. The only value derived was the realisation that the British torpedo firing device was of superior design and its introduction into the German navy. Lamsdorf, now called Łambinowice, is a small town in Poland, once the location *of one of Germany's largest prisoner of war camps for allied servicemen. The camp originally opened during the Franco-Prussian War of 1870-71, and was also a prisoner of war camp in the First World War. In 1939 it housed Polish prisoners, then from 1940 until it was evacuated in January 1945, it housed more than 100,000 prisoners from Britain and other Commonwealth countries, as well as from the Soviet Union, Poland and various European countries occupied by the Germans. In 1943 many prisoners from Lamsdorf were transferred to other camps, and the number was changed from VIIIB to 344.*

In 1941 the Germans opened a Navy (Marlag) camp at Sandbostel (Stalag 10B), between Hamburg and Bremen. Here also were taken the Seal's officers. However, on June 19, 1941, the whole of Marlag was shifted to Westertimke, 20 miles away, where the Officers, Petty Officers and ratings were put into three separate sections. A year later 500 ratings said farewell to their officers when they were taken to Silesia to build factories. Here many of the crew were split up into different working parties and lost contact till after the war. From the end of 1942 till the end of the war, life at Westertimke went on as well as the prisoners could make it. Some were pre-occupied with escape, others with the Marlag Amateur Operatic Society. Some found a faith in God which was not just another form of "escape" but was to change their lives. Rupert Lonsdale already had a strong Christian faith and had led his men in prayers during the enemy attacks on the submarine. He went onto serve God in the Anglican Church. Of those who continued to try and escape – "Tubby" Lister, Trevor Beet and Clark – it was Lister who was later to make a home run from Colditz. Accommodation was a great improvement at Westertimke, and Clark shared a room with Lonsdale and four others. Other inmates included Peter Buckley, the CO of the submarine Shark.[28]

Another luminary of the Apprentices joined *Caledonia* on 3 January 1943: John Worsop went on to gain a Cadetship to RNEC Keyham qualified as a watchkeeper in HMS *Theseus* in 1948 and after completing the Advanced Engineering Course at RNEC Greenwich he went to sea in HMS *Superb*. He then served as the Senior Engineer of HMS *Ark Royal*. While serving in Bath on the Polaris team he was promoted Commander and after a time in Washington and Bath he went back to sea as the Commander (E) of HMS *Blake*. On promotion to Captain in 1972 he was at one time the Captain of *Fisgard*. He was promoted to Rear Admiral in 1981 and was appointed Companion of the Most Honourable Order of the Bath in 1984; he retired in 1986 and died in 1995.

By 1943 the Fleet Air Arm Apprentices spent the first year of their apprenticeship in either *Fisgard* or *Caledonia* before moving to an establishment at Clayton Hall in Newcastle-under-Lyme, which was known as HMS *Daedalus II* and which remained in commission from 1940 until 1946. The arrival of Aircraft Apprentices at *Fisgard* necessitated the formation of extra divisions, the first group, joining early in 1943, forming Hood Division and the second group, who joined in September of that year, forming Raleigh Division. It must be said that these "Fleeties", as they were called, were looked on with deep suspicion by the regular members of *Fisgard*. After the year at either *Fisgard* or *Caledonia* they were united at *Daedalus II*, where they completed their training, but in three years rather than the normal four.

In 1943 a daring plan to sink or disable the German Battleship *Tirpitz*, using midget X-craft submarines, was formulated. *Tirpitz* was hiding in a Norwegian fjord near Trondheim, where it was believed that she would be safe from Allied air attack. During the raid by the X-craft there was considerable damage inflicted on *Tirpitz* and the bravery of the attackers was rewarded with many decorations. One of these was to CERA Vernon "Ginger" Coles:

Vernon "Ginger" Coles, was born on April 16 1920 at Tilehurst, Berkshire. Orphaned at the age of 5, he was brought up by an uncle and aunt He left the local school at 14 to become an apprentice toolmaker at Huntley Boome and Stevens, manufacturers of biscuit tins which are now collectors' items.

Inspired by Sunday school outings to see the fleet review at Weymouth, he joined the Navy in 1938.

His first ship was the destroyer HMS Faulknor, the first British destroyer to sink a German U-boat, Ginger Coles served in her during the Norwegian Campaign of 1940, with Force H in the Mediterranean on the Malta convoys and escorting convoys to Russia and across the Atlantic. He volunteered for the submarine service in 1942.

Ginger took part in several daring raids using four-man midget submarine known as X-craft.

X-craft were 51ft long, 5ft 9in in diameter with internal headroom of 4ft 8in and powered by a reliable 42-horse power Gardner diesel engine giving a range of 1800 nautical miles. Each carried two 2-ton explosive charges to be placed under the bow and stern of the target and detonated by a time fuse, set from inside the submarine.

Operation Source *was the attack, using midget submarines, on the heavy German warships* Tirpitz, Scharnhorst *and* Lutzow *hiding in the northern Norwegian fjords, Ginger Coles was the designated engineer and steersman of X-9. He recalled: "As the German fleet would not come out to fight, X-craft were the only means of sinking German ships that was likely to work."*

The craft, manned by passage crews, were towed by normal submarines into position off the Norwegian coast where attack crews were to take over. "During the training exercises," Coles continued, "It was realised that the manila tow-ropes stretched under tension and after anything up to five days, snapped. The best tow-ropes were of nylon used by the RAF for towing gliders, however the RAF was only willing to supply three ropes."

When, on September 11 1943, six X-craft left their base at Loch Cairnbawn, one of the suspect manila ropes was attached to X-9. The line parted at the parent submarine end and the weight of 500ft of wet 4in manila rope attached to the bow of the X-craft dragged it down to below the safe diving depth and beyond. The towing crew, Sub-Lieutenant "Paddy" Kearan, Able Seaman "Darkie" Hart and Stoker "Ginger" Hollet were all lost.

"I honestly thought Tirpitz would have been blown sky high," Coles continued "If everything had gone to plan she probably would have been, what with 12 tonnes of explosive under her that would have broken her back without a doubt, the real problem was the tow ropes. I lost three very close friends three dedicated people – Ginger Hollet in particular. He and I were the only two engine room people in the crews, he was a bubbly fellow, full of life and always working, doing something for the betterment of the boat"

As it turned out, three of the remaining boats, X-5, X-6 and X-10 (later portrayed in the film Above Us the Waves *(1955) starring John Mills,) extensively damaged* Tirpitz. *But nine men had been lost, three in X-9 and six taken prisoner, Two Victoria Crosses, four DSOs, one DSC, one CGM and three MBEs were awarded.*

Later, Ginger Coles teamed up with the Australian X-craft captain Lieutenant Max Shean, first lieutenant Joe Brooks, and diver Frank Ogden for **Operation Guidance**. *A lesson learnt from* **Operation Source** *was the potential for confusion during multi-craft attacks. So, on April 14 1944 Shean's X-24 was towed to Norway for a solo attack on shipping in Bergen harbour. Explosive charges were successfully laid under a German merchant ship* Barenfels, *24 hours later, sick and suffering from headaches caused by the stale air in the boat, Shean and his crew rendezvoused at sea with the submarine Sceptre* *to be towed home. Coles had steered X-24 continuously for 19 hours. Shean was awarded the DSO for his courage, Coles was awarded the Distinguished Service Medal, the highest award with the exception of the Victoria Cross, then available to ratings for bravery and resourcefulness.*

"Max Shean was the only captain I would sail with," Coles said later. "When we went into Bergen one would have thought we were going on exercise. He was cheerful, confident and pleased that we were doing something useful with no thought of not coming back."

After D-Day the X-craft were deployed to the Far East for **Operation Sabre**. *When the experienced submariner, US Admiral Chester Nimitz, Commander-in-Chief, Pacific Ocean Areas, first saw one of the midget submarines he declared it a "suicide craft" which had no place in the Allies' order of battle. But when orders came from Washington to cut two underwater telegraph cables off Japanese occupied Saigon, he soon pressed them into service. Shean designed special grapnels to hook the cables and ERA Coles manufactured these in the workshops of the depot ship before they set off, once more under tow, from Queensland to the Mekong river.*

On July 31 1945 they began a submarine trawl for the cables and after Coles had steered X-24 across the river several times he snagged a cable and was suddenly brought to a halt, just 13 minutes later the diver, Australian Sub-Lieutenant Ken Briggs, returned with a short length of cable as a souvenir. Coles continued to steer underwater across the Mekong and a second cable was found an hour later. This time Sub-Lieutenant Adam Bergius emerged from the airlock brandishing a length of cable as proof that it too had been cut. ERA Coles was mentioned in despatches.

Post-war Vernon Coles served in submarines in Sydney and Singapore and twice in Malta before leaving the Navy in 1952.[29]

Clayton Hall was a fifteenth-century manor house with Tudor and Georgian additions and a now-dry moat. The house was home to the wardroom and the various necessary ship's offices while the Apprentices were accommodated in wooden huts for junior Apprentices and brick-built air raid shelters for the more senior Apprentices, both described as too cold in winter and too hot in summer, Frank Wootton joined *Fisgard* in 1943 and remembered Clayton Hall from his time there:

The house itself housed the various ship's offices together with the wardroom. The accommodation for the apprentices was in wooden huts (junior) and brick built air raid shelters (senior). The various instructional centres were remote from the stately home, the factory had once been a large garage and was situated in the town itself as was the technical school for electrical training. These establishments entailed a march or truck ride of about 1.5 miles. In winter we marched in boots and gaiters (which was the rig at all times) in the road, the right hand man of the leading section of threes carried a white lantern while his counterpart in the rear carried a red lantern. Hook boys, ever conscious of their dignity and safety, marched on the pavement. Some of the machine tools in the factory could be classified as archaic, one lathe in particular had been salvaged from the German battlecruiser Derfflinger lying at the bottom of Scapa Flow...

The electrical technical school was situated in an old mill, in which James Arkwright would have been quite at home. Our electrical instructors included a couple of Chief EAs and a number of ancient Chief Torpedomen. One such was known as Jettison Joe, he imparted wisdom on his specialised subject, bomb release circuits. The classroom was loomed around the walls with the appropriate aircraft wiring, and bomb racks were stoutly bracketed to those walls. Joe used to cock all the release and fuzing units before the class assembled. He would deliver his spiel and finish with a flourish saying, "The pilot then presses the bomb release 'tit'". There would then be a metallic click as a salvo was released over an imaginary Japanese fleet. This pantomime pleased Joe mightily, or it did until the racks were surreptitiously loaded with 20lb practice bombs. The resultant salvo failed to impress.[30]

The academic subjects were taught in what had been an "Academy for Young Ladies" in an affluent area on the outskirts of the town. It seems the classrooms were light and spacious and relatively modern, but, as had been the case with Stoke Damerel Girls School, the original female inhabitants were long gone. As well as far better school facilities, there were several extramural activities to occupy the Apprentices; there was a military band, which was in popular demand for civil and civic parades, and there was a dance band and an orchestra. Against all Apprentice sensibilities there was keen interest in the provision of the ceremonial guard for divisions. It provided certain privileges, such as extra leave, which resulted in intense competition to be a guard member. Such an outlook at *Fisgard* or *Caledonia* would have been seen as beyond the pale and such activities were well avoided.

In 1944 Mike Simpson joined *Fisgard* as an Artificer Apprentice (Air). He completed his apprenticeship and was commissioned in 1952; this was fortuitous as he had twice been court martialled; on the first occasion he was treated leniently for the offence of leave-breaking. However, the second occasion involved a charge of drunkenness and it was ordered that his papers as an officer candidate be destroyed, but due to a fortunate stroke of luck these papers had already been dispatched and the Chief Writer agreed to keep quiet on the matter in return for Mike's daily tot, a very fair swop. He qualified as an Air Engineer Officer in 1956 and was promoted to Lieutenant the same year. As a Lieutenant Commander he served an exchange with the United States Navy as a helicopter production manager. Promoted to Commander in 1969 he served in HMS *Ark Royal* as AEO and as a Captain was Director Aircraft Maintenance and Repair from 1975 until promoted Commodore in 1981, when he was the Commodore of RN Barracks Portsmouth. He was promoted to Rear Admiral in 1983 and retired in 1985. (During the writing of this book it was learnt that Admiral Mike Simpson died on 26 June 2018 following a scooter accident in Bali.)

As well as new establishments at *Fisgard*, *Caledonia* and *Daedalus II* there was also another established at Warrington, known as HMS *Ariel*. This catered for the electrical aspects of the Fleet Air Arm, particularly radar and W/T instruction. There was also an incident at *Daedalus II*, which was related by Frank Wootton:

> *Matters went over the top when a full scale mutiny broke out in the senior divisions. This was triggered by the over reaction of the Commander to the pilfering of grapes from the Clayton Hall greenhouses. This became something of a cause célèbre known as "The Grapes of Rothwell". As one of the junior divisions at the time the seniors confined us to our huts so that we would not be involved. Actually it became quite a serious affair, the white ensign was struck and replaced with a red gym shirt and a mutinous throng marched on the hall, to be repelled by a stalwart divisional P.O. armed with a rifle and fixed bayonet. Eventually matters returned to normal when armed units were brought in from outlying sites. This left the authorities with a problem, how to deal with the culprits, they being in boy's service. Nothing daunted, their Lordships came up with a cunning ploy; the malefactors being over 18 years of age were rated Acting, Temporary, Air Fitters 2nd Class and dispatched to Preston army glasshouse for their sins. They returned, in the fullness of time, as born-again Apprentices, folk heroes in their own time. Needless to say the saga lost nothing in the telling.*[31]

This could have been treated far more harshly in a wartime environment but was perhaps tempered by the ethos of Apprentices' training establishments. The upshot, as many Apprentices at *Daedalus II* saw things, was the splitting up of the Apprentices, with "G" Class being moved to RAF Worthy Down, which was however shared with the Royal Navy and known as HMS *Kestrel*, to complete their training. Later HMS *Condor* was established to consolidate all FAA mechanical training.

In *Caledonia* as the years rolled on life matured for the Apprentices as they became more senior, as Ian Rogers wrote"

E class and we were seniors! We now used the senior dining hall and rec. room, which, incidentally were both identical to the junior versions. Our pay went up to 11/- (55p) a fortnight (27 1/2p a week). Being seniors did not change the general routine times of starting and stopping work, Divisions, meal times and the rest. The main difference between junior and senior was in the factory and in our classroom studies.

The hard flogging with hammer, chisel and file was practically at an end. We had fitting jobs still to come but we now learned how to work with machine tools. Each ERA (fitter and turner) was allocated a centre lathe; my first was a 6" Lang and later I had an 8" Denham. We were lucky to have machines that were brand-new at the beginning of the war. Training was also carried out on surface grinders, vertical and horizontal milling machines, the big "Kearns" borer and other machines, but our main love was for our lathes which we cleaned and cared for.

Also in the past were the school subjects of maths, science and English. These were replaced by technical subjects, marine engineering, workshop practice and mechanical drawing, (and in G and H classes, applied mechanics and electricity). Classroom time was extended from two to three nights a week from 17.45 to 19.50.

The EAs broke away from us, in that they now did their own electrical technical subjects in school time, and they also had their own partitioned off corner of the factory where they trained on small precision lathes. Of course they also had different test jobs.[32]

After the end of the war Artificer training was consolidated, when RNATE Torpoint was commissioned as HMS *Fisgard*, RNATE Rosyth became HMS *Caledonia* and RNATE Arbroath became HMS *Condor*. This was followed in 1947 by a major reorganisation of training that had remained unchanged since the introduction of Fisher's "Second to None" Boy Artificers in 1903. This started with the alignment of the terms at *Fisgard* with those of civilian schools; the entry would change from two a year to one each term. This it was hoped would give a better flow of Artificers to the Fleet. As well as these changes, the alphabetic nomenclature A, B, C and so on would become numerical: 1, 2, and 3 onwards. Further, the system of divisions was streamlined so that all divisions contained members of all the classes then under training, while keeping the existing divisional names.

At the same time the selection of specialisation, previously made by successful candidates before joining, was delayed for one year until after each apprentice had been able to demonstrate his aptitude and abilities. Hitherto the only career option available after entry was to ERAs who, at the end of A class, chose to become a fitter and turner, coppersmith, engine-smith or boilermaker. At this juncture, the training of naval Shipwright Artificer Apprentices, recruited from candidates who sat the same entrance examination as Artificer Apprentices, and previously carried out in the dockyards, was brought into the naval training scheme. At the same time the Civil Service Commission examination was discontinued as an entry method and was replaced by an examination set by the RN to more suitably reflect their requirements of apprentices.[33]

So now we see the full range of trades that remained for some years, until the introduction of Marine Engineering Artificers.

John Gurr was now in the Pacific Fleet, based at Trincomalee, where they were welcomed by Rear Admiral Sir Philip Vian, who said that they would find this theatre of war different to fighting the Germans and indeed in the next few weeks the ships, which included four aircraft carriers, *Victorious, Illustrious, Formidable* and *Indomitable*, were tasked with making raids on Japanese shipping off the coast of Sumatra. There were the inevitable losses of aircraft but nothing like on the scale that the Japanese claimed, as John said: "Japanese radio, broadcasting in English, claimed '104-British aircraft shot down'. I doubt we put a hundred into the air in the whole day."[34]

After this initial sortie the fleet sailed to Freemantle and then on to Sydney for a seventeen-day rest. This gave John a chance to look up the relatives of friends in England. However, the address given was little help at first, there being nineteen streets called Campbell Street, and it was only serendipity that John was able to find them and enjoy some home hospitality.

This was a period where the Japanese resorted to any method to sink ships, including "Kamikaze" suicide planes and the doomed mission of the huge Japanese battleship *Yamata*, which was sunk by American aircraft. A British ship, HMS *Ulster*, suffered damage and casualties from a near-miss "Kamikaze" and *Indomitable* also had a near miss but suffered no damage. John reported that during a mission to bombard an air base on Honshu:

> The "Kamikaze" came out in waves of up to thirty in each group but our fighters had the measure of them and shot most down although slight damage was caused to our ships. However, weight of numbers did allow three "Kamikaze" to penetrate the screen; one crashed itself onto Formidable's flight-deck to destroy several parked planes and starting fierce fires. A second suicide pilot hit the deck of Indomitable at too shallow an angle and bounced straight over into the ocean while the third missed his aim – and the Indefatigable by a few yards – to enter the water and disappear in a spectacular explosive splash and once again we were thankful for the darkness.[35]

It was a blessing to all who served in ships in this theatre of war that these suicide pilots were sent out with the bare minimum of training. It is salutary what could have been achieved with fully trained pilots.

By June the ship was in Brisbane for some well-earned maintenance and the ship's company some well-earned rest and recreation. Later, on 28 June, the ships sailed and prepared for the final thrust against the Japanese homeland; fortunately, the loss of life this would have entailed was spared by the dropping of the atomic bombs on Hiroshima on 6 August and Nagasaki on 9 August 1945. This resulted in a cessation of activity by the British Fleet and was followed by the surrender of Japan on 15 August.

In the aftermath of the conflict one of the first actions was to send home "hostilities only" ratings in the age group 18–20, though one would have thought there were more pressing problems confronting the ship at the time. This caused some upheaval as some of those to return home were on watch and reluctant reliefs had to be found; this was down to John and did not make him popular. Once these men had left the ship sailed for Leyte and on to Hong Kong.

Hong Kong Dockyard, when John passed through, was a shambles and much of the damage had been inflicted by the British before the Japanese arrived in 1942. But there was much that had been inflicted by British bombardment and Japanese sabotage. The purpose of John going ashore was as part of an armed landing party sent to distribute food and other necessities to a civilian internment camp about ten miles outside the city. Among the many internees was the Eurasian wife of a Petty Officer who had been transferred from one of the carriers to *Euryalus* so that he could search for his wife; to everyone's joy the couple were reunited, though the poor girl had been through years of Japanese mistreatment.

The war might have been over but *Euryalus* continued her commission in the Far East. She travelled extensively throughout the region, visiting Fiji, Tonga and Samoa. Naturally during this time many were thinking of going home and many "age and service" groups from other ships had left for the UK. This naturally caused some resentment and apathy, particularly as the food was of poor quality due to an overspend of the catering account in Sydney. Christmas 1945 was spent in Hong Kong and John considered it a good time to approach Commander (E) about his relief and subsequent return home, only to be told there was a great deal of difficulty in finding suitable replacements.

The ensuing months seem to be ones of continued steaming around the area and mounting ennui in the ship's company. Any number of rumours were circulating, particularly regarding going home, and, as is quite often the way, none had any substance and the ship remained on the Far East Station, visiting Shanghai before going to Labuan, in north Borneo, and Saigon, though it would be fair to say these exotic destinations did not hold much allure for John or the ship's company as this soon after the end of the war there were shortages of almost everything and little or nothing to do ashore.

At last the news John had been waiting for arrived: his relief would arrive on 7 June and he would be leaving the same day. John travelled home on the aircraft carrier HMS *Indefatigable* and after a long and tiresome voyage home arrived in Portsmouth on 7 July and after twenty-eight days' leave John entered the depot at Chatham for the last time. This time he would leave as a civilian and having collected a "De-mob suit and pork pie hat"[36] on Monday 30 September 1946, John's fortieth birthday, he left the Royal Navy.

In 1946 Hugh Thompson joined as an Artificer Apprentice and became a Cadet (E) in 1948 at BRNC Dartmouth and subsequently at RNEC

Manadon. He went to sea in HMS *Manxman* and after completing the Advanced Marine Engineering Course at RNEC Greenwich he was appointed the Senior Engineer of HMS *Duchess*. He then passed the first Nuclear Advanced Course and served in the Dreadnought Project. In 1963 he was promoted Commander and served in the Repair Ship HMS *Triumph* in Singapore. He was promoted Captain in June 1975 and returned to the Submarine Project as Assistant Director of Marine Engineering Submarines. After promotion to Rear Admiral he was appointed Chief Marine Systems Engineer. He was promoted to Vice Admiral and knighted in 1986.

Another radical change was the realisation that four years in one establishment was too long, particularly in *Fisgard*, where Apprentices of nineteen and twenty with over three years' service had less shore leave than newly entered stockers in HMS *Raleigh* across the road and poorer conditions and fewer facilities than those at a similar stage of training in *Caledonia*. To ensure the training was suitable for the more technological Navy that had emerged from the war, it was decided that the first twelve months would be devoted mainly to craft training, followed by four months of training specific to their specialisation prior to moving on to *Caledonia*, *Collingwood* and *Condor* to complete their apprenticeships.

The practice of "sprogging" was still to be addressed, as Roy Whittington remembered all too well:

> *In Drake Division we A class sprogs were mustered in front of H class to be selected as individual fags. As we outnumbered H class there were 3 or 4 of us extra and I was fortunately not appointed as a fag. However I made my first mistake soon after in the dining hall. We ate at tables within the division as classes. Unfortunately one teatime our A class table did not have a pot (large, tea for the use of), but across from us was an empty H class table with a teapot, which was obviously not in use. Using a degree of initiative I "borrowed" the said teapot, filled our cups and returned the pot to the H class table. However someone "snitched" on me and I was called to the senior dormitory to offer an explanation. Sadly, to take H class items was not acceptable! As a penance I had to clean H class shoes, numbering, to my recollection, about forty-five pairs.*[37]

It is clear that this type of behaviour needed to be addressed and it was some years later that the first efforts, unsuccessful as it turned out, were tried.

The Fleet Air Arm Artificers who had joined the fleet as Air Fitters, Engine or Airframes, Electrical and Ordnance with only three years training could remain as Artificers by completing a further year of training in a second trade. At the same time what became known as the "Series" training was introduced:

> In the Autumn of 1947 the apprentices of 9, 8, 7 and 5 Classes were transferred by special train to Caledonia in a journey which took 35 hours to complete, (so much for the golden age of steam)! In December 1947, the senior class (12) passed out of both Fisgard and Caledonia and 6 Class (made up of part of ex 1945 Grenville and 1946 Frobisher), left Fisgard to join up with their counterparts at Caledonia, leaving only the new 12 Class and 4, 3, 2 and 1 Class behind. Thereafter, on completion of 4 Class, one term after their categorisation, ERA, OA and Shipwright Artificer Apprentices were transferred from Fisgard to Caledonia, EA Apprentices to Collingwood and Fleet Air-Arm Artificer Apprentices to Condor. Thus began the Series classes and, after 12 Class (ex 1944 Anson) passed out as 5th Class Artificers in August 1948, Fisgard became dedicated solely to the initial training of all Artificer Apprentices of 4, 3, 2 and 1 Class.[38]

It was hoped that this segregation of the older Apprentices would bring to an end the tradition of "sprogging", the provision of menial tasks by the junior for the benefit of those senior, with the imposition of minor, but often degrading, punishments for both real and perceived breaches of the standards laid down by the senior Apprentices. As was to be expected, the "sprogging" merely moved from the twenty-year-olds bullying the sixteen-year-olds to the seventeen-year-olds now ruling the roost. But there does seem to have been an improvement in general behaviour.

> The splitting of all artificer apprenticeships between Fisgard and one of three other sites did however reduce the level of indiscipline among fit, high-spirited young men confined for four years in one place with little liberty. It was a blessing to many earlier apprentices that their conduct sheet was wiped clean when they left Fisgard, Caledonia or Condor and their youthful misdemeanours were not recorded as a loss of VG conduct on their Service documents. A number of apprentices given a Captain's Warning for Conduct during this era heeded his dire threat, (doubtless under parental pressure), turned over a new leaf and subsequently enjoyed successful naval careers.[39]

The mention of HMS *Collingwood* earlier went hand in hand with the introduction of the "Series" system and on 3 September 1948 the first forty-seven Electrical Artificer Apprentices joined *Collingwood* and formed Fisher Section, which was to continue until the demise of the branch. There was also for many years Jellicoe Section, where the Third Class Artificers returned after their year of sea training.

That at this time there was a considerable bias towards craft training can be discerned from this article in the *Second to None*:

For the first half of the 20th century, 80% of the RN Artificer Apprenticeship was devoted to craft training. No history of Artificer Apprentices would therefore be complete without a mention of the test jobs over which generations of Boy-Arts toiled and by which, until the 1950s, the Admiralty assessed the competence of its future craftsmen.

Throughout the apprenticeship, an apprentice's measured progress from A or 1 class to H, J or 12 class, was governed by the skill with which he tackled the end of term scholastic and technical examinations and test jobs which became progressively more demanding...

Whilst each class test job held its own terrors, the Big One was undoubtedly the Admiralty Passing-Out Test Job. The ERA Boilermakers, Coppersmiths and Enginesmiths faced a selection of three jobs from a total of eight or nine and had to rely on classmates or more junior apprentices as mates.

Throughout the 1930s and 40s, until 1946, The Admiralty Passing – Out test job for EAs, ERA(F&Ts) and OAs were selected by the Admiralty from sets of test jobs, the ERAs and OAs undertaking the full size version and EAs (at first) a half-size replica, later replaced by a special set of miniature jobs. All work had to be done on the lathe or bench, the use of milling and slotting machines, chasers, taps and dies was not permitted...

Towards the end of 1946, a new series of Passing-out Test Jobs was introduced by the Admiralty to test the craftsmanship of each apprentice. Fitters and Turners were tested in the use of all hand and machine tools, (except a Capstan lathe), and all metals including aluminium and alloys. No apprentice had any sight of the test job or drawings of it until he was ready to start and his first task after seeing the drawings was to manufacture the special tools required for the job. ERA (F&Ts) and OAs undertook the full scale version and Air Artificers (Ordnance), EAs and EAs (Air) the half scale replica...

The high degree of skill imparted to those thousands of Craftsmen Artificers by dedicated instructors, proved invaluable to the Navy before the advent of "repair by replacement". Their worth was particularly evident in damage repair situations in ships and submarines and in the work of Fleet Maintenance Units and Depot ships, where their experience of practical engineering enabled them to assess the feasibility and viability of repairs and to carry them out professionally.[40]

These sentiments were echoed in an article published in 1945 that at a length of some twenty-seven pages extolled the training afforded to Apprentices at *Caledonia*. It started with the methods of entry, the necessary qualifications and the opportunities for advancement to commissioned rank. It went into great depth at all stages of training, detailing the craft skills necessary to progress from class to class and even the day-to-day activities from the moment they arrived at *Caledonia* through to the duties of an ERA at sea. Sport, welfare, extramural activities and even the daily menu were pored over in great detail. But perhaps the greatest exposure was given to the progressively difficult craft tasks the boys had to complete; these were given in both illustrations and words, with both dimensions and tolerances allowed and detailed the way marks were allocated, or in the event of poor fitting how marks were deducted.[41]

That a civilian publication should go to such lengths indicates in what high esteem naval apprenticeships were held in the engineering fraternity. And it is difficult to think of a better recruiting aid at nominal cost to the Admiralty. Whether there was a need for recruitment at this time is a matter of conjecture; there were many "hostilities only" Artificers keen to return civilian employment and, unlike after the First World War, there was no axing of whole classes of Apprentices. So, perhaps it is safe to assume that new recruits would have been welcome and possibly the reduced numbers required would allow only the best applicants to be selected.

There remains one more hybrid of the war years that deserves a mention and that is the ERA (Air), which was mentioned in a letter to the editor of the *Fisgardian*:

On the subject of Artificers in the Fleet Air Arm, there was a strange being – the ERA (Air), he was neither fish nor fowl. At the beginning of the war, before Aircraft Artificers were available to man machine shops at maintenance units and airfields, highly skilled craftsmen, machinists, toolmakers and sheetmetal workers were recruited on a hostilities only basis to fill the gap. But what to call them? In their wisdom their Lordships decided on ERA(Air) much to the chagrin of those in the engine rooms of the Fleet.[42]

chapter seven

The Fifties,
Movement and Change

• • •

But a sudden change came o'er his heart,
Ere the setting of the sun;
And Tubal Cain was filled with pain
For the evil he had done:
He saw that men, with rage and hate,
Made war upon their kind,
That the land was red with the blood they shed,
In their lust for carnage blind.
And he said—"Alas! that I ever made,
Or that skill of mine should plan,
The spear and the sword for men whose joy
Is to slay their fellow-man!"[1]

It was at the beginning of this decade that the progressive change from a craft-orientated apprenticeship to one where the bias was on academic rather than workshop skills, such that by 2002 it had changed from 80% workshop and 20% schoolroom to 18% workshop and 82% schoolroom: a dramatic reversal of emphasis.

In 1950 David Sherval arrived at *Fisgard* to begin life in the Royal Navy as an Artificer Apprentice. His potential was soon recognised and he passed the Special Entry Examination and joined BRNC as a Cadet (E) and went on the study at RNEC Manadon. He was promoted to Lieutenant in 1957 and Lieutenant Commander in 1964, when he served as Assistant Chief Engineer Gibraltar. He was promoted to Commander in 1970 and Captain in 1977 when he served as the Fleet Marine Engineer Officer. He was promoted to Rear Admiral in 1985 and was appointed CB in the 1989 New Year Honours List.

It was also true that the facilities provided at *Fisgard* were not as good as required. In 1950, when the then Captain, Captain C.M. Morrell, relinquished his command, he wrote:

Unfortunately, some of the programme works proposals which my predecessor turned over to me still remain undone. It is true that ere have been certain improvements made in the living quarters, but we still lack what I regard as essential to a boy's training establishment, such as adequate playing fields, a swimming bath, our own laundry d cinema. In these days, when the Navy estimates are cut to the bone, it is the very things that we need so badly that invariably go by the board. I know that my successor will carry on the fight where I leave it, and I hope that during his time at least some will receive official approval.[2]

As is always the case when funds are in short supply, there is much to be said for self-help and so in 1952 the Apprentices were allocated into working parties to excavate a hole as the beginning of a swimming pool and it must have been a source of great pride to all those involved and by the completion in 1965 that must have been many thousands. The foundations were completed by 1954 and the pool itself was operational by 1958. The final project was the erection of the roof; the total cost was £22,000, though this is probably far less than it would have cost through official channels.

Bryan Marshall, who joined in 1951 Series 14, remembered life at *Fisgard*:

King George VI was still on the throne when I joined HMS Fisgard. *My entry had just over a month in the King's Navy (7 Jan to 6 February 1952). Civilian Identity cards, a hangover from the last war, were abolished a fortnight later. But another, more memorable relic of the war – food rationing, lingered on and* did not officially end until July 1954. We were growing lads, so food was an important factor. From the bread spirited away from Fisgard's dining room for Saturday afternoon toast; to the mass boycott of meals in Collingwood in protest at the weekly fare of ghastly "layer pie". At Fisgard we browned our toast on the "Tortoise" stove that stood on round white stones in the middle of each dormitory and provided what passed for central heating at Torpoint.

The Conservatives under Winston Churchill had defeated Labour in the General Election and were to stay in power for the next 13 years. 1951 was the year of the Festival of Britain and no doubt some of us would have visited this exhibition on London's South Bank.

Just seven years after the war, its reminders were powerful. Blitz damaged Plymouth with battleships, cruisers and a monitor in Plymouth harbour, blast walls in the dormitories, and be-medalled long serving officers and ratings (some with medals from World War 1). The Navy's personnel had fallen from 865,000 in 1945 to 148,000 in 1951. By 1956 it had fallen to 125,000. Now it's 42,000! We were lucky to escape the Korean War (1950–53) but some of us were caught up in the Suez campaign. Life for us was monastic, with severe restrictions on time ashore: initially no "open gangway" ("Liberty men fall in") and we had to be back at times by which today's youth would not even be ready to go out "clubbing". "Sprogging" (fagging) and some mild bullying were rife, but it had the effect of bonding junior classes in mutual protection against adversity. Our schooling was generally good (small classes) and even the most fumble fisted of us developed skills in the workshops.

With our grammar school or similar educational background on joining, our lengthy training and rapid advancement to senior rate, we were conscious of being a lower deck elite. Indeed this had been Admiral "Jacky" Fisher's aim when he had the first "Boy Artificers" recruited in 1903. Even our "fore and aft" uniform with its red cap badge became unique in 1956 when all other branches using this uniform switched to square rig. It wasn't until 1999 that junior artificers made this change. By today's standards our lives were innocent, almost naive. Apart from alcohol (a navy preoccupation – think of the rum ration) and tobacco (officially endorsed "blue-liners" and duty-frees) addictive substances were unheard of.

Television was in its infancy. Elvis made his first record in 1953 and Bill Haley's "Rock Around the Clock" became the first million seller in 1956. Singers now long forgotten, warbled their melodies over the Fisgard "Tannoy". Kay Starr's "Wheel of Fortune", Guy Mitchell's "She Wears Red Feathers". Radio was *the prime source of entertainment: Radio Luxembourg, the Goon Show, Ted Heath and his Band.*[3]

This gives a very clear picture of life in *Fisgard* in the early fifties and it is apparent that despite the best efforts of all in authority in *Fisgard* that "sprogging" was still very much alive and would remain so for many years to come, though Bryan does think it bonded the juniors together in an attempt to alleviate its worst effects. There was also the perennial moan about the quality of food, a subject dear to the heart of any Apprentice, but with the continuation of wartime austerity this can possibly be excused.

At *Caledonia* Electrical Artificers had moved out to *Collingwood* and shipwrights were fully integrated in the training regime, much of their training taking place on HMS *Artifex*, which had started life in Swan Hunter and Wigham Richardson's shipyard as the TSS *Aurania*, working for the Cunard Line. She served as an armed merchant cruiser during the war and in the later stages she was refitted as a fleet repair ship with the name *Artifex*. She returned to the United Kingdom and in 1948 she was adapted to provide the workshops for Shipwright Artificer Apprentices, some of the modifications being carried out by the first classes of Apprentice. Some of the workshop output from the days of *Artifex* were in evidence around *Caledonia*, such as the figurehead, the rugby posts and the factory welding bays.

As is often the case, people's time at *Caledonia* can be clouded by time: the good times remain clear and precise while those not-so-good times fade into obscurity, as Jack Pearcey recalled of his time in *Caledonia*:

As I remember it, my time at Caledonia *was not marked by any momentous happenings. There were however, lots of little things that I recall as being part of the life I led at that time. There were the trips into Dunfermline to go to the cinema, possibly dropping off on the way back at Wesley House, (which was run by the Methodist Church and provided affordable refreshment for impecunious apprentices), to get some beans on toast for 6d (2½ p) Some of the apprentices would save up for a month and go and blow the lot on an evening at the pub. Even in those days, when your pay in your final year would usually be only £1 to £1.50 a fortnight, you needed to save if a rousing night was intended. As licensing laws in Scotland stood at that time we had to have "travelled" for a minimum of three miles if we wanted a drink on a Sunday, so we used to walk into Inverkeithing and sign in as travellers at the hotel there...*

During my last year, because nobody more competent could be found, I was the Chapel organist. Mercifully the choir sang lustily enough to drown my wrong notes – of which there was a plentiful supply. The Chaplain at the time was named Clutterbuck, and when a few years later I joined the cruiser Glasgow, a hand fell on my shoulder as I reached the top of the gangway and a voice said, "You're the chapel organist." It was Clutterbuck, so perhaps I underestimated my musical prowess. Time seems to blot out the unpleasant memories in life and although I was not miserable at Caledonia I vaguely remember times when I was less than happy, but the reasons escape me. By and large I think I enjoyed life there.

This also gives some idea of the pay Apprentices received in the early fifties, though through the ages Apprentices have always complained of being poorly paid, underfed and over-disciplined. Subjected to far too long in the factory and schoolroom and far too short a time ashore, thus it ever was.

Life in *Collingwood* followed much the same pattern. The Electrical Branch was still very much in its infancy, having only been created in 1946 under its first director, Rear Admiral Stuart Bateson. Admiral Bateson has been claimed as one of our own for many years; the Fisgard Association believed him to be ex Boy Artificer who joined in 1916. In the light of some research in the National Archives this seems unlikely; his father was a barrister and Kings Council and Stuart's service record shows his date of entry as 15 September 1916 and indicates that he joined as a "special entry".[4] This was reserved for slightly older boys, seventeen years old, who were mainly taken from public schools. It was not designed to be a democratic method of entry, and they spent eighteen months in dedicated nautical training aboard a ship before joining the fleet as Midshipmen. Entry was to be once a year in September, which increased in 1917 to twice a year when the exigencies of wartime also made it necessary to shorten the eighteen months to three. This time would be spent at RNEC Keyham, studying seamanship, signalling, navigation and boat handling, though not engineering.[5] The fact that Stuart went down this route may well have led to the assumption he had started in the RN as a Boy Artificer.

Returning to *Collingwood*, as Jim Gibb wrote, remembering Fisher Block:

Fisher Block was situated as far as you can get from the main gate and was a good 15 minutes march from the workshops. We were very fortunate to have, as our first boss Commander RH Eddhey, one of the original 12 EA Apprentices selected from ERA Apprentices at Indus, who was transferred to Fisgard when Indus closed in 1922. He was very proud of being an ex EA apprentice and of taking command of his boys.

The Electrical Branch was in its infancy and the training problems were enormous. Innumerable conversion and career training courses were in progress: Leading Torpedo Operators to Electrician, Leading Telegraphists to Radio Electrician and even Dockyard Foremen doing sword drill on the parade ground in shiny black gaiters before being translated into Commanders (L). There were also early classes of EMs and REMs doing their initial training.

Each class of Apprentices was shared between two divisions Walker and Middleton, (and later two more, Phillips and Bateson), named after Admirals who were involved in the formation of the fledgling branch, rather than traditional sea-dogs. This paved the way for the later practice at Fisgard of using the names of ex-apprentices who have achieved Flag Rank, ie Burgess, Cooke, Frew and Lane and later Tribe, Griffin, Spickernell, Harcus and Sherval…

Collingwood was of course the principal training establishment for the whole Electrical Branch and was run as an RN Barracks. It was a culture shock for all apprentices, particularly those with three years previous service in establishments dedicated exclusively to their training and well being, to find that they were no longer special. No longer was their accommodation kept clean by "Gobbies", but only by themselves; their sartorial eccentricities, particularly regarding headwear, were deemed unacceptable and discipline was imposed by staff who had little understanding of or affection for "Tiffies" and no connection with Fisher Block. Apprentices had to take particular care coming offshore for they had to pass through the main gates and run the gauntlet of any number of members of the staff only too keen to report errant apprentices to Fisher Block Divisional office. Conversations with my old classmates indicate that life at Caledonia was somewhat easier. The training given at Collingwood was very good and the workshop facilities were excellent, no belt-driven lathes! All of the Instructors were ex EAs though not all were ex-boys. Our mechanical training was completed in 9 Class. Common electrical training took place in 5 and 6 Classes. In 7 Class we took the old Admiralty Part 1 examination and on its results chose to be EAs or REAs. The REAs did less workshop training than the EAs and consequently more schoolwork. Thus when we came to our final test job in 9 Class the EAs job, with more machining, was more demanding.[6]

Collingwood then was an enormous, sprawling establishment that had seen much use as a new entry training establishment for "hostilities only" seaman ratings during the war. It was a wet and boggy site, a condition that would come back and bite in the 1960s, laid out in four identical self-contained sections, each designed to hold 2,500 men with a weekly intake of 1,000 men; thus the establishment held 10,000 men at any one time. With the arrival of the Electrical Branch, further building was undertaken, including the area known to all who passed through *Collingwood*'s gates as the "White City".

Initially Electrical Artificer apprentices were accommodated in Excellent Road but in April 1949 they moved to the south-west corner, known as Fisher Section. By 1963, numbers dictated that they had to be split into four divisions: Bateson, Middleton, Walker and Phillips. The last Electrical Apprentice, with the grand old English name of Osuwu Banahene, passed out in the autumn of 1964.

The Fisher Section mascot was a German sheepdog, adopted in 1955, called Carl (Collingwood Apprentice Radio and Electrical). He spent several years in Fisher Section, joining in many of the Apprentices' activities, but let himself down with the bitch belonging to the Captain's wife.

The training at *Collingwood* was considered to be of very high standard. It was nice that none of the lathes in the workshops were belt-driven, as had been the case in *Fisgard*: progress indeed. The instructors were all ex-EAs and the Apprentices followed their chosen path of EA or Radio Electrical Artificer after 7 Class, with the mechanical training completed in 9 Class.

Fisher Section was almost an establishment within *Collingwood*, with its own regulating staff, PTIs and GIs. There were separate training staff and the Apprentices were alone in holding Sunday divisions. This separateness caused some friction with the other trainees, though as the Apprentices spent much longer in *Collingwood* this was easily ignored, particularly when seen in respect of the contribution that Fisher Section made to the establishment in terms of the numbers supplied to sports teams at all levels, to the band and to the provision of honour guards for visiting dignitaries. As Bryan Marshall (1952, Series 14) put it,

For four very formative years in our lives we lived in close proximity, sharing a wealth of experiences, good and bad. It is clear that this period of time set a

common seal on us, as we so effortlessly pick up the threads of comradeship and
acquaintance fifty years later.[7]

This is a very succinct view of the value of training together for all that time
and getting to know and appreciate the foibles and virtues of those you had
to spent so much of your youth with, for better or worse, and for Artificers
it was normally for the better.

Now that the training regime had settled into *Fisgard* providing the
Part I training for all specialisations with *Collingwood*, *Caledonia* and *Condor*
effectively providing the specialised Part II training, a period of stability
returned to Apprentices' training that was to remain until the end of the
1960s.

As well as Apprentices from this country there were also some from
Commonwealth countries. Initially this was only Apprentices from New
Zealand, who had completed Part I training in New Zealand and arrived
at *Caledonia* and *Collingwood* to complete their apprenticeships. In later
years there were also Apprentices from Nigeria and Malaysia, who added
a certain exoticness to *Fisgard* in their time there. There were some strange
and interesting stories about some of these young men that will appear later.

In *Caledonia* training continued without the EAs and in early 1950
there was a most unfortunate incident that resulted in a fatality to a young
Apprentice. Ken Nicholson (Howe 1947) remembered the accident:

Another accident occurred in the workshop in about 1950 when a coppersmith
apprentice called "Pip" Plummer was repairing a cracked water jacketed casting,
but he had not been told to reduce the pressure by removing a blanking plug or
by drilling a vent hole. The inevitable happened. Under heat there was an air
expansion and an explosion that killed "Pip". I believe that he is buried at Christ
Church, Widley near Portsmouth.[8]

This suggests a lack of proper supervision by the instructor, though there
is no mention of any repercussions or inquiry into any negligence of the
part of the instructors. Such accidents were possibly more common than
is reported in Apprentices reminisces, though hopefully fatalities were the
exception not the norm.

As has always been the case, what was considered a poor rate of pay as
an Apprentice, though much ameliorated by higher pay than non-Artificers

once training was complete, there were all manner of wheezes to accrue extra cash with many an illicit scheme, as John Watts (Grenville 1947) recalled:

A monthly occasion was the issue of a ration of duty free tobacco and "blue liner" cigarettes, this supply was much cheaper than the equivalent in the civilian shops. To the smokers the ration was a lifeline for their habit, to the non-smoker it was goods to be bartered or sold. It was against the rules of the Navy for Apprentices drawing their ration not to consume the allowance themselves and spot checks in the first two weeks after the issue were a hazard for the non-smoker who was selling his allowance. The tins of tobacco were often emptied and either cotton wool or tissue paper plugged in about fifty per cent of the tin and tobacco replaced on top. This subterfuge passed muster for quick spot checks by the Duty PO. The cigarettes came in packs of two hundred (10 packets of twenty cigarettes). A pack would be carefully slit open and a number of the full packets that had been sold would be replaced with packets filled with paper. Again these bogus packs generally passed off as the real thing. A good profit could be made selling the cigarettes off base so the real challenge was to smuggle either full tins of tobacco or packs of cigarettes. The simple method when one was wearing a raincoat or greatcoat was to take half a dozen packets and spread them among the pockets so that when the "liberty boat" was inspected they did not show up as a bulge.

Smuggling tins of tobacco and packs of two hundred cigarettes was another story! One method was to make a hanging string-cradle between the legs and suspend either the tin or the pack between one's thighs. This method was generally successful but on occasions the goods would slip to the ground and the group marching to the gate would dribble the package or tin into the centre of the party where someone would bend down and retrieve it, returning it to its owner outside the gate. There did not seem to be any advice regarding the perils of smoking in those days so "ciggy and baccy" ration days were red-letter days on the calendar.[9]

This seems to have been a reckless method of gaining a little cash and the consequences of discovery would have been out of all proportion to the profit and may well have resulted in court martial and possible discharge. Whether these consequences ever passed through the mind of the individuals concerned must be doubted as any thought would have shown the dangers of what can only be called reckless disregard for authority.

There seems to be a sense of the ridiculous in many of the escapades concerning with young Apprentices, with shades of "Stalky and Co" for getting into and out of situations that could give rise to serious disciplinary actions, as George Bedhall (Benbow 1949) remembered with some pride:

The HMS Devonshire *was in port and being used as a training ship, the trainees of which kept trying to take the mickey out of us trainee engineers. One Sunday afternoon we were out sailing with a whaler when a bunch of the seamen tried to humiliate us. Me being me, we overhauled them and boarded, taking their sheets (control ropes) and all but two oars leaving them miles out in the Firth. Returning back at the jetty feeling quite pleased with having had the better of those "dabtoes" (seaman branch), we tidied the boat and stowed all our gear away, leaving their gear on the jetty. At the top of the gangway was a Military Police van and a Lieutenant Commander Provost Marshal with bright shining gaiters asking who was in charge of the party. It was me. I was terrified! The "snowdrops" (military police) were never taken lightly in the forces. He asked me to accompany him in the van, saying nothing. I was taken to the C in C's headquarters and told to wait. After a time, a Master at Arms came and told me that I was on a charge of "piracy on the high seas". "Here we go again," I thought. He then quick marched me into the Admiral's office, stated the charge to the admiral who was sitting behind his desk. I was still in sailing rig. The Master at Arms explained to the C in C who I was and what we were doing. When he learnt that I was an ERA apprentice from* Caledonia *he burst out laughing, while I was still quaking in my boots. He then told me to stand at ease and told me he had been watching my escapades on the water from his house, which overlooked the Firth of Forth. He then congratulated me on my seamanship, and offered me a cup of tea and cakes and said he would send a signal of commendation to my commanding officer. The "Jossman" then took me back to my ship in his car. Not many naval personnel have been charged with mutiny and piracy during their career!*[10]

How nice to see a Senior Officer with a keen sense of humour. The outcome could have been so different, though "piracy on the high seas" seems perhaps a little over the top for an incident on the River Forth far from the sea.

The "chippies" who spent much of their time at *Artifex* had a long march back from the dockyard at the end of the day and would go straight into the dining hall for tea. This consisted of bread, butter and a "dollop" of jam. The butter was not considered enough to cover the amount of bread a young Apprentice would consume so all manner of tricks were tried to procure more butter; to ask for more was akin to Oliver Twist asking for a second helping. One trick was to quickly lower your plate onto the one below, hoping the butter would adhere to the bottom of the plate, from where it could be retrieved, with luck, before anyone noticed.

As with many close-knit communities there is always some form of ritual and rite of passage to mark the end of the association and the passing out classes at *Caledonia* were no exception. There was always a passing out dinner and dance, with the inevitable result of many suffering the effects of over-indulgence of alcohol. There were also the usual "high spirits", which normally involved the discomfort of the more junior classes and the disruption of some part of the ship's routine that, while, annoying, was not difficult to remedy, such as running a pirate flag up the flag staff, perhaps with the added annoyance of the removal of the bottom halyard, making the flag's removal that much more difficult.

There were all manner of japes and wheezes attempted by Apprentices down the years and truth to tell they were not always successful; some rebounded and authority had the last laugh. This could be particularly true when it came to the choice of port division; the Royal Navy has a predilection for giving people the opposite of what they ask for. This may on occasions be aided and abetted by a divisional officer, as Algy Preston (Rodney 1947) discovered: his choice was Portsmouth, Chatham and finally Devonport; needless to say he was selected for Devonport and he always harboured a suspicion this was payback for previous misdemeanours.

There is a recurring theme throughout all reminisces that has been highlighted before. The reduction in the time spent at *Fisgard* being reduced from four and a half years to four terms was supposed to herald the end of "sprogging" and lead to a more egalitarian system, however there were many amongst the Apprentices who saw things in a somewhat different light. There was a view that having been subjected to the humiliations of "sprogging" when in the junior classes that there should be recompense when in the senior classes and consequently the practice continued but, as Bill Spong (Rodney 1952) remembered, there were ways to avoid being used as a skivvy:

Until I became eligible for one of my own, I found the concept of sprogging unacceptable. I expect that every 12 class had a few bullies in its midst, ours certainly did. One in particular, whom I won't name, had such a broad "Brummie" accent that my classmates will immediately know to whom I refer. Whilst in 5 class, having more than enough chores of my own for comfort, I resented being forced to char for others. Thus I devised a cunning plan, and feigned incompetence to several degrees lower than I actually was. At first I only burnt his toast and managed to dull with oil the bullshit shine on his boots, but it was my severely singeing his best doeskin trousers that earned from him the title of idiot. D'you know I was given no more such chores![11]

There were of course different priorities once the Apprentices had passed out and joined the fleet. Life at sea did not allow for the hijinks of *Fisgard* or *Caledonia*; life had to be altogether more serious. With this came the added bonus of travel to places the majority of men at home could only dreamt about in the 1950s. Such a destination was Vietnam, at that time a colony of France and engaged in a war of independence against the "Viet Minh". While serving in HMS *Warrior* in 1954, Gad Howe was detailed to go to Saigon Airport to assist in the recovery of a Sea Fury that had had to divert there. He flew off *Warrior* in a Firefly; the catapult launch caused him to black out.

At Saigon Airport all was in chaos: the Viet Minh had already cut off the water to the city, but this did not stop Gad making the necessary repairs ready for takeoff. No sooner were the repair complete and two of what Gad refers to as "Hooray Henrys" turned up, who were in fact the naval and Air Force attachés in Saigon. These two individuals insisted that the party accompany them to the airport restaurant, where, being greeted by the head waiter like a bad smell, possibly due to Gad's get-up of dirty blue overalls and stained sweat band, they tucked into smoked salmon sandwiches and champagne. On leaving there was disappointment expressed by the French that the RN planes would not be helping against the Viet Minh.[12]

Such occurrences must be unusual but add spice to what can be a humdrum existence on board ships at sea or, indeed, ashore, as Derek Spencer (Series 3) remembered. He was an EA3 serving in HMS *Alamein* while it completed a short refit in Gibraltar. The shoreside accommodation left a lot to be desired; the walls were liberally coated in the remains of generations of mosquitoes, which he and his cabin mate added to with the liberal application of a flip flop. Even this carnage did not prevent the two of them waking up in the morning with numerous bites; as he commented, the lack of a ceiling did not help. There was some consolation in the availability of cheap Spanish brandy. Caporal was somewhat rougher than Fundador but it was only 3/- a bottle.

It has often been suggested by many who were not Artificers that they were not "real" Leading Hands, POs or Chiefs, however this next story suggested that was not the case even back in the 1950s, as Frank Mould remembered:

It was early September 1953. I stood aft on the main deck of HMS Whirlwind (F187), taking in all the sights and sounds of what seemed like pandemonium going on around me. Whirlwind was a "New" AS frigate. She had just completed a long refit in Chatham Dockyard, and only three weeks earlier, had joined the 5th Frigate Squadron of the Mediterranean fleet. I had joined her only three days before and was even newer than she was! The pandemonium I was witnessing was the CinC's harbour inspection of Whirlwind, prior to her acceptance into the Med Fleet. I was completely in awe of all that was going on around me, Fisgard and Cale had not prepared me for "General Drills". Just over a month before I had been a "Boy Tiff" in THE BEST 12 class ever, on top of my known world and thought I knew all there was to know about naval ordnance. Now here I was an insignificant OA5, and totally at a loss in understanding my present world. I had already taken an active part in the Harbour Inspection by dropping the breechblocks of the 4-inch, in a timed exercise. I thought Cale had taught me all there was to know about the 4" Mk 19, but I had quickly learned that she hadn't taught me much about simple maintenance! I now knew with certainty that I had an awful lot to learn. I had done my bit and now I was standing back watching and learning from my new shipmates. "Oi you, 'Ooky," I became aware of somebody shouting above the noise, and chaos. Looking around I saw this huge second row forward with the most unlikely title of "Buffer", glowering at me. "Who me Chief?" said I in awe of this giant of a man. "Yes you," said he, "that's what's on yer arm aint it?" Oh so that's what that badge is, I thought, and dutifully replied "Yes Chief." His next words left me flabbergasted. "I have written orders for you, but since you don't know you're an 'Ook, you probably can't read either, so I'll briefly translate. Get six armed men, and a signalman, rations for 24 hours and get ashore to set up a blockade on Manual Island. Make contact with the ship for further orders." "B b b but Chief," I said, "I am an OA5" "Name?" He shouted, "OA5 Mould," I said, springing to attention as if I were back in One class. "Well OA5 Mould you're an 'Ook, Killick or Leading Hand first and last, it says so on yer arm, and right now I need an 'Ook, and you're it – now move!" he roared at me, and went off to ruin the day for some other unsuspecting sprog. With the help of my Chief OA (God bless you Ernie, wherever you are) I managed to gather six other bewildered people and a signalman, get them armed with Lee Enfield rifles and bayonets, (no bullets of course!), get them suitably attired, and ashore by Manuel Island Bridge, then made contact with the ship as per my orders, both verbal and written. On contact with the ship I was given further orders to challenge everyone who came onto the Island and get them to identify themselves. This last was no problem as everyone whom I challenged, whether a Captain (RN) (in civvies), or a passing housewife, all were very helpful and all civilly passed the time of day, whilst I dutifully stood to attention and glanced importantly at their relevant identification. The day wore on and I was beginning to get the hang of this "Ooky" lark, and even to enjoy the temporary taste of power! Then this obnoxious person turned up in a battered old car. He wore a well-worn gabardine mac, and a soft woollen hat full of fly fishing hooks. He just sat in his car and glowered at me. "What's going on?" he snarled. "Just an exercise sir," I said politely. There followed a few heated moments where he was belligerently demanding to be let through, and I, as courteously as I could, refusing to let him pass. I was actually toying with the idea of letting him by and get on with the easy life, when he suddenly revved his motor and yelled at me, "I haven't the time or patience to play silly buggers with the likes of you!" That made me mad, so I poked my Lee Enfield through the window of the car and close to his ear and slapped the bolt. "You go and tell that to the silly bugger who sent me here! Meanwhile either identify yourself or leave!" I said with feeling. He suddenly smiled and my heart sank, for I knew that smile; who didn't, for it was known world wide!! It was the Earl Mountbatten of Burma, Commander in Chief of the Mediterranean Fleet, Governor of Malta, and the Boss's Uncle!!! I was paralysed, helpless, gob smacked, and rooted to the spot, but he continued to smile that mesmerising smile of his. "Be good enough to remove that weapon from my starboard ear, as I am the silly bugger who placed you here," he said gracefully, handing me his identification. Without a glance I passed them back and muttered sheepishly, "Pass Sir." I think I also managed to give him the general salute. "Oh I don't need to go any further thank you," he said, so very politely, "Good day to you," and drove off! Soon after that we received the recall, and as I got back on board I was met by a midshipman, "OA5 Mould?" he asked. I nodded, "The Captain would like to see you on the bridge!" "Oh God," I thought as I followed the Snotty up to the bridge. Well you would, *wouldn't you? After all I was on my way to see Commander Evans the "Master and Commander" of HMS Whirlwind, on his own bridge, – and me, just an 'Ook! Aboard Whirlwind HE was God. Even I knew that much! I waited in the wings whilst the Midshipman reported to the Captain, who was sitting in his chair, and after a 10 while the Skipper looked over to me and beckoned with his index finger for me to approach, which I immediately did. "OA5 Mould," he said in a fatherly sort of voice, "I have a message from our Commander in Chief, especially for you. Had you let him pass, you would have lived to be the oldest OA5 in the Royal Navy." – "Carry on!" I believe the original signal read, "I would live to be the oldest Leading Hand in the RN". Ever since, when ever informed by some Old Salt that I was not a "Proper Chief" or whatever, I would simply reply "I have been addressed as such by some very senior officers, and a 'Buffer'. If my title was used by them it must be so"!!!!!!!!!!!!!![13]*

Bill Spong remembered joining his first ship after the euphoria of passing out and being able to sew on the gold hook on the left arm of his jacket. He actually went to the wrong ship initially as there were three battle-class destroyers alongside each other and for some reason he was mistaken for a new Stores Accountant (SA), thinking only of Shipwright Apprentice. Once this was rectified he was, of course, adrift, and possibly because of this his first job on board was to clear the seamen's heads; being unfamiliar with the methods to employ, Bill proceeded to undo various pipe unions until one gave up some noxious liquid, which splashed onto the mess deck table and – horror of horrors – into the rum fanny. Bill was not a popular man and to compound his faux pas it was the stokers' rum.

There is one subject that is always dear to the heart of a young Apprentice and that is his stomach; for, of those young men who joined *Caledonia*, many had not been north of the border before and were ignorant of certain national dishes, as Gil Harding (Series 20 1955) remembered:

All of my class were born just before World War II started, so war and bombings and the need for the Armed Services were not questioned by us, they were facts of life. National Service was going strong and every able-bodied young man was called up to do his two-year stint almost as soon as he left school. Uniforms were worn for leave by all the Services, so everywhere you went there would be Servicemen in uniforms. We had been raised on war-time rations so very few of us were fussy eaters, but some of the food produced in the galley at Caledonia would have been a test to anyone. Two items I still recall with a shudder; sheep's hearts, which looked like a miniature rugby ball and tasted similar but with the arteries in them, and meat pies, which came to be known as "cow pies" that I would have challenged "Desperate Dan" to eat. They were made of all the gristle and waste bits cut from the meat, which were then hidden by a pastry crust. The latter resulted in a "food strike" that became known as the "Cow Pie Mutiny".

While on the subject of food, our move to Scotland introduced us to several dishes that we had not previously encountered, haggis, black pudd'n, mealie pudd'n, salty porridge and fish in all their glory. I personally came to like most of them but it was a shock to my southern constitution when they featured on the "menu" for breakfast.

Every week there was a "menu" produced by the galley staff. There was no choice, but some of the dishes would have sounded good at the Savoy in London. Unfortunately they were figments of someone's imagination that were probably way outside the ability of the cooks, let alone their production for eight hundred young lads to eat in half an hour, and stay inside a meagre budget![14]

There was an incident in 1955 that is worth repeating as it demonstrates the independence of Artificer Apprentices and shows how there are those who scream and shout to little effect while a more conciliatory approach will pay dividends. This episode concerns Her Majesty the Queen's proposed state visit to Norway. It was intended that the Queen would join the Royal Yacht *Britannia* in Rosyth Naval Base. Traditionally the Royal Guard would be made up of sailors in bell bottom trousers and round hats but it was found that there were insufficient seaman ratings to form the Guard. The fallback option was to form a guard of Artificer Apprentices in fore and aft rig. This caused some consternation amongst the fraternity of gunnery instructors from Whale Island but it was either Tiffies for the guard or no guard at all. Hugh Simpson takes up the story:

Consequently hordes of GIs descended on Caledonia *where the senior classes, ie nine class and above, were formed into a rudimentary guard. The GIs then spent days screaming at, I mean drilling the guard by marching it round and round the factory and up and down the lower road. After a time it appeared that all the GIs' fears were to be well founded as the guard was a shambles despite the intensified screaming of the GIs. As the Queen's departure date came closer, panic was setting in when the Chief Hook of the School, Pete Beck of Exmouth*

Division, suggested that perhaps he could take charge of the guard for a trial demonstration. Much to the GIs' scepticism it was agreed to give it a try. At the Chief Hook's command the guard snapped to attention and proceeded to give a demonstration of guard drill that would have put the Brigade of Guards to shame. The Chief Hook then explained to the GIs that if they treated the tiffies with respect, they would then get respect and co-operation in return. After the Queen's departure the GIs reluctantly conceded that it was one of the best guards that they had ever seen. The footnote to this episode occurred when the guard had to return the special rifles and bayonets to the armoury for return to Whale Island. The rifles were returned without incident, however the majority of the bayonets were not. It appears that the guard wanted a souvenir of their unique day. An armistice had to be declared to allow the bayonets' return without penalty to the guard members.[15]

This shows clearly that when treated with the respect they thought they deserved the Apprentices could rise to the occasion and provide something "second to none" that Jackie Fisher would be proud of. It also, perhaps, highlights the often poorly hidden antipathy felt for GIs and the assumed superiority of the Artificer as seen by themselves.

In 1956 there was a concession that was guaranteed to bring a smile the face of all Apprentices: the withdrawal of gilt buttons that had happened in 1926 was reversed and once again the Tiffies' no. 1 uniform was resplendent in gilt buttons. This was something all at *Fisgard* looked forward to, the passing out parade being the first chance to show off this finery.

To continue in the vein of pranks that Apprentices got up to and the lengths they would go to is illustrated by an episode that took place in *Fisgard* in the autumn term of 1957. Graham Ford remembered walking down the covered way behind Anson Division when he was stopped in his tracks: tethered outside, happily eating the grass, was a goat. Now, this was not a run-of-the-mill goat but a "ceremonial" goat that had been "liberated" from its pastures in *Raleigh* to graze happily in Anson Division.

Later that morning, while "both watches" were mustered, two Apprentices were seen approaching the east side of the parade ground, marching smartly and leading the goat. They proceeded to report to the duty Lieutenant Commander that "Operation Billy Goat" had been successfully accomplished. There was little the DLC could do but acknowledge and order them to "carry on". The Commander was duly informed and the miscreants summoned but it appears the only punishment was an invitation to make a donation towards a new ceremonial coat for the goat. However, the sentries in *Raleigh* were rewarded with extra duties for failing to spot either the intruders or the fact the goat was missing.[16]

There is a further twist to this story, provided by Arthur Bailey (Series 28) who after forty-eight years admitted to being one of the instigators. He remembered that the plot was hatched as a "passing out" wheeze to beat them all. Walter, the goats name, was selected as an innocent victim of the scheme who could have no say in his abduction. There was a need for much intelligence before the operation was put into practice; there was an insider in the form of a stoker who looked after Walter; his sister worked with Arthur's sister and they often met ashore. It was discovered that where Walter was stabled was near to gates leading out to the Trevol shooting ranges and that the locked gates could be lifted off their hinges for easy access.

Secrecy was of the utmost importance and only a select few were allowed to be in the know. On a suitably dark night the perpetrators made their way, suitable camouflaged, through the playing fields, across Anthony Road, through *Raleigh* married quarters to the gate with the dodgy hinges. After a slight scare when the boiler man came to dump the clinker, the intrepid intruders set about luring Walter to pastures new. As is the way with animals, Walter was not coming easily and he exited his stable at full speed with an Apprentice gamely holding onto the rope that had been put round Walter's neck. Fortunately for reasons best known to Walter he did this in silence and allowed himself to be led back whence the Apprentices had arrived. Taking turns overnight to babysit the goat, he was as already mentioned presented at "both watches" in the morning. The finale was remembered by Arthur:

After a brief "discussion" with the DLC, we were told to march Walter down to the Regulating Office. The Duty RPO was "Donk" Davis Together with Walter, we waited outside his office until he was ready to see us. When called in, we all went in, goat and all. To "Donk's" horror, Walter planted two feet on his desk and started to empty his ashtray. By now, all hell had broken loose and every man and his dog, including the Commander, wanted to know what was going on. Eventually calm descended, and Walter was ceremoniously returned to Raleigh accompanied by a Guard and Band. Raleigh was not amused, because while we *had been pinching their goat, some classmates had also sneaked into Raleigh and had hoisted an RNATE flag on the Main Mast on the main parade ground, which nobody noticed until they fell in for "both watches". The fall out was pretty heavy. On the grapevine, we had heard that Raleigh was going to get revenge by pinching Fisgard's Christmas tree, which was on our parade ground. So the Commander decided that the goat-pinchers should sleep in the school rooms to guard the tree. We had fire hoses run out to repel boarders, but to no avail, the b*****s came and pinched the clapper out of the Ship's bell, right under the nose of the Quartermaster. We had sleepless nights, but the QM nearly got busted. The outcome was that about an hour before our Passing-out Parade, resplendent in boots and gaiters, we "appeared" before the Commander. The charges were:*

a) Absent from place of duty, namely bed

b) Absent without leave, namely, breaking out of HMS Fisgard

c) Entering an Out of Bounds area, namely married quarters

d) Breaking into HMS Raleigh

e) Removing Government property from said HMS Raleigh

f) Breaking into HMS Fisgard

g) Bringing an animal onboard without permission

h) Absent from place of duty namely Both Watches.

The Commander was highly amused about the whole incident but felt that as Walter was old and arthritic we should contribute the princely sum of five shillings each toward a new winter coat for him.[17]

There were episodes that were not so light-hearted and perhaps reminded many that there was a very much more serious side to life. One such incident happened in *Caledonia* late in 1958, as Alan Petrie (Series 27) recalled:

A sad episode happened on the 8th Nov 1958 when Nigel Spragg (Alky) one of our New Zealand classmates was killed in a motorcycle accident in Inverkeithing. He was one of our more promising Apprentice classmates and could have gone on to great things, but it was not to be. We provided a guard of honour for a full Military Funeral with Kiwi Kelly, another of our class, providing the drum beat. It is common Naval practice to auction the kit of a messmate who had died, in order to raise money for his family. Alky's kit was auctioned many times over. The class was very sombre for a long time after that. I can report that the grave is very well tended in the Commonwealth War Graves section of Douglas Bank Cemetery Rosyth.[18]

The auctioning of the deceased's kit is a time-honoured naval tradition originally to ensure there were sufficient funds for the possible widow and children and this has been used for many years. Each item of kit is auctioned and then returned to be reauctioned; this will be done any number of times until sufficient funds have been raised.

While it was decided in the mid-1950s that HMS *Daedalus* would be the primary technical training establishment for all Fleet Air Arm Apprentices, this meant the closure of two establishments that had a long association with FAA Apprentices, namely *Ariel* for electrical training and *Condor* for airframes and engines, though *Condor* did not actually close until 1971, when it was handed over to the Royal Marines. The name *Ariel* remained as *Daedalus* was renamed *Ariel* in 1959 and the old *Ariel* at Worthy Down was handed over to the army in 1960. This would not be the end of the story of *Daedalus/Ariel* as *Ariel* was moved to the Naval Air Station at Lee-on-the-Solent in October 1959.

Air Electrical Apprentices spent the time from 5 Class to 9 Class at *Collingwood*. It was only then that they moved to *Ariel*, which was very different to *Collingwood*, as Ron Towns remembered fondly:

Life at Worthy Down was dramatically different from that at Fisgard and Collingwood. A smaller establishment – most unlike the large one just left behind. Life there was very relaxed. There was no resident divisional staff, we didn't march to school and, most importantly, the food was great. Fisgard food, everyone will agree, was pretty bad. Collingwood was a little better, but at Worthy Down it was great. The choices were numerous and the serving sizes tremendous. There was also an extra meal, tea, served at tea time. Apart from tea and toast there were treats like grilled kippers and poached eggs.

There were no machine shops at Ariel, just class room instruction.

The class rooms were easy walking (not marching) distances from the living area. Modern, glass filled school rooms with central heating. One could look out across the sports fields or open country where 848 Squadron was forming up with Wessex helicopters. We had real live Artificer instructors, kindly people who filled us with a real sense that the end of the long haul apprenticeship was coming. It was almost as if the last three years need not have taken place. This was the

real stuff learning about Identification Friend or Foe, (IFF) radar altimeters,
Doppler radar and other airborne electronic aids. The class was small due to all
the trade subdivision we had been through. We all talk about the "esprit de corps"
and the feeling of being the "best", "second to none", but we felt really special – our
small band of REA(A)s.

No liberty boats here, it was open gangway. There were two entrances. The
main gate through which most of the traffic entered and left and the small back
gate close to our accommodation block. There was just one sentry there and, for
those of us with cars or motor bicycles, it wasn't necessary to dismount-just drive
through.[19]

So everything was in a settled state and training was well established;
the next ten years would see considerable change in both training and
organisation. Whether for good or bad is all a matter of opinion, but those
who go before always consider that any changes are normally not going to
be an improvement.

chapter eight

The Sixties, More Reconstruction and the End of the ERA

• • •

There's letters seal'd, and my two schoolfellows,
Whom I will trust as I will adders fang'd—
They bear the mandate, they must sweep my way
And marshal me to knavery. Let it work;
For 'tis the sport to have the engineer
Hoist with his own petard, an't shall go hard
But I will delve one yard below their mines
And blow them at the moon.[1]

In the early 1960s there was little change to the training regime, entry requirements or length of training. And from of the stories of this time little had changed with regard to the belligerence of Apprentices, particularly when it impinged on either their welfare or their stomachs. This is clearly illustrated by what was known at the time as the "Breakfast Roll Mutiny", as Trevor Waddington (Series 32) recalled:

The "Breakfast Roll Mutiny"! Technically it was a mutiny, but was probably never recorded as such. The catering officer, most likely trying to save money,

Indus 1904

Reg Bennett 1916

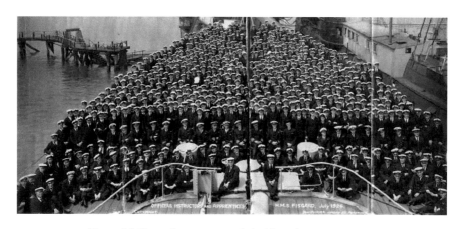

Fisgard Officers, Instructors and Artificer Apprentices 1926

Caledonia *1937*

Ron Calverley at RAF Kaldadarnes, Iceland 1943, Front row forth from left

RNATE Arbroath 1945

Series 14 1952

HMS Caledonia *Royal Guard 1955*

HMS Condor *Divisions 1959*

HMS Fisgard *Main Gate 1962*

HMS Fisgard *Lane 1 New Entry September 1967 (Author second from left front row)*

HMS Fisgard *Bennett Division ready for Captains Rounds 1977*

HMS Fisgard *831 Class Tribe Division*

HMS Raleigh 903 Entry note blue cap badges on the girls tricorns.

HMS Raleigh *Passing out Class 2001*

061 Entry Walker Division (the final class of Artificer Apprentices)
2006 with 'George' the Fisgard *Figurehead.*

had decided to do away with the bread rolls served at breakfast. His mistake was in underestimating the significance of this menu item. For the senior app who had left his bed at the last minute, as was customary, the bread roll made into a "bacon sandwich" was his breakfast. We gathered on the parade ground that morning for both watches and the senior class started chanting, "We want rolls for breakfast. We want rolls for breakfast. etc." This was quickly taken up by the remainder of us and must have lasted for several minutes before the noise brought out the Duty Officer, a SD sub-lieutenant. He handled the situation well, saying that although he understood our feelings, this was no way to behave in a disciplined service. We marched off the parade ground quietly but with heads held high. The next day bread rolls were back on the menu, never to be removed again![2]

This incident once again demonstrates the tolerance with which Apprentices were treated; it is likely that in any other establishment such behaviour would not have been tolerated. The similarity with a minor public school appears again. As well as the lenient response to the incident, it is evident the mutinous actions had the desired effect: bread rolls reappeared at breakfast the very next day.

Throughout the modern history of Apprentices, much store has been set on adventurous training in all its forms, whether it be trekking in the Scottish Highlands or the Brecon Beacons or sailing, skiing or canoeing. All manner of activities were sanctioned and they gave the Apprentices healthy activities where it was hoped they could not get into too much trouble. Wishful thinking indeed, as Nick Hartland (Series 33) wrote:

From the barn in the tiny place of Dall in The Highlands of Scotland, some five miles from Schiehallion, orienteering exercises in the Scottish wilderness were given to small parties of five or six apprentices. On each occasion a different apprentice took on the job of leader. My turn came after a day of kayak training on Loch Rannoch. I came to every inch of that flimsy boat as we struggled down to the edge of the loch. That, by the way, was frozen over and it seemed, not for the first time in the Royal Navy, a mark of insincerity of purpose to spend the allocated day attempting to float a kayak, when two inches of ice stubbornly impeded progress. The GI patiently explained, in choice and very old English, how to crack the ice, "Or else…!" The following day I took the Ordnance Survey map, compass and K-rations and four very weary, foot dragging, colleagues off to find the signs, or markers, that had been left at various places indicated on our maps. Almost immediately, the survival lessons we had learned at HMS Fisgard *came back to me. It may have been that in a desert situation you did not eke out the water you had but drank the lot to heighten the head of fluid in your body, which was then lost at a more beneficial rate and could be strained through a sock. I reasoned that similarly and without dissent from the other four, we ought to demolish all the rations there and then, explaining, as if it was necessary, that at least there would be less to carry. Those rations were very good and, as I recall, included a type of tinned plum pudding with a density that had to be bitten into to be believed. There were also slabs of dark chocolate, which resembled what we would come to know as Kye but which, in later nights at sea, we would consume in the form of thick hot chocolate, during middle watches which stretched endlessly from midnight till 4 am.*

Two or three markers were traced on the route, then the Scotch mist closed in. Using the compass, I led the party to the heart-stopping edge of a deep ravine. That's when the mutiny started and, with so little resistance, one might have thought I led it. Three decided to follow the edge of the steep bank downwards to distant civilisation and two wanted to try for more markers but common sense finally prevailed and we eventually reached the road between Dall and Kinloch Rannoch; yes, where the pub was! The next decision was unanimous. We strode out for the pub!

This was our undoing, because the subsequent smell of beer and the lack of identification markers resulted in double marching round and round the parade ground after we had returned to HMS Caledonia. *There we doubled with Lee Enfield rifles held above our heads in relentless sleeting rain. The memory of the gradual accumulation of water inside my sleeves, slowly saturating my clothes from within, is undimmed.*[3]

This type of extramural activity was strongly encouraged throughout Artificer training, whether on the moors of Devon while at *Fisgard*, the Welsh hills while at *Collingwood* or even while enduring the Petty Officers Leadership Course in the Black Mountains. It is of course debatable whether the Apprentices shared the same enthusiasm for these outdoor activities, particularly if they had to be endured in the midst of winter. The areas for the expeditions were without exception some of the bleakest, coldest and most inhospitable parts of the country.

As well as the "Exped", there was perennial love of sports that young men and particularly Apprentices have. This love of sport was nurtured and encouraged, with many Apprentices being selected for teams at Command and Navy level. There was also a keen fixture list with local schools and other military establishments, which always engendered a fierce rivalry. There were the fixtures against the RAF at RAF Halton in the 1920s mentioned previously and in the 1960s there were annual fixtures, summer and winter, against the army Apprentices at Chepstow. There were advantages to playing for a ship's team: there was free gangway after the match and an extension of leave of half an hour. The only downside of these slight privileges is that they were not well publicised; it was a matter for the individual to trawl through ships' standing orders to find the relevant entry and then being able to convince any sceptical gangway staff of your legitimacy.

As well as sport and Exped there were other extramural activities. One popular with budding musicians was the ship's band. Those with no musical aptitude were soon sent on their way, but being the drum major did not require any musical ability as such, though there was an "audition", as John Bowden learnt at the end of 1 Class:

Like many other Artificer Apprentices before and after my time, I carried out the duties of drum major with both the "Fisgard" and "Caledonia" Apprentices' Volunteer Brass Bands.

At the end of 1 Class, December, 1958, along with other apprentices, I attended an audition held on the .22 Rifle Range at "Fisgard" for the position of drum major for the Artificer Apprentices Volunteer Brass Band. This audition was arranged by the ship's Gunnery Officer, Sub-Lieutenant Williams RN, together with the Bandmaster, his name sake, Mr. Williams. I was the successful applicant and took over the task at the start of 2 Class, January, 1959, holding the position for the rest of my time in "Fisgard" in 2, 3, and 4 Classes. The band and its drum major were under the tutelage of "Bandy" Williams, a retired Royal Marine bandsman of great musical knowledge. The band thrived under his leadership, and gave many displays in local Carnivals and Gala Days, culminating in the first ever full "Beat Retreat" ceremony held on the "Fisgard" Parade Ground in the summer term of 1959...

On "Passing Out" of "Fisgard" in December, 1959, I was one of the very lucky ERA, OA, and Shipwright Apprentices to go to "Caledonia." Here, in 5 Class, I joined the brass band as the Junior Drum Major, the Senior DM being my immediate predecessor from "Fisgard." He was, I remember, an OA/ App, but sadly, his name escapes me. Being senior, he had the pick of duties, and at the 1960 Royal Tournament appearance, he did the afternoon performance, leaving me to do the one in the evening. This meant that he could have the remainder of the weekend with his family and girlfriend. I was the duty "bod". Our Bandmaster at that time was a great character, a Band Sergeant RM, called "Shady" Lane...

My days as a Royal Navy drum major finally ended in 1963 at HMS "Sultan." I arrived there in January 1963, having left the Dartmouth Training Squadron, (HMS Urchin"), the previous month, at the end of the seagoing term, 12 Class. I was to attend the then new Type 81 Tribal Class Frigate COSAG Machinery Course before joining HMS "Gurkha." On joining "Sultan," I spent some six weeks prior to the course as a member of the Ships Company as an ERA 3rd Class, working in the Outside Trades shop. Funnily enough, my task was to assist in the making of the 1/6th scale Mk VI 4.5 twin gun turrets for model GMDs that were to be the Royal Navy's contribution to that year's Royal Tournament. During this time, and whilst on the course, I carried out drum major duties for the "Sultan" Volunteer Brass Band.

However, it was not the same as the bands of "Fisgard" and "Caledonia," or I dare say, those Art/App bands of "Collingwood" and "Condor" There was something very special about the Art/App bands, both Brass and Pipe. They were a group unto themselves, they were great fun, and although they were amateurs, they were in their way, very very professional, but above all, they were GOOD! I can only say that I have always felt extremely honoured, yet humble, to have been allowed to spend some of my time as an Art/App.[4]

There seems to have been a consensus amongst Apprentices through the years that the bands made up of amateur Apprentice musicians were of an overall very high standard. Again, one of the perks of being in the band was the issue of the coveted "blue" station card, with its concomitant privileges and status, privileges not to be passed up if of a musical bent.

At the start of the 1960s there were several changes that are worth noting. In 1960 the five classes of Artificer were reduced to three, with Third Class being equivalent to Leading Hand, Second Class to Petty Officer and First Class to Chief Petty Officer. There were still right up to the early 1970s some ships where the Third Class were still messed in the Petty Officers' mess rather than with junior ratings, but it became less and less the norm.

With this restructuring came the last allocation to Ordnance Artificers from the September 1960 entry. From 7 July 1961 a new Artificer Branch was formed with the introduction of the Control Artificer (Weapons). [5]This followed the increasing complexity of the weapon control systems and allowed a more even distribution of resources and a way of improving the deep specialist skills required to manage the new technologies, both surface and sub-surface.

For Apprentices in May 1961 it was decided that the four terms spent in *Fisgard* would be reduced to three, starting with Series 42, the extra term being added on to the Part II training, so there was no reduction in the overall length of the apprenticeship. Just after this change, in September 1961, there was a decision to allow those of a higher academic prowess to complete the training in *Fisgard* in two terms rather than the now-normal three.

If there is one thing that will remain with any Apprentice for all time it is the initial shock of kit issue marking and worst of all the kit muster. As Apprentices spent such a long time in training there were many of these hurdles to overcome, but the first was the biggest shock, as Ian Pile (Series 45) remembered all too well:

However, the most peculiar aspect of getting used to life in uniform was just that; the uniform itself. The initial kit issue was like being outfitted for a WW2 movie, with lots of webbing. blanco, boots, King George cap badges and ill-fitting garments. The kit list went on and on, including items as diverse as long woolly underpants. boot-brushes, housewife. paybook wallet, pyjamas and stiff detached collars. The tropical shirts came in three sizes; large, huge and enormous. After kit issue, the first step was kit marking. This involved assembling a wooden name stamp, dipping it into gloss paint and stamping the name on to every item of kit (hopefully the right way up). My first attempts were encouraging, with my name I PILE clearly standing out, but as the name stamp got more clogged with fluff and setting paint, the results deteriorated to *****.

The next step was to sew over the name, on selected clothing, with red silk thread. (The wiser Apps waited until the paint dried before attempting this). I was lucky, with only five letters to sew in, but unfortunate souls with long names had to burn the midnight oil! We should have been issued with two pairs of boots and one pair of shoes, but Slops had run out of shoes. As an alternative, we were given deck slippers, which were black leather creations, with chrome buckles. These could only be worn with night clothing (trop shirt and SB suit), so the runs ashore to the Rendezvous Cafe in downtown Torpoint had to be in boots. The

Naval approach to breaking-in new boots was novel; they sent us on a 15 mile road march, which broke-in my feet, not the boots! After the last Apprentices' kit muster, items such as the pyjamas and woolly underpants became very good car polishing rags, but the boot brushes have survived 36 years of continuous use and still proudly display the name I P***.[6]

Such memories will be only too real to many old Apprentices. Even without having to embroider your name with the introduction of white tape and using the wooden type block with black dye to emboss your name on working rig and with a small metal name type to mark many other items of kit without having to resort to red silk thread and needle, it was still an ordeal to have to lay out your entire kit for inspection on so many occasions.

While there were changes to training throughout the Apprentice time for those at sea, there were still places in the world that are now long gone as an area in which to serve. One such station was in the Persian Gulf. In the early 1960s there were ships based in Bahrain at HMS *Jufair*, which will bring back memories to many. Len Murrell (Series 24) served in HMS *Loch Lomond* in 1961–1962 and remembered that there were duties expected of a Petty Officer that had not been mentioned at all during training:

In the summer of 1961 I was serving on HMS Loch Lomond stationed in the Persian Gulf, based at Bahrain, HMS Jufair. Our purpose of being there was guard ship/peacekeeping patrol of the shoreline of the Trucial Oman States (7 in total) – now the UAE. The aim was to apprehend shipping/boats/dhow's that were suspected of gun/arms running sourced from the Yemen. Not that we ever caught anyone, most could outrun our 18 knots flat out. We had a mixed bunch as the crew that included 22 marines, some 20+ Somali sailors (picked up at Aden en route), Chinese laundry crew, Indian tailor, interpreter and a Southern Irish canteen manager.

At the time I was a 4th Class OA, not yet old enough for his first good conduct badge. Being messed in the PO's mess, the only Tiff I learned that as a Petty Officer I was required to carry out duties as PO of the Day and PO of the shore patrol, I don't recall any mention of these additional responsibilities during our apprenticeship at Fisgard or Caledonia? Nevertheless, I shrugged and took it in my stride. Come late December of 1961 we found ourselves in Kuwait, Mina Al Ahmadi, and a rare occasion when we had a jetty to step on to. Seems the Brits helped finance the building of the jetty that qualified RN ships a single parking space.

Christmas Eve arrived and I found I was duly appointed PO of the patrol – I was obviously not wise to duty rosters. Part of patrol neighbourhood was the Habara Club, this was an exclusive ex-pats club that the manager had throw open its doors as an appreciation of our presence and being Christmas Eve. I had as my patrol two AB's. We were picked up at the jetty – the RAF I recall and taken to the Habara Club. We had no sooner crossed the threshold when greeted by a rather irate Manager, demanding that we extract some drunken yobs, he led us to a two chaps in civilian clothes, both were much the worse for wear. I should add that some of our crew were present in uniform and not causing too much disruption. Seems these two were off HMS Dalrymple – survey ship. She was anchored off and I was unable to arrange passage for their return, they became increasingly stroppy and aggressive at my suggestion that they should go elsewhere to sober up – to no avail, so I cautioned them that they were being arrested and would be accommodated on Loch Lomond overnight and returned to their ship in the morning.

On arrival back onboard I reported the situation to the Officer of the Day who scratching his head as to where to accommodate these two characters, he decided the chain locker was the safe option for all concerned. By this time it was 23:00 and I returned to the Habara Club to complete the patrol, the manager was very welcoming on our return and we were expecting no further issues, how wrong could you be! I'd lost sight of my two patrol members only to find that the manager had been a little over generous with his gratitude and I was faced with my second case of inebriation that evening, fortunately I was able to get them on board without incident, the Officer of The Day was not to be seen on the brow – some experience that day was.

Some 6 weeks later we caught up with the Dalrymple and I was summoned aboard to support the charges on these two characters. A very hostile CO tore me to shreds, claiming I had no right to incarcerate his crew members in the way that I did, I had no backup with me for support. He dismissed the charges; conduct unbecoming (drunk & disorderly) claiming it was just high spirits on a on a festive occasion! I was just relieved to get back on board the Loch Lomond and shot of the wretched experience. Loch Lomond decommissioned in Singapore in 1962. On return home I was drafted to Royal Arthur for a leadership course, I often wonder why?[27]

This is a timely reminder that during training much emphasis was put on academic and craft training but, while expressing the accelerated

advancement to senior ratings that Artificers would benefit from, there
was no time spent in explaining the duties and responsibilities that came
with being a senior rating, whether Artificer or not, and perhaps some
explanation of these duties and responsibilities might have prevented much
embarrassment later.

In *Fisgard* there were some strange goings-on that Stuart Wakefield
(Series 43) wrote about. One of these concerned Ghanaian Apprentices,
who were a little bit older than the usual Apprentices:

Term 1 – Ghanaian Hypnosis
*During the late summer of 1961, I was one of about 350 members of S43 entry
of Artificer Apprentices who joined HMS Fisgard. Unusually these included a
dozen Ghanaians, who, unlike us teenagers, were all in their twenties. I especially
recall one of the two Ghanaians in my Division called Abu, and his lack of any
initials placed him at the front of every line in alphabetical order, whilst also
allowing him to rapidly complete the task of sewing his name in almost every
item of kit in red silk chain stitch. It became apparent during conversations with
Abu that he was an experienced hypnotist, and a demonstration of this skill
was arranged where he would mentally transport one of our class to the United
Nations building in New York. The event was planned to take place during the
evening in an accommodation hut, and our Chief Hook selected me to maintain
a look-out at the entrance, with strict instructions to permit nobody to enter the
hut as it could be dangerous for the subject.*

*Whilst I took up my position on the outside, I still managed to occasionally
peep around the door to observe the goings-on. The hut was illuminated in the
centre by a single candle between Abu and the subject, and every space was
crammed with silent Apprentices gazing in anticipation. Suddenly, I heard the
familiar shout of "Stand-by for Evening Rounds", which was a warning that
the Duty Lieutenant and his small accompanying group were about to enter
our accommodation to ensure that no harm was coming to naval property, and
possibly of lesser concern, to us Apprentices. It was apparent that I needed to
comply with the Chief Hook's order, and as the Duty Lieutenant put his hand on
the door handle, I said "You can't go in there Sir, as there is a séance." Although
I considered that I had made the situation perfectly clear, the Duty Lieutenant
rushed past me into the hut, and there were screams as he switched the lights on
and confronted the two performers. Whilst I ran away as fast as I could and
witnessed nothing further, it soon became apparent that no further action was*

to be taken due to no harm having been done. However, I considered it to be best to maintain a low profile for a few weeks in the hope that the Duty Lieutenant would forget my face.

Term 2 – Factory Riot

My second term at HMS Fisgard took place during the stormy first few months of 1962. All classes had a weekly hour of evening instruction in the Factory, which is the building behind the great majority of Class photographs taken at the establishment. One evening, about one hundred and fifty Three Class Apprentices entered the Factory for instruction and proceeded up the steps under the clock and past the Office of the Regulating Petty Officer. They may have felt like herded cattle as they moved along the narrow passageway and started to moo, which immediately resulted in the Regulating Petty Officer yelling "Stop, that mooing." Whilst this seemed to have the required effect, their return along the passageway after the hour was accompanied by sheep-like baaing.

It was unacceptable for the Regulating Petty Officer to accept being outmanoeuvred by Apprentices, and he immediately demanded that the entire Class form up in threes on the now dark Parade Ground in front of the Factory. A ritual haranguing relating to fundamental aspects of naval discipline commenced as soon as the Class was assembled. However, the stipulated formation may have been a less than ideal, as it provided the opportunity for Apprentices at each end to quietly slip away in the darkness. Eventually, the Regulating Petty Officer found himself berating only a small fraction of those who had been in front of him a few minutes earlier.

This situation required an immediate and firm response, and the whole class was instructed to assemble on the Parade Ground with their bed mattresses. The Apprentices were instructed to run around the Parade Ground carrying their mattress, and the large number of senior rates positioned around the perimeter undoubtedly emphasised the severity of the situation. Whilst it would be reasonable to expect that Apprentices would quickly become exhausted by such a demanding workout, the lack of Parade Ground illumination provided opportunities. Many Apprentices completed two or three laps before diverting behind one of the four surrounding blast walls to rest for on their mattress before re-joining their colleagues. In reality, one hundred Apprentices running around a dark Parade Ground could appear much the same as one hundred and fifty. After about thirty minutes with no indication of the Apprentices becoming fatigued, they were instructed to return to their huts and prepare for an immediate kit inspection. *Three Class received considerable help to arrange their kit, and it seemed that the Divisional Chief Petty Officers who came to carry out the required inspections had lost much of the enthusiasm that they may have had to instil discipline at such a late hour. Interestingly, there was subsequent discussion with the Divisional Chief Petty Officers as to what constituted a Mutiny and the related punishments.*

Term 3 – Queen's Birthday Parade
We received our brass buttoned tailored doeskin uniforms during the summer of 1962, which made us the obvious choice to form the one hundred and fifty strong Guard of Honour for the Queen's Birthday Parade. Whilst we considered that we knew almost all there was to know about naval drill after a year of weekly sessions on the Parade Ground, we were still required to undertake a number of practice parades. The weather remained fine as we practiced marching across the road to HMS Raleigh where the parade was to be held at the much larger facility.

On the Saturday morning we assembled for the event, and I was to be the right-hand marker for our three ranks of fifty. We undoubtedly provided good photo opportunities for the many guests that were gathering on the bank of seats in front of us. At the appointed time, we smartly responded to the various commands given by the Lieutenant appointed as Guard Commander. We were inspected by an unknown senior naval officer, and then advanced in Review Order before manoeuvring around the Parade Ground for the concluding march-past accompanied by the Royal Marine band playing nautical themes. As we reached the bottom corner where we were to turn from our column of threes, the order was given, "Into line abreast, right turn". I had turned left exactly as we had practised countless times before realising that the Guard Commander had given a wrong order, which even he ignored. Chaos reigned as many of my classmates, being more disciplined than me, marched off in the direction that they had been ordered. I followed the Guard Commander and somehow sensed those behind me that were scampering about in an attempt to reposition themselves correctly. Although we achieved a semblance of marching past in line abreast, it was impossible to salvage our, until then, near perfect performance. We were no longer the confident Class that we had been an hour and a half previously as we departed through the gates of HMS Fisgard.[8]

In 1964 the last Ordnance Artificers left *Caledonia*, which had had its title changed to the Royal Naval Engineering School, and during this period His Royal Highness Prince Philip laid the foundation stone for new accommodation to replace the "temporary" huts that had been used since the establishment opened. Prince Philip commented in his speech of his concern that in many cases after he had laid a foundation stone it immediately disappeared into store; much to everyone's amazement, as soon as Prince Philip had left the stone was moved into the foyer of one of the lecture blocks, not to reappear until the new accommodation was opened in May 1966, as was reported in the May edition of *Navy News*:

One hundred and fifty-eight years after the launch of the first HMS Caledonia, *a first rate of 120 guns, apprentices of the RN Engineering School are starting to move into the sixth* Caledonia, *the new buildings of which have been rising slowly on the hill overlooking Rosyth dockyard over the past eighteen months.*

The first of the six new accommodation blocks is already occupied. Apprentices live in cabins of four, each block having thirty cabins. The new Caledonia *should be complete by 1969.*[9]

Away from *Caledonia* and *Fisgard* there were other stories to tell, as Stuart Wakefield (Series 43) remembered about *Condor*:

A Drill Order, Never Previously Heard.
After a few terms during the 1960s at H.M.S. Condor, the Fleet Air Arm training station at Arbroath, many Aircraft Artificer Apprentices visited Hepworths, Britain's largest clothing manufacturer at the time, to purchase a new No. 1 uniform. Such visits created an opportunity to somehow make the uniform a bespoke item that reflected the wearer's personality. Doeskin was invariably the material of choice, and the only possible visible modification was to slim down the trousers at the bottom to eighteen inches, or even to seventeen inches at a push. Although this measurement does not matter as much as it did when "drain-pipes" were the height of fashion during the 1960s, the Admiralty was reluctantly wrestling with the need to accept modern trends; (that were also to soon accept sailors' sideburns down to the bottom of the ear).

Whilst the manager at Hepworths well understood that it was in his best interests to remain within the limitations of acceptance, the trick up his well-tailored sleeve was to offer exotic jacket linings. The available range included bright silks in blue, orange and green plus various tartans and paisley patterns, and even embroidered Chinese dragons. In addition, it was not unusual to order the lining to be quilted, without a thought for its subsequent practicality in a warmer climate.

It may be reasonable to presume that any exotic embellishments would remain unobserved during occasions when No. 1 uniform was the required dress. However, during one Wednesday afternoon Divisions, the Captain was inspecting the Ship's Company, and initially doubted what he had seen peeking from the chest of an unfortunate Apprentice. The exposure of a slender scar of orange silk may have been due to corporal development since measuring for the uniform, and heaven forbid that there should be criticism of Hepworths tailoring skills.

Although Apprentices' were generally well tuned to the Captain's moods, nobody was really sure what he was thinking as he completed his inspection without any discussion. However, he spoke briefly to the Chief GI before granting permission for the parade to be dismissed, that is except for Apprentices who were ordered to "Stand Fast". There was palpable unease as the Chief GI marched decisively towards those left standing to attention on the Parade Ground and bellowed "Apprentices to hold open jackets – Open Jackets". If only somebody had thought to summon the ship's photographer to save the scene for posterity. The Apprentices managed a to achieve a semblance of order as they responded to the never previously heard order, and the Chief GI stared silently at what had been revealed for what seemed like five minutes before ordering "Apprentices to close jackets – Close Jackets". The Apprentices were then instructed that they were to attend a parade in No. 1 uniform in four weeks, when the jacket inspection would be repeated. Whilst there was no implied threat, there was categorically no confusion as to the consequences of any future instance of abnormal jacket lining. Suffice to say that Hepworths stepped up to the mark and did not charge excessively for the privilege of fully rectifying the situation within the stipulated period.[10]

Sometimes the sartorial elegance that Apprentices sought was not conducive to the financial well-being of these boys and as in so many cases there were the unintended consequences of defying dress regulations in favour of a snazzy suit to wow the girls.

After the grind of workshops in *Fisgard* it was a nice change for these Aircraft Artificers to have trade tests more attuned to their eventual employment, though the methods of negotiating these tests was not always conventional, as Stuart wrote:

Another Way to Complete a Trade Test

After the common fitting and turning syllabus at H.M.S. Fisgard, Aircraft Artificer Apprentices received instruction upon sheet metalwork in the "Factory" at H.M.S. Condor. Whilst learning such new skills was stimulating, occasional opportunities presented themselves for extending the learning process, these included establishing the reaction of a steel roller taken from one of the large "G" rolling machines after being held against a buffing machine wheel and then placed on the concrete floor. Other investigations included experimenting with blowing oxygen from a gas welding torch through the vent hole in a lit Brasso tin that was provided to ignite the torch, and projecting magnesium rivets from the hole at the end of a twelve inch rule so that they skimmed the surface of the salt bath.

The advanced sheet metal requirements included the crafting of a double curvature sheet, which required many heat treating, beating and rolling sequences before the required number of contact points on the test gauge could be achieved. The definitive test job was the "Vampire Tail Boom", which had the appearance of an enlarged Norman helmet, and was primarily held together with a large quantity of solid 3/32" rivets. In an effort to inspire Apprentices, a locked glass-fronted cupboard displayed samples of previous test jobs that could be handled by Apprentices ahead of starting a new job.

Whilst in excess of fifty hours were allocated to this job, it soon became clear that no time had been built in for the large amount of double curvature work not going to plan. The preliminary internal structure requirements were soon completed, and the process then required the metal sheet to be pounded once it had been annealed in the salt-bath. The sheet soon had numerous indentations which had to be smoothed out on the "G" rolling machine before being optimistically held against the test gauge. The whole process could become demoralising, as it invariably needed to be repeated many times before even the minimum number of contact points was achieved.

More than one Apprentice became frustrated to find that attempts to increase the number of contact points actually resulted in a decrease, and they often sombrely sought inspiration from the display samples. However, one went as far as to consider how he could compare his job with those on display. The highly skilled and forgetful civilian Instructor routinely left the display cabinet key on a hook beside his desk, so believing it to be reasonable to avoid disturbing his well-deserved coffee break, the Apprentice borrowed the key to make a hasty inspection of one of the display jobs. However, another possibility then arose which required that he shuffle four display jobs to fill the space that had been allocated to five, and took the sample back to his bench for detailed examination.

The Apprentice noted none of the anticipated hullabaloo over the missing sample, and began to wonder if an impudent swap was possible. A plan quickly developed to partially de-rivet the sample job and install his own internal structure over the course of a couple of coffee breaks to avoid being overlooked by the Instructor. The plan's weakness was that the required hand riveting would require another Apprentice to assist and therefore be implicated in the scheme. However, he was now committed, and furtively completed his plan to the point of submitting "his work" for marking after disposing of his original work. It appeared as if he could get away with such audacity, as all evidence had been destroyed, and there was no hue and cry over the missing sample. Soon, the marks were posted on the Notice Board, and he was aghast to note that he had been awarded a mere 52%, and he was left to ponder if he should complain that inadequate work had been put on display.[11]

Here once again we can see the effects of unintended consequences; having acquired the test job from the display cabinet the perpetrator could, at least, expect a higher mark than he actually managed. Perhaps the instructors had a more rigorous marking regime than that in place when the original was marked. But it does show that the best laid plans of Apprentices could easily come to nought.

Even the best of intentions of the training staff could be thwarted by the lack of suitable subjects to work on and antiquated equipment, as was the case for Stuart prior to his year at an air station:

Sometimes Apprentices Were Defeated by the Basics...
A four week Advanced Sheet Metal Course was scheduled shortly prior to departing from H.M.S. Condor for one year of Field Training at an Air Station. This course was designed to prepare Artificers to undertake structural repairs to pressurised aircraft. It may therefore not be difficult to imagine the astonishment Apprentices felt when they were directed to a pre-world war two Walrus amphibious bi-plane. This antiquity had a metal hull which was undoubtedly not pressurised, and even its four wings were fabric covered. Apprentices were unimpressed to learn that the aircraft had been dragged from a dump, and their "advanced" training would be to bring it up to museum standard, after which it would be transported to the Fleet Air Arm Museum at Yeovilton.

Whilst there were a small number of more interesting tasks, including the refurbishment of a wing float that had been masquerading as a merry-go-round child's boat, most Apprentices were tasked with reapplying the fabric to the wooden ribbed wings. The only available reference was a pre-war Walrus manual, and it soon became apparent that a whole range of basic fabric handling skills were presumed to exist. Although the Gliding Club Instructor came to offer guidance, it soon became apparent that there was a significant thirty year technology gap, which could only be filled by detailed archive research.

Eventually the required cloth, substances and tools were obtained along with a simple diagram showing the procedure to be used. A small representative wooden training aid was manufactured, and the Apprentices got down to work. Whilst there was initially little concern for the likely overall, appearance of the completed assignment, this changed by week two when Apprentices began score each other's work. Although a few had undeniably developed a degree of expertise, the required skills were never achieved by the majority, and the poor appearance was becoming more apparent as each day passed. Eventually, discussions with the museum representative, who knew what was required, but not how to achieve it, resulted in those having "it" being given a supervisory role over those without. Although this equitable solution ultimately led to the production of a museum standard aircraft, it left the question of what these future Aircraft Artificers would do when presented with the requirement to repair a damaged pressurised structure. With appropriate aplomb, all whose training had been diverted to this noble cause had their service documents annotated "To be given advanced sheet metal training if required for employment".[12]

As so many Apprentices have learnt, the "exigencies of the Service" could always be suborned to some project that was short on funds but deemed to be of value to the Service and which could easily be passed off as suitable training when clearly that was not really the case, but it was normally in a good cause and quite often more fun than the proper training would ever be.

Among those joining *Fisgard* in the mid-1960s was Mike Doyle (Series 56), who served for fourteen years leaving in 1979 as a Chief Shipwright. He remembered joining *Fisgard* with two schoolmates, leaving his native Corby in Northamptonshire:

I entered the Navy as an apprentice at HMS Fisgard in Cornwall on 10th January 1966. I joined with about 100 other new entrants who were designated class S56. There were three of us who joined together from my town, Corby in Northamptonshire. We were recruited after a visit from an RN recruiting team to our school, Corby Grammar School in late 1965. Faced with the prospect of the local Steelworks or the RN, it was the Navy that won out. I was particularly struck at the prospect of being an Artificer Apprentice and more specifically, to fulfil my love of woodwork and metal work (the only thing I was good at in my wasted school years) becoming a Shipwright apprentice. So after taking the Navy exam and two days of aptitude tests at Victory barracks in Portsmouth, I was offered a place to begin an apprenticeship along with John and Willie. Willie made it as far as HMS Collingwood as an electrical artificer apprentice but then left the Navy after falling in love. John and I went through training together. He became an Engine Room Artificer and ended up serving in Nuclear Subs.

My memories of HMS Fisgard are scant; the passage of time (some 50 years) has eroded my ability to recall events and places to some extent. However, there were patterns and moments that I remember and broadly, I seem to recall that I did enjoy my time there. The first term was general engineering training, basic Naval discipline, fitness, leadership training etc. Then I think that in the second term you opted for your chosen branch. My first choice unequivocally was to be a Shipwright, and my second choice was Engine Room Artificer (ERA) but only because you had to make a second choice. Then to my horror, I was allocated to become an ERA apprentice. I immediately put in a request form protesting that I always wanted to be a Shipwright and eventually had to appear as a "requestman" before the Captain of Fisgard. As I stood there as a trembling 16 year old, I told him that my heart was set on being a Shipwright and if that were not possible I would leave the Navy. In those days leaving the Navy was almost impossible without taking some form of drastic action such as deliberately failing exams or trade tests but even then, the process was a tortuous one. To his credit, the Captain looked me in the eye and said "request granted". I was then told me to go and join the new class of Shipwright apprentices assembling in the woodworking shop. I think there were about 12 of us destined to be shipwrights.[13]

As with many, the years have dimmed the memories to some extent, but many things seem to stay firmly rooted in the brain, as Mike continued:

There was the time I was caught smoking by my Divisional Officer who told me to lay out my kit for inspection outside his office at 6:30 on a stormy Sunday morning. After waiting for hours, in a drafty corridor, the b-----d never turned up! How bloody stupid was I! Bitter complaints but to no avail. Then there was the time we went to sea for the first time; a trip to Jersey on HMS Carhampton, a minesweeper. Landed in St Helier and put on a truck to "ambush" some soldiers returning from a night exercise on the island. We lay in wait and then I remember a thunder flash and they chased us into a field where I hid amongst the cabbages! One of our group was "captured" by the soldiers and pinned up against the wall where he was slapped about a bit. But we got our own back on the return to Plymouth where we had the bunks and they slept on the deck and were all seasick (but so was I).

The rest of the time is a blur of school work, workshop, parade ground drill and sport. I played a lot of rugby for Fisgard and travelled across the South West to play matches. Then there was the pride I felt when we were issued with a full set of woodworking tools and then used them to make our large wooden tool chest to put them in. That tool chest would then follow us from ship to ship during our naval career. Mine did until one of the most stupid and idiotic events took place whilst I was on HMS Norfolk.[14]

There are, of course, some events that time never dims and one such tragic event happened on 21 October 1966 with the catastrophic collapse of a colliery spoil heap. The tip had been created on a mountain slope above the Welsh village of Aberfan, near Merthyr Tydfil, and overlaid a natural spring. A period of heavy rain led to a build-up of water within the tip, which caused it to suddenly slide downhill as a slurry, killing 116 children and twenty-eight adults. Such a disaster is unlikely ever to be forgotten by those touched by it; there were other tragedies that affected Mike during his time in *Fisgard*, as he wrote:

Other memories are embedded in tragedy. I remember hearing the news of the Aberfan disaster in 1966 and seeing one of my messmates go into shock as the news unfolded on the TV. His young sister was in the school at the time and lost her life I believe. On another occasion, I grudgingly lent my plastic mug one Sunday morning to a "loud" cockney messmate, Terry Phillips who was told he would get what for if he lost it. He was going diving with the sub-aqua club in Cawsands Bay which is just outside Plymouth Sound. Later in the day we were piped to clear lower deck and we gathered in the Dining Hall to be told by the Captain that there had been an accident and Terry and a Lt Anton (who taught in the classroom) had both drowned. In the Naval tradition, as his messmates, we auctioned Terry's kit and all the monies raised went to his family. It was a poignant moment a few years ago to see both their names engraved on the wall at the National Memorial Arboretum in Staffordshire. What strikes me now was that there no counselling for us young lads following these tragedies as there is now. That was it, he was gone, life just went on, get over it.[15]

There was, of course, the important business of ensuring that all exams and trade tests were successfully completed. The price of failure was to be "back classed" and miss passing out with those who you had joined with; this is something that happened to Mike Doyle, as he explained:

I should have focused more on my school work as I failed a mechanics exam by 4% and was subsequently "back classed" from S56 to S57. There were no resits in those days! I was devastated and heartbroken when all my contemporaries passed out and went on their way to their different establishments to complete more specialised training for their chosen engineering branch. I was left behind to complete another term but luckily there were others who were also back classed including some good mates Geoff and Vic (more about Vic and Geoff later). Following this set-back, I swore then I would never, never fail another exam in my life and I didn't. So I knuckled down and passed out of Fisgard in the Spring of 1967 and was bound for HMS Caledonia at Rosyth to further my training as a Shipwright Artificer.[16]

There were further changes at *Fisgard* in September 1966. The reduced number of Apprentices entering brought about the restructuring of the divisional system within the establishment. The existing divisions of Anson, Blake, Collingwood, Duncan, Exmouth, Frobisher, Grenville and Hawke were rationalised to four. The new divisions were named after former Apprentices who had reached flag rank, boys we have met before: Bennett, Cooke, Frew and Lane. With Lane and Frew to the east side and Bennett and Cooke to the west side of the establishment, a separation guaranteed to ferment rivalry, both on and off the sports field.

Mike Doyle remembered arriving at *Caledonia* and being accommodated in huts even more basic than those at *Fisgard*, but only for a short time, or so it was expected at the time; however, as is often the case, things did not go according to plan as far as this outdated accommodation was concerned. But notwithstanding the accommodation Mike enjoyed his time in *Caledonia* and enjoyed the training:

> *Arriving in Caledonia, as at Fisgard, we were accommodated in dormitory blocks*
> *– only these were a lot more primitive (wooden sheds as I recall). However, our*
> *stay in this basic accommodation only lasted for a few months before we moved*
> *into brand new prefab concrete accommodation blocks with four men cabins and*
> *all mod cons – luxury. But then a few months later, after a severe storm blowing*
> *down the Forth valley, they discovered the blocks were falling down so it was*
> *back to the "sheds" until they carried out major repairs; but we were soon back*
> *in our modern accommodation. Caledonia was great for me. I really enjoyed the*
> *more specialised academic and practical subjects in the massive and well equipped*
> *workshops. Around 50% or time was spent in the classroom (maths, mechanics,*
> *naval architecture, ship construction etc) and the other 50% in the workshops*
> *where we were taught a wide range of craft skills: copper smithing, black smithing;*
> *sheet metalwork, welding, woodwork, boatbuilding and a variety of other*
> *supplementary skills. At different stages there were exams and trade tests to test*
> *knowledge, skills and ensure progression through training.*[17]

Despite having failed an exam and been "putback" a term, this did not affect Mike, as he did not suffer in the end and there was also much else to enjoy in *Caledonia* as he remembered:

> *But there was so much more to do beyond the schoolroom and workshops (the*
> *"factory"). I joined the brass band as a drummer (only had to press one leg of my*
> *uniform trousers as the drum hid the other one), and we played at gala days all*
> *over Southern Scotland and even went down to Earls Court to play at the Royal*
> *Tournament. I continued to play sport, and trips to Dunfermline and Edinburgh*
> *provided us with an active social life. And so the two years in Caledonia flew*
> *by and we eventually passed out in summer 1969. Paradoxically, I passed out*
> *with my original entry group S56 as they reduced the length of the shore based*
> *element of the apprenticeship from 11 to 10 terms and therefore two classes S56*
> *and S57 left together.*[18]

Another major decision was to end the long-running "craft" apprenticeship in favour of the more highly favoured and modern "technician" apprenticeship. To many this was the beginning of the end of "proper"

Artificers. But times change and the Royal Navy could not continue with what was regarded as an outdated system of training in isolation. There was now much more emphasis on the academic training of the Apprentices and far less on the skill of hand for so long nurtured in the Artificer. Perhaps this lack was most keenly felt in deployed ships far from a repair facility or dockyard when improvisation and that skill of hand were at a premium.

One of the final acts of the 1960s was the demise of the Engine Room Artificer after 101 years. Engine Room Artificers were rebranded as Marine Engineering Artificers (Propulsion) and Shipwright Artificers were renamed Marine Engineering Artificers (Hull). Just prior to this change there was a reorganisation within the Weapons Electrical Department that saw the introduction in February 1967 of Ordnance Electrical Artificers (OEA) and Control Electrical Artificers (CEA) and the still-quite-new Control Artificer (Weapons) joined the ranks of CEAs.[19]

The loss of ERAs was not greeted universally with delight, as Fred Davies (Series 64) remembered:

After our first term we were informed that we would be the last class of ERA and Shipwright Apprentices and very shortly we would become MEA(P), (H),(L),(OA),etc. This didn't seem to matter to us but everyone around us said how sad it was. During the second term we were given our trade and I was delighted to become an MEA(P), as were most of my close friends, and our ultimate destination would be Caledonia along with the MEA(H)s.[20]

On a final note for the 1960s Stuart Wakefield had a few words on the perennial lack of funds available to Apprentices and the strictures it placed on runs ashore:

How to Reduce Car Running Costs
Not many Apprentices owned a car, as few could afford sufficient fuel for the entire range of pleasant undertakings that are routinely associated with car ownership by young men, let alone the accompanying costs of maintenance, insurance, and tax. Understandably, the few Apprentices who had succumbed to owning their own vehicle invariably focussed upon locating the garage selling the cheapest fuel, and other costs were pushed aside for another day. Whilst bringing others along to share costs undoubtedly contributed towards having

"wheels", it was also often incompatible with the coincident desire to take a local young lady for an outing.

Whilst all Artificers possessed sufficient knowledge to undertake car maintenance, the limited area outside of the Accommodation Block was the only space readily available for this purpose. However, although such use was frowned upon, it was not unusual for these facilities to contain more than one car that was temporarily immobilised due to needing a spare part that the owner could not immediately afford. The MoT test had been introduced in 1960 with vehicle inspections commencing at ten years of age, and, fortunately for many car owners, did not at that time include body or chassis checks. Reducing the cost of the test depended upon finding a sympathetic garage that would not permanently take an old car off the road. Another cost related to insurance cover, and significant administrative effort was always applied to finding an elusive low-priced quotation, and the cover eventually purchased was always reduced to the minimum.

Car owning Apprentices normally spread the cost of the inescapable Road Tax by paying every four months rather than opting for six months, let alone twelve. One Apprentice found himself in a dilemma with his tax due on Friday, a keenly anticipated date was on Saturday and payday was on the distant horizon. At the time, it was accepted practice to claim to any official enquirer that the required application was in the post, which prompted creative thinking to kick in. The Apprentice wrote a letter that requested the recipient to find enclosed a cheque for four months Road Tax", which was placed in an envelope with the completed tax Application Form, but without any cheque. A follow-on letter to be posted after pay-day was already composed along the lines of "Please find enclosed the required cheque that I unfortunately overlooked for inclusion with my Application Form." However, within a few days the Apprentice received a letter containing a four month tax disc, and his emotions swung between extreme gratitude for such an astonishing fluke, and substantial resentment at not having applied for six months.

This may have a resonance with Apprentices in *Collingwood* in the late sixties, where the authorities took great umbrage at those Apprentices who used the fire hoses on the ground floors of the accommodation blocks nearest the car park to wash their cars at the weekend and, as is so common in such matters, issued instructions that anyone found flouting the ban on using these fire hoses for any purpose bar the one they were designed for would be "subject to disciplinary action". It seemed the ideal use for the fire hoses to many at the time.

Leaving *Caledonia* Mike was due to join HMS *Chichester*, based in Chatham, and after his summer leave he and his friend Vic Hodgson travelled down to Chatham to await the arrival of their first ship. During this wait they were accommodated in HMS *Pembroke* and it was during this period that they had what can only be described as a naive reliance on customary routines at *Caledonia*, customs that as they were to find out were not universal across the fleet, as Mike recalled:

> During our stay in Pembroke the two of us were accommodated in the vast Victorian brick dormitory blocks together with the junior rates from various ships that were refitting in the Dockyard. It was here that one of the most embarrassing moments in my life took place. When we were in Fisgard and Caledonia all of us apprentices wore pyjamas – it was normal. If you were really cool, you left the top half off. And so, as was normal for us, we wore them on our first night in this dormitory block. We both decided to go for a wash and as we walked the length of the block we were… Well dear reader, I will leave it to your imagination what we were called by the other ratings in the block as we did the "walk of shame". Now I know why it is called a barrack block! Nobody but nobody wore pyjama's in the Queen's Navy and if you did apparently your sexuality was questionable – even worse when the two were walking together. But nobody had told us! At this point I should point out that there was nothing between us! Since that day, the only time I ever have worn pyjamas was the rare time I was bed-bound and a doctor had to make a home visit.[21]

The final act of 1969 was the end of the series method of entry identification that had been in place since September 1947. The new method would employ the first two digits, which would indicate the year of entry into *Fisgard*, and the third digit would indicate the term – 1 for spring, 2 for summer and 3 for autumn – so the first entry using this method was 691 entry in spring 1969.

chapter nine

The Seventies, Expansion and Contraction

• • •

And for many a day old Tubal Cain
Sat brooding o'er his woe;
And his hand forbore to smite the ore,
And his furnace smouldered low.
But he rose at last with a cheerful face,
And a bright courageous eye,
And bared his strong right arm for work,
While the quick flames mounted high.
And he sang—"Hurrah for my handiwork!"
And the red sparks lit the air;
"Not alone for the blade was the bright steel made,"
And he fashioned the first ploughshare.[1]

The 1970s started with several innovations. The first, which was fleet-wide and not limited to Artificers, was the introduction on 7 August 1970 of the warrant rank of Fleet Chief Petty Officer.[2] To reach this rank one needed to be recommended and more significantly there was the requirement for those in contention to have two passes at GCE O level, with one being English. This requirement was almost universally achieved amongst the Artificer Branch and so nearly all Chief Artificers were potential Fleet Chiefs. This title was finally laid to rest on 30 August 1985, when the title was superseded by Warrant Officer,[3] as used in the other Services and the Royal Marines; it does beg the question why Warrant Officer was not used right from the introduction of the rank.

Also in 1970 the long-lasting saga of Air Engineering training was finally resolved, with training moving from *Condor* in Arbroath down to HMS *Daedalus*, the name of which was finally settled on after much chopping and changing over the years. This, of course, brought to an end the long-running association of Artificer training in Arbroath.

Another significant change to tradition also occurred in the early days of 1970: an event that went to the roots of naval tradition but one that was not compatible with the modern technological Royal Navy was the abolition of the daily rum ration. Many mourned its passing but to many others it was an anachronism from the past and really the loss of the daily "tot" of rum was not greatly missed by the majority, particularly senior rates, who could now benefit from a range of spirits in lieu of the rum, hence greatly enhancing the ability to provide suitable refreshments when entertaining.[4] This loss of the rum ration did not affect Apprentices under training regardless of age. There was, however, a new initiative in *Fisgard* with the opening of the "Tiffin Club", which allowed Apprentices over the age of eighteen to buy and consume alcohol on board for the first time.

In these early days of 1970 Mike Doyle was now on his first deployment aboard HMS *Chichester*. The messing arrangements particularly stuck in Mike's mind:

> On the domestic front, food was served individually in metal trays from the galley and then taken down to the mess to eat – no central mess hall and a real trial in rough weather. It was worth remembering however that we were not Stokers/MEMs and so strictly speaking we were supernumerary to the mess and in some senses I guess we added to the overcrowding issue? But we were still part of the mess and participated in all mess duties. However, we were not watchkeeping 24 hours a day in the engine rooms, as most of the mess were, but were day workers ("Idlers" in old Navy speak). This meant that we spent a lot of the time during the day in dimmed lighting and dodging hammocks which were perpetually rigged in some part of the mess. Despite this, we never really experienced any serious animosity from our messmates – a lot of banter but no

real resentment. However there were a couple of individuals who I never really
got on with.[5]

So the perceived privations of the messing and accommodation at *Fisgard*
and *Caledonia* show how cosseted they were as Apprentices ashore in the
protected bubble of Artificer training.

Having sailed from Chatham, *Chichester*, or Chi as she was affectionately
known by the ship's company, sailed down the west coast of Africa on
passage to the Far East. This was the time of the closure of the Suez Canal:
after the 1967 Six Days War, Israeli forces occupied the Sinai peninsula,
including the entire east bank of the Suez Canal. Unwilling to allow the
Israelis to use the canal, Egypt immediately imposed a blockade, which
closed the canal to all shipping until 5 June 1975. This forced all shipping
to transit around the tip of South Africa to reach the Far East. It did have
the benefit of providing a run ashore in South Africa, something that had
not happened for some considerable time and something that Mike had not
forgotten. It was primarily the segregation of Black and White that was the
result of apartheid that Mike remembered with considerable abhorrence, as
so many who had witnessed it also did.

My first run ashore into Simonstown was a major shock to the system. At that
time the apartheid regime was still in force and to see the extent of the segregation
was horrific. It seemed as if everything was segregated into black or white only:
telephone boxes, benches, taxis etc. On the Chi we had 2–3 black guys (not in our
mess) and because of the segregation, they were not permitted to come ashore in
the normal way. I seem to recall they were collected by local black organisations
and taken to separate social functions. So bloody sad and I have never forgotten
that.[6]

At this time there was considerable tension in Central Africa following
the unilateral declaration of independence (UDI) by Ian Smith's Southern
Rhodesian minority white government in 1965. This led to sanctions being
imposed on Southern Rhodesia. Black nationalists in Rhodesia and their
overseas supporters urged Britain to remove Smith's government with
a military invasion, but Britain dismissed this option because of various
logistical issues and the possible confrontation between British and
Rhodesian troops. Harold Wilson instead decided to end the Rhodesian

rebellion through economic sanctions; these principally comprised the expulsion of Rhodesia from the sterling area, a ban on the import of Rhodesian goods, and an oil boycott of Rhodesia.

When the Rhodesians continued to receive oil, Wilson attempted to directly cut off their main supply lines, namely the Portuguese Mozambican ports at Beira and Lourenço Marques. This blockade, the Beira Patrol, was endorsed the following month by UN Security Council Resolution 221. The United Nations also passed a resolution making sanctions against Southern Rhodesia mandatory on all its members.

The Beira Patrol continued until June 1975, when Mozambique became independent from Portugal and gave an assurance to Britain that no oil would pass through its ports to Rhodesia. It had never been totally successful and with careful rationing Rhodesia had managed to survive, with the help of South Africa allowing oil shipments to pass through its territorial waters.

During the early part of Mike's patrol there was a serious incident to which *Chichester* provided assistance, having to conduct an emergency breakaway while replenishing fuel from the Royal Fleet Auxiliary tanker, as Mike recalled:

> It was during one RAS that we did an emergency fuel shut off and breakaway from the RFA tanker. We had received a distress call from the SS Mactra a very large oil tanker that had suffered an explosion and fire. We proceeded at full power and on reaching the ship, sent over our PO medic to render first aid. A number of people lost their lives including wives who were sunbathing on the main deck. The explosion had been caused by static electricity generated when they cleaned the empty tanks igniting residual fuel vapours. I understand there were explosions on similar ships until they devise a system of filling the tanks with inert gas before cleaning.[7]

When *Chichester* had completed her turn on Beira Patrol the ship sailed into the Persian Gulf to take part in the Ethiopian Navy Days when there was a tragic incident, one of many that Mike was to witness, which was then followed by a more mundane disaster to the ship itself.

> Leaving Mombasa, we represented the British navy at Ethiopian navy days in Masawa and then went on our way to the Persian Gulf, scheduled for 3 months, based in Bahrain. It was during this time that two dramatic events

occurred. Our skipper was Commander Tim Sex (yes that was his name) who was well respected on the ship. One afternoon I heard a pipe for the PO Doc to go to the captain's cabin at the double. Shortly afterwards we saw the captain go off the ship and into a waiting ambulance – still in his sports gear, apparently he had been playing hockey. The ship's company were later told he was rushed to RAF Muharak for emergency treatment and then flown to the UK where he died shortly after arriving – reportedly from a brain haemorrhage. Rumours said he had fallen in the bath in his quarters, others that something may have occurred playing sport but whatever happened we were devastated to lose him.

A new skipper duly arrived from the UK to takeover command (I can't recall his name) and a few days later the plan was to leave Bahrain in company with a US Destroyer on a routine patrol. However entering and leaving the naval base at Bahrain is apparently a tricky business as there are a lot of reefs and shallows. On that day there was only one pilot available and our navigator "graciously" let the US ship have him. So we departed the base mid-morning without a pilot. It was about mid-morning and stand-easy in the mess. We were having a cup of tea when suddenly the ship lifted into the air and there was a loud crash. We immediately thought there was a collision and there was a mass evacuation from the messdeck led by one of our leading hands, Nobby Hall, who supposedly had a damaged foot and had been excused watch keeping. He was lying on his bunk at the time and I have never seen anybody move so fast. To this day I am convinced it was him that crawled over my back on the way up the ladder!

The engines were stopped and we sent down a diver to check for damage. I vividly remember the Marine Engineering Officer (MEO) asking the diver when he surfaced "Was there any damage to the propeller" and the diver replying "What propeller?" We had lost the whole of the starboard prop – blades stripped completely leaving just the propeller boss (the bit in the middle)!

Our new captain was severely reprimanded after that event and the Navigating office was "dismissed his ship" and sent back to the UK in disgrace.[8]

The next months were spent in the Far East, with visits to Honk Kong, Australia and Mauritius, until the ship started on its way home, arriving in Chatham in October 1970, by which time Mike had been rated MEA(H)3. After a further period of fishery protection around the North Sea and eighteen months onboard the ship Mike left as an MEA(H)2 and joined the Fleet Maintenance Group at Rosyth.

Another young man to join *Fisgard* was Ken Enticknap. He joined Frew Division with 703 Class and has written a few memories of his time as a young Artificer:

Memories of Artificer Training
FISGARD
- *Saluting the flag when transiting the main gate*
- *Having to return our entire civilian clothes home; resigning ourselves to a life in uniform.*
- *Static tanks*
- *Sprogging*
- *Div-Raids – sneaking behind the Workshop after midnight to spring a surprise raid on Westside messes. Tipping everyone out of their beds and sprinting back, only to await the return raid.*
- *Building great structures with the beds*
- *Having to file flat (or try to!) for the first time; the 1" cube!*
- *Saturday morning divisions after 2hrs in the workshop and struggling to put a starched collar on and not get dirty finger marks on it whilst attaching to collar-studs. I never was successful!*

CALEDONIA
- *The elation when the new captain granted plain-clothe privileges to all apprentices. This happened in the first few weeks of me being in Caledonia and was part of an initiative to improve morale – It did!*
- *The last of the Series Classes passed out without incident. There had been serious trouble with the previous class, painting the factory roof and some equipment going missing. The follow on class was threatened with all sorts of repercussions if any high jinxes happened prior to their passing out parade. Well, everything when swimmingly well, no issues whatsoever! Until the following spring when it was apparent that they had painted some very disparaging comments about the senior management team in weed-killer on the lawn outside the captain's office window. They couldn't call all them back, because they had all been spread around the fleet.*
- *CPO Apprentices with higher powers of punishment than you Divisional Officer*
- *Sleeping in a hammock aboard HMS RAPID during the sea training term.*

- *Having to paint the systems on the evaporator as a punishment. I never could flash up an evaporator to get clear water out of it.*
- *Writing the stage pressures on my hand prior to taking my HPAC AMC – I've always been a bit miffed that all they do today is press a button in the SCC – the very modern ships have them start and stop automatically – Such the price of progress!*
- *Club 61 fortnightly discos and the influx of hordes of females from Inverkeithing – colloquially called the Inverkeithing Knicker Factory. Escaping CALDEDONIA without being hooked into marriage was a feat in itself!*
- *Bunking off school work to attend Band Practice and consequently not catching up with instruction but enjoying the summer pageants with the band in places like Biggar and Linlithgow.*
- *Being back classed for failing the academic exams!!!*

1st Draft – HMS LONDONDERRY

- *Learning first-hand about the World as we travelled to the far-east and back. No tales on the grounds that I might incriminate myself.*
- *Learning too that it's not what you actually did on your run ashore but the way that you embellished the story during the next day's stand-easy post mortem.*
- *As an apprentice working toward all of his tickets – Boiler Ticket being the first hurdle. Becoming absolutely and deeply familiar with where every pipe comes from and goes to, the statement that someone never know systems as we as he knows those in his first ship is so true. After 2 and half year and a junior no-badge Petty Officer it was really good to be the go-to guy for detail on the marine systems.*
- *Being capstan operator in the opposite watch to Chippy. He did all the entries into harbours in lovely sunshine and I did all the RAS's in Force 6 and above. I was afforded 1 entry into harbour when Chippy had gone on leave. The head-rope had just been passed across and the 1st Lieutenant shouted from the bridge "Down slack on the head-rope". Not being familiar with the term, I put all of the slack in the rope down onto the deck, veering the capstan (rather that hauling it). The call to down slack came again so I veered out more. A very irate and panicky call came from the bridge – "Pull the fucking thing in, you prat!" Lesson learned: The Seamanship World seem to shroud the bleeding obvious with antiquated jargon, not taught at CALEDONIA.*

- *As you start to get comfortable with life aboard your first ship and everything begins to become familiar, the young artificer Enticknap began to look beyond the horizon and was intrigued with the mysteries of what went on behind the ever closed doors of the CPOs' Mess and the smell of stale booze and fags that wafted out of it. I admit that secretly I held these illustrious people in high regard and really couldn't wait to get my tickets and join the elite society. That was all except one, of course. Mechanician 1st Class GM had taken a disliking to me and when on watch constantly harangued me that I could dip a tank and got all of the readings. He made my life a misery for a while... well, only until I discovered he would change the tanks over while I was out on rounds and that my readings were in fact accurate. Later on in my career he was an inspiration for me to pass the commissioning exams. I so wanted to become his Divisional Officer so I could fuck him over, too. Sadly, it was not to be.*

- *From my lowly position, CPOs looked to have so much fun. I recall being alongside in Gibraltar when the Chief's mess arranged to have a banyan on a nearby beach. They had booked the whaler and I witness them departing with the buffer at the helm and the senior engine-room tiffy, wearing his blue peaked yachting cap, at the engine controls (complete with his toolbox, his pride and joy, with its preciously guarded contents). With a full complement of passengers and loaded to the gunwales with CSB (I reckoned there must only have been inch or two of freeboard). It was very obvious to me that they had already completed a very successful DTS and were in high spirits. Two of three hours later, I watched them return back to the ships. The buffer, a true professional, put the whaler deftly alongside the Mediterranean ladder. Now with a much more noticeable freeboard and everyone started off loading gear back up the ladder onto the flight-deck. Last but one to leave the boat was Sam, the senior engine room tiffy, cradling his precious toolbox. Unfortunately at the very moment Sam put his leg out to begin climbing the Med-ladder, buffer let the boat drift away and Sam step straight into the water. As he went down he very casually placed his toolbox onto the Med-ladder's platform and slipped slowly below the surface leaving only his yachting cap floating. He bobbed back up moments later and the buffer grabbed his collar. Once Sam had been reassured that his toolbox was safe he allowed himself to be rescued. Lesson learned by me – Even when your pissed... look after your tools!*

- *As a junior PO a few months later having to pour the contents of my toolbox into a skip as the Navy had stopped issuing personal tools to artificers. Tools would be held in the ship's workshops. It was likened to losing the tot – we had tears in our eyes.*[9]

The recent changes in the nomenclature of those Artificers who had been ERAs caused some ribaldry when the first Apprentices from 691 entry reached *Caledonia*, as Fred Davies (Series 64) wrote:

After our first term at Caledonia, *entry 691 came up from Fisgard and they were the first "bisexual" apprentices (ie they were neither (P) nor (H)) to go through* Caledonia. *They were going to become "Super Tiffs", capable of "welding wood to mild steel and of unblocking the heads with the left hand while painting a crest for the MEO with the right hand, all whilst recovering from a main FL failure". Indeed they were awesome! So awesome that they went back to* Caledonia *later to do the "hull adqual" course.*[10]

At this time there was a change in the vessels used as "afloat training ships", with HMS *Eastbourne* replacing the ancient and venerable HMS *Rapid* and HMS *Duncan*, a Type 14 Frigate, becoming the harbour training ship. While *Eastbourne* was an improvement on *Rapid*, *Duncan* was not the best ship to cope with over-enthusiastic Apprentices, being rather small and restricted in machinery.

With the cyclical nature of Artificer recruitment and the numbers required there was a need in September 1972 to increase the number of divisions from four to six. The new divisions were named Shepherd and Tribe, maintaining the new tradition of naming divisions after Admirals who had risen from Apprentice. And in May 1973, after a further increase in Apprentice numbers, two further divisions were added, named Griffin and Spickernell. However, this increase in numbers was very short-lived and in the following year two divisions were disbanded with the loss of Cooke and Shepherd Divisions, the last being very short-lived.

Away from the training establishments some Artificers sought drafts to ships in build, always considered a plum draft. One such was Roger Bateman (Series 25), who had no hesitation in his choice of draft:

On completion of my Chief ERAs Course in 1970 I was offered a "Draft" to HMS Maidstone *(Prison Ship in N Ireland?) or to HMS Bristol – which was* at the early stage of build in Swan Hunters (Newcastle-on-Tyne). It didn't take much hesitation to accept the latter.

HMS Bristol (D23) was a Type 82 Destroyer, the only vessel of her class that was built for the Royal Navy. Originally intended as the first of a class of large destroyers to escort the CVA-01 Aircraft Carriers – projected to come into service in the early 1970s, Bristol turned out to be a unique ship: the rest of the class were cancelled along with the CVA-01 carriers in the 1966 Strategic Defence Review.

The shoreside Office for Ships Staff during the build was located just opposite a Bone Yard where the bones of various animals were melted down and processed. Alongside the Bone Yard was a Factory where Pickle Onions were manufactured. The aroma in the shoreside Office, to say the least, was absolutely putrid; unfortunately the combined smell of bones and onions clung to ones clothes and overalls. However, we were never short of Pickle Onions at home and the occasional sheepskin rug from the Bone Yard were often made available.

As any matelot who has visited Tyneside on a ship will testify, the Local population in and around Newcastle think the world of "Jack". Ships Staff on HMS Bristol were well looked after in approved lodgings. The drafting officer detailed a Leading Patrolman (assumedly to collect the fortnightly pay for Ships Staff from the Bank). In his wisdom the Leading Patrolman decided to "Check" on the authenticity of some of the ratings approved lodgings; the first address he checked turned out to be the Morgue at N. Shields, his next check involved prolonged banging at a door contained in what appeared to be an intact row of Tenement buildings in Wallsend. Imagine his surprise when the door he was banging at slowly fell in exposing a derelict building site being cleared, after being bombed during WW2.

The address/house number of the flat I shared with Ch.Mech Dick Bentley and CERA Stew Herd was 982 Walker Rd, the number on the House next door was 486 Walker Rd; I can only assume that the houses were built starting from Opposite Ends i.e. Newcastle (from 1 end) and Wallsend (from the other end) – it could only happen in Geordie Land.

I was asked to Manage the Ships Football Team, we were entered into the Wednesday Business Man's League. It didn't take long for me to notice that the "Business Men" in the League resembled extremely well built and hairy warriors averaging about a foot between the eyebrows. All of the Local Police areas fielded teams along with Coal Miners and Shipyard Workers. In many matches against these teams we were lucky to get NIL goals. One consolation about the opposition teams was that they all had a Sports Club where our team were invariably entertained grandly.

There was one occasion – after a match when, having played against – and consequently being hosted by the Byker Police at their Pavilion there was a "raid" by another Police Unit who were looking to apprehend custodians of premises that were permitting drinking out of "licensed" hours. Our hosts didn't appear too happy with the intrusion and a big punch up ensued between the two factions of police – and they took no prisoners. – Again, it could only happen in Geordie Land.

The Senior Engineer of HMS Bristol (Lt Car Wilf Blacker) was a qualified Football referee who would often officiate at our matches. It was a very sad occasion when he died suddenly after a bout of influenza/Pneumonia. This large as life "Bluff" Cornishman was sorely missed by all who made his acquaintance on Bristol. Wilf was relieved by Lt Cdr Maunder (Mumbling Sid) whose personality was in direct contrast to Wilf Blackers.

Successful Contractors Sea Trials were completed under the control of Swan Hunters Management with BRISTOLS Commanding Officer (Capt. Roddy McDonald RN) and Executive Officer (Cmdr R Ram RN) onboard. The Swan Hunter Foreman of Caulkers during the trials was a certain Mr Hogg, the Contractor in charge of Ships Cleaners was a Mr Bullock and 1 of his cleaners was aptly named Mrs Hens.

A Classic broadcast was made during the Trials period by a Geordie "Wag" over the ships Tannoy system as follows: – "Mr Hogg, Mr Bullock, Mrs Hens and Cdr Ram report to Capt. McDonald on the Bridge". Shades of Old McDonalds Farm!!

The ship was accepted into service on 15 Dec.1972 and Commissioned in Bristol (Avonmouth) on 31 March 1973. Many social events were laid on by the Bristol Council, a separate event was a Tug of War between the Ships Staff and the Bristol and Avon Police on the Clifton Downs. The Police team won this event by virtue of using 1 of their Police Horses as the Anchor Point of their team. I was invited by Alan Dicks (Manager) to take the Ships Football Team to play his Bristol City Colts – we lost.

Shortly after Bristol we visited Glasgow, the Officers held their normal "Cocktail Party" and afterwards the Ships Commander brought several guests to the Chiefs Mess. When the guests entered the Mess I thought our Chief Yeoman was going to have a heart attack. He was an ardent Glasgow Rangers supporter and the guests included The General Manager of Rangers (Willie Waddell) and

The Manager (Jock Wallace) together with John Grieg and Willie Thornton (Star Players from Rangers and Celtic).

I was invited to take the Ships soccer Team to play against a Rangers team at Ibrox – we lost!! Our normal goalkeeper was not available for the match and we had to play our bespectacled Leading Writer who insisted that he keep his glasses on whilst playing in goal during the match. I didn't see much of the match as the 2 Managers wanted to show me around their magnificent Rangers Trophy (Blue) Room and the remainder of the complex. What I do remember of the tour was that in each room within the complex, was a safe with a chubb lock which, when opened by 1 of the Managers revealed a bottle of Malt Whisky which I was obliged to sample. Hence the hazy memory of the tour.

The CERA's, ERA's and Mechanicians were accommodated in their own (watchkeepers) Mess; 3 Computer Tiffs and the NBCD Chief made up the numbers. There was a separate Chiefs Recreation Space where any social events would take place. The NBCD Chief (Brian Crawford) was in fact a Chief PTI and was also the current Captain of the RN Soccer Team. He often said that playing for the RN was like a stroll in the park after having played for Bristol's team during the build period whilst at Newcastle.

The NBCD Chief (Brian Crawford) forever complaining that he was constantly requesting the requisite allowance of Fire Fighting Foam. Try as he may, he was not able to obtain the correct and laid down quota of Fire Fighting Foam for use in the event of a ships fire. This lack of Foam was to play an important feature during the large boiler/engine room fire which happened not long after – in 1974.[11]

Bristol was to be the centre of attention in 1974 but for all the wrong reasons and the failure to maintain the requisite firefighting equipment complement was seen by some as a major factor in the ensuing fire, important but only one of several factors that made the fire into such a major incident, Roger remembered the time of the fire only too well:

The large part of 1973/1974 was spent trialling and building up experience using the new weapons and integrated computer systems. The ship was undergoing trials off the Welsh coast and would invariably anchor each evening off Fishguard, where leave was granted. The inability to receive any TV reception and the fact that on that particular evening Cassius Clay was being shown on TV in a fight, possibly prompted the Command to change the anchorage to just off Milford Haven. This action – in my own opinion probably saved the ship from a watery grave.

I can clearly remember coming back from ashore at Midnight and going into the Chiefs Recreation Space. The Ships Fire Alarm was sounded at 0029 that morning.

Whilst at anchor the Ships Machinery was in the Auxiliary State under the control of a POME) in the Machinery Ship Control Centre (SCC), with a Main Boiler providing steam and 1 of the Steam Turbo Generators providing the Electrical Power requirements. The Ship was also fitted with 2 "Stones" Auxiliary Boilers and 3 Diesel Generators. 1 of the Diesel Generators was stripped down undergoing repair.

With the change of the Auxiliary Watch at 2359 the procedure was to change from the "Steaming" boiler to the boiler at "Standby". It is important at this stage to point out that on each boiler, 2 of the Boiler Steam Stop Valves (Main Steam Stop and Auxiliary Steam Stop) were automated and could be operated from the Control Room Machinery Console. The 3rd Steam Stop Valve (Saturated Steam Stop Valve) on each boiler was however, NOT automated and could only be operated by hand locally at the Boiler Front within the Engine Room. This again was a very important point when attempting to extinguish the ensuing Boiler/Engine Room Fire.

During the Auxiliary Steaming State of a boiler the Auxiliary Steam Stop Valve is "Open" (supplying the Steam Turbo Alternator and auxiliary pumps); the Main Steam Stop Valve (providing Main Steam Turbines) and Saturated Steam Stop Valves (providing steam for Calorifiers etc. and for "Steam Drenching" a fire) are "SHUT".

The fire was located in the region of the Boiler Front (within the Engine Room) and was caused by the failure of a flexible Rubberised hose connected to the discharge of the running Dieso Fuel Pump. The Fuel Pump was supplying the Burners of the "steaming" boiler. It is assumed that immediate combustion took place when the discharge hose failed and the fire started and quickly took hold – with Dieso Fuel spraying over the whole face of the boiler front. A young M(E) in the Engine Room at the time, confirmed that the fire had spread very quickly and was burning fiercely, hence he was unable to gain access and use the Machinery Broadcast to inform The Ship Machinery Control Centre (SCC) of the fire. He made his way as fast as he could to report the fire to the POME) running the Watch in the SCC.

Such is the design of the control system as fitted on the steaming boiler, when the Steam Pressure started to fall off in the boiler (due to lack of fuel to the

Burners), the running Dieso Fuel Pump speeded "UP" to increase the fuel supply, in order to maintain the Desired Steam Pressure in the Boiler. The increase in fuel leaking from the fractured hose of the fuel pump, and spraying across the boiler front obviously exacerbated the problem and the fire became more intense. The M(E) coming from the Engine Room was able to inform the POME) in the SCC of the fire who in turn raised the Alarm – Fire! Fire! Fire! – Fire in the Ships Main Machinery Space. The POME) immediately stopped the Dieso Fuel Pump supplying fuel to the steaming boiler. The 2 serviceable Diesel Generators were started and eventually put on load to supply the ships electrical supply. At this stage the Duty Engineer Officer (Chief Tiff) took over the watch as the Engineer Officer of Watch – EOOW in the SCC.

The initial method used to extinguish the fire was to decant Foam down through the Foam Tubes from the stowage drums located on the deck above the Engine Room and down through the Port and Starboard sides of the Engine Room into the bilge of the Compartment. As stated earlier – the limited supply of foam turned out to be totally inadequate hence the fire raged on. It is unknown that "If" the correct allowance of Foam had been carried and used, whether the fire would have been extinguished.

When the EOOW recognised that access to the steaming boiler "Hand Operated" Boiler Saturated Stop Valve was impossible – the Engine Room was confirmed clear of personnel and the hatches were "SHUT". It is assumed that "if" the Saturated Stop had been accessible and able to be "Opened" then this method would have been the alternative way to possibly extinguish the fire (with what steam was still available in the boiler) to "Steam Drench" the Engine Room.

The next method to try and extinguish the fire was to Steam Drench the Engine Room using steam from the Auxiliary Boilers. This action could not be achieved however since the 2 "Stones" boilers relied on a remote servo-air supply to support the flame. The Servo-Air compressor (supplying air to the air system for the boilers) was located adjacent to the running Dieso Fuel Pump in the Engine Room with the fractured Discharge hose; it transpired that the reason no air was available was because the fire had burnt through the rubberised discharge hose of the Air Compressor. There was no alternative air supply fitted to supply the Auxiliary Boilers.

I cannot recall why there was so much Salt Water laying in the passageways on the Port and Starboard Side of the ship. What I do remember clearly is that the water laying on the deck in the passageways immediately "above" the Engine

Room was boiling hot. I can also clearly remember the ship being in a state of "Loll" and slowly rolling over from Port side to Stbd side and back again. Clearly a perilous condition. Another clear memory was the presence in the passageways of thick black acrid smoke. It was necessary to take ones face as low as possible to the water filled deck to try and suck in some air.

As mentioned earlier, the ship was anchored off Milford Haven. There is/ was a large oil refinery in Milford Haven where the oil tankers would discharge their cargo of crude oil. To this end there was a flotilla of vessels that could fight any fires that occurred at the refinery or on the tankers. This factor turned out to be the salvation for HMS Bristol and the firefighting vessels.

When "The Command" on HMS Bristol realised that the fire was out of control and beyond the capabilities of Ships Staff to extinguish the fire – the flotilla of firefighting vessels, moored nearby, were requested to attend. From memory, the firefighters put their hoses into the Engine Room at approximately 0230 and discharged large quantities of Foam into the Compartment. I am unsure what time the fire was finally extinguished but can remember the first entry into the compartment was approximately 0630.

I ventured into the Engine Room at some stage early in the morning where I encountered the Cmdr (E)-Rusty Robertson RN and the Commanding Officer – Capt. Hugh Janion RN. They were both obviously very despondent. All of the Aluminium Deck Plates had burnt through and it was necessary to manoeuvre oneself around the Engine Room stepping on and using the steel Deck Support Ribs that normally had supported the Deck Plates. Rusty Robertson's future in the RN, as a result of the fire, was done no good at all; Hugh Janion was appointed as Commodore Royal Yatch.

With just the 2 Diesel Generators available and running the ship was experiencing a severe power shortage. However, during the following forenoon, one of my Artificers (Tom Lunn) and myself spent time and were finally able to get both Gas Turbines running. We were not too concerned about the shortage of electrical power since having got the Gas Turbines running, power was required to stop them.

Again, if my memory serves me correctly, we sailed from Milford Haven and entered Portsmouth on a Sunday Morning. I kept the "Morning" watch (0400–0800) and was the EOOW during the entry into Portsmouth. The Fire damage was intense and resulted in there being no Telegraph or Telephone Communication (TCB or Main Line) between the Bridge and the EOOW Console in the SCC. There was however a serviceable telephone communication loop from the Bridge to the Electrical Control Room which was adjacent to the SCC. It was necessary to remove a hardened glass partition between the Electrical Control Room and the SCC. Telegraph orders and Revolutions were passed by voice through the telephone to the Electrical Control Room and then by "Voice" through the removed glass to the EOOW in the SCC. Many other distractions were occurring during the passage into harbour including the incessant action of Electrical Breakers – (Making and Breaking) which of course affected the running machinery and lighting which was dimming then brightening again. Thank goodness the propulsion system (Gas Turbines) were not affected by the Power Failures. I should have been relieved at 0800 by 1 of the Section Officers, I knew that this was foolhardy as these Section Officers never kept any watches as EOOW. Sure enough the young Lieutenant taking over the Watch asked me if I would remain with him, and to that end he informed me that he had brought several Bacon Rolls and Coffee for me from the Officers Galley. I could not refuse him and carried on running The Watch until "Finished with Main Engines". The Section Officer concerned ended up as a Captain (E) in (MoD) Foxhill and obviously did not forget the favour, he was instrumental in granting me a nice "Contract" when I was working for YAR(D) – An Engineering Consultancy – which was eventually taken over by BAe (Systems). What goes around – Comes around.

On going down the gangway and looking from the jetty, the ship looked in a sorry state, the Dockyard personnel were hastily rigging tarpaulin over the damaged area of the ships superstructure. I can only assume this was done to prevent the prying eyes of the media.

For about a week later I was bringing up the remnants of black smoke from my lungs– not nice. I had to attend an Enquiry (held onboard Bristol) to give an account of my actions before and during the fire. The Enquiry Team (it appeared) were possibly looking for any sabotage action which may have taken place. Shortly after, I was drafted from the Ship.

In my opinion HMS Bristol was superbly designed for its future planned role and was years before its time. She ship underwent patchwork repairs and was able to sail using just the Gas Turbines.

As a final note, it can be stated that you cannot "Design" for "All" eventualities. As far as I know, aluminium deck plates were never used again in future design ships – As was found out on the T21s during the Falklands Campaign – Aluminium structures only add fuel to a fire. "Stones" Auxiliary Boilers were fitted with their own self – contained servo air compressors on future ships. Anomalies and mis-judgements will be made in the best of designs.[12]

The lessons were learnt, but it was a close run thing and had the ship not been anchored off Milford Haven the outcome could have been very different. It is worth dwelling on this incident as it highlights the dangers that any ship can face even in peacetime. Roger mentioned that the ship was in a state of "loll", this was much more serious than was perhaps appreciated at the time, with large quantities of surface water from the firefighting effort adding to the instability of an already top heavy ship. This is, perhaps, the closest a modern warship of the Royal Navy came to foundering in peacetime until HMS *Nottingham* hit Wolf Rock near Australia.

Mike Doyle, meanwhile had married a girl, Eleanor, he had met while in FMG in Rosyth. However, while still single he had requested to return to sea and as is the way in these things that is where he went and in early 1974 he joined HMS *Norfolk*:

Before I met Eleanor, I had requested a draft to join a sea going ship again. As a single man, I was getting bored being on shore. However, once I was smitten with Eleanor, I desperately tried to cancel the request but too late; I was drafted to HMS Norfolk, a Guided Missile Destroyer (GMD) refitting in Portsmouth. After we were married at the end of March 1973, we bought a small bungalow in Dunfermline. Then 6 weeks later I had to join the ship. The ship was still in dry dock and was being refitted with the French Exocet missile – the first Royal Navy ship to do so. It involved removing B 4.5 inch gun turret and replacing with a launch structure for 4 missile pods. After refit the plan was we would proceed to France for extensive testing of the missile in 1974.

Arriving on Norfolk as a MEA (H) 2, a Petty Officer, I was part of a team of four MEA (H)s. Our role was to maintain all aspects of the ship that related to its hull structure, ventilation; fresh and salt water services; fire-fighting, and many ancillary items such as boats, anchors etc. As the newest joiner, I was put in charge of the fire-fighting pumps and systems which in a large ship carrying missiles was a big and complex responsibility. My first job was to locate all the valves, pipes and pumps as most had been removed to the dockyard! Eventually, all were refitted and fully tested. I really enjoyed the work but having to live in HMS Nelson on my own during the week was a trial for a newly married man. At that time I had a Vauxhall Viva and drove nearly every weekend from Portsmouth to Dunfermline. Leaving at 12 noon on Friday (I did a "deal" with the Chief Shipwright to work extra hours during the week) and ended up driving over the Forth Road Bridge at 10pm Friday night!

By September 1973, the ship had completed the refit and we left for Portland and our 6 week "Work-Up" began. This consisted of intensive training and testing of all aspects of the ship and her crew to bring her, and us, to a full state of readiness as a fighting machine.[13]

It seems as if Mike had more than his share of attending disasters and mishaps and as the ship was returning to Portsmouth fate struck again:

It was end of October 1973 and the ship was returning from Portland to Portsmouth for a welcome weekend leave (I was to drive to Scotland on the Friday after we docked). At around 1am, we received a distress call from the Lebanese registered MV Barrad Crest which was a small cargo vessel of around 1,500 tons transporting Fyfe bananas.

The ship was on fire in the English Channel (I think it was somewhere off Start point). When we came upon the ship, the crew had abandoned her and she was ablaze in the bridge area. Norfolk drew up a short distance from her and we played fire hoses onto the rear section of the ship. I was duly woken by my boss and told I was to be part of a boarding party who were to get the ship ready for towing. My role was to "break" the anchor cable and connect the towing hawser. I gathered some tools together and we were transported to the ship in one of our boats. I remember climbing the rope ladder on the ship's side and swinging out into mid-air as the ship rolled in a heavy swell, hanging by one hand as the other was clutching my tool bag. Luckily the ship rolled back the other way and I was able to complete the climb.

The anchor cable was so badly maintained that I had to hacksaw through sections of the cable which was some 1.5 inches in diameter. As I was doing that, a fire-fighting party was sent over and when I was finished I then joined with them. I recall, seeing the deck glowing red hot right beside some gas canisters and thinking "not a good spot to be in". However, after many hours of effort, we could not reach the seat of the fire which was somewhere deep in the ship. Because of the volume of water used to fight the fire, the ship was listing badly and becoming unstable. Then eventually, after some 24 hours, we had to stop our fire fighting efforts to prevent her capsizing.

The decision was taken to tow the ship to Plymouth where we handed her over to Plymouth Fire Brigade in Plymouth Sound. However a short time after we left the ship to return to the Norfolk, there was a large explosion and a number of fire-fighters were hurt. Apparently the fire had reached containers of refrigerant which exploded. It was unfortunate for those brave men but lucky for us? We arrived at Portsmouth on the Saturday and as a newly married man desperate to see my wife, I drove for 10 hours to Dunfermline for just the one night, returning back to the ship on the Sunday!!

A few days after the fire, I was visiting the MEMs mess deck on routine maintenance where, lo and behold, there hanging in the mess in pride of place was the bell from the Barrad Crest! I asked one of the mess members how they had managed to get the bell back to the Norfolk without anybody noticing? They told me that they had hid it in my tool bag – and I thought I was just too exhausted when I could hardly carry the bag back to the ship![14]

While *Norfolk* was carrying out Exocet firings on the ranges off Toulon Mike heard that he had successfully passed the examination for MEA(H)1 and so was now a Chief Petty Officer, with all that entailed:

During my time in France I heard that I had passed my professional examinations for MEA (H)1 which meant I was promoted from Petty Officer to Chief Petty Officer. I had also won the Herbett Lott Memorial prize for achieving the highest grade in the navy examination. Being promoted to Chief Petty Officer meant I had to change messes and it was with regret I left the best mess I had ever experienced in the Navy, number 4 PO's mess on Norfolk – a really great bunch of guys. Having said that, I found Norfolk to be a generally "happy" ship (old navy hands will understand what I mean). There was a lot of banter and teamwork – even when things got rough literally and figuratively. Our team of Chippies worked well as a team, always had a laugh and joke and tried not to treat life too seriously which was important in keeping you sane.[15]

There were many incidents to keep life from becoming boring while Mike was in *Norfolk*, which he was happy to relate:

During our time in the Med we had an Admiral on board (not sure why but for diplomatic reasons because we were working with the French Navy I guess?) His name was Rear Admiral ("Whisky") Wemyss. He was a great character who was popular with the ship's company (and in our PO's mess when he fell through the door one day and demanded that we open our bar for him). Onboard we had a Fairey Huntress which was essentially the Admiral's speedboat. It was a beautiful craft but as we were returning to Toulon after experiencing a heavy storm (yes it can get very rough in the Med) the boat suffered major damage. Because it had not been properly lashed in the davits, it crashed against the steel structure of the davit and the result was a hole the size of a football punched in its side. The admiral had plans to entertain some local dignitaries on the craft the following day and insisted the boat was repaired and ready for him to use. So a fellow Chippy, Pete Coombes, and I set about repairing the hole. This meant working through the night, at sea, with the boat hanging in the davits. Fortunately, just before leaving HMS Caledonia, they had put us apprentices through a course in how to make repairs using Glass Reinforced Plastic (GRP). The boat was made of wood but could be repaired using this method which was faster and just as strong. So we set about making the repair and by the time we docked in Toulon in the morning the repair was finished and painted to the extent that you would never have known there had been any damage to the hull. That earned us both the gratitude of the Admiral in the shape of – what else – a bottle of whisky!

As shipwrights, one of our tasks on board Norfolk was to unblock drains and toilets – not the most pleasant of tasks but essential. As one old chippie was heard to remark "It might be shit to you but its bread and butter to me!"

There was one occasion when another member of our happy band of Chippy "brothers", Mick Gent, was tasked with unblocking a large deck drain from the main galley and asked me to help him. This was a sizeable 6" diameter pipe that ran down two or more decks so was a considerable length. The pipe was full of smelly waste water and food waste from the main galley – not very nice! To unblock the pipe, Mick decided to remove an internal access cover at the point where the pipe left the ships side on a lower deck. This involved him catching the contents of the pipe in a large plastic dustbin once the cover plate was removed. Now, as he undid the bolts, I did a quick mental calculation to determine the total volume of the pipe and decided that the contents of the pipe would not fit into the dustbin he was holding. Knowing this, but not telling him, I removed the access plate as he held the bucket. I then watched as Mick balanced on a stool with the dustbin held up on his shoulder to collect the contents and listened to the rumble as the bin started to fill. As it got heavier, Mick's knees started to buckle and eventually the disgusting contents started to spill over the rim of the bin and over Mick who was screaming at me to help him; but watching him struggle with all the mess running down his face caused me to collapse in a fit of laughter. However Mick had the last laugh as the weight of the dustbin became too heavy and he dropped it, covering us both in the smelly mess. But it was worth it!

On another occasion we were issued with a new compressed air "gun" for unblocking drains. The idea was you pumped it up and then pulled a trigger to fire a bolt of high pressure air down the drain to clear the blockage. It was a useful device, but potentially lethal in the wrong hands, as we subsequently found out. One of our MEMs who worked with us was sent to unblock a sink drain in the Officer's cabins. However, he did not realise that the drain was connected to other sinks and, after inserting the gun into the pipe and pulling the trigger, the bolt of air took the path of least resistance and flew out of the Commander Store's sink next door, just as he was working on a large stores ledger. The Commander, his ledger and most of his cabin were decorated with speckles of the black sludge that inhabits the inside of drain pipes.

The first we knew of it was when the said MEM crashed through the workshop door and, partially paraphrasing astronaut Jim Lovell on Apollo 13 said "Chief we have got a problem" A phone call for me to report to the Commander's cabin swiftly followed. As I viewed the damage, I have to confess to some difficulty keeping straight face as I had to look into his black speckled face.

One of my regular tasks onboard was to test all the missile sprinkler systems. The new Exocet missile launcher was on the upper deck where "B" gun turret used to be. The four missile pods were surrounded by a network of pipes with sprinkler heads and was designed to spray the whole area in a deluge of salt water should there be a fire. To test the system involved opening a valve which was just inside the superstructure and then to stand below the launcher and watch to ensure that water issued from each sprinkler head. After making a broadcast that testing was about to take place, I stood on the foc'sle below the launcher whilst one of our MEMs opened the valve from inside. I shouted: "Okay Nobby, open the valve". At that moment, the Executive Commander came around the corner right beside the launcher. He looked at me and I could see the puzzled look in his eye. Frantically, I shouted for the valve to be closed but too late – a beautiful spray cascaded all over the launcher and the Commander. He retreated back down the deck uttering words and I am sure that the F word was used! Needlessly I had to explain to my boss what was being done but I was in the clear as the Commander evidently hadn't listened to the broadcast.[16]

It is at this juncture that we can return the saga of Mike's toolbox, mentioned earlier:

But there were other times when life became farcical. You will recall at the beginning of this story I commented how each Shipwright apprentice made their own large tool box for all their tools which then followed them through their naval career. On the Norfolk there were four shipwrights and we each had our own personal toolbox which we had made as apprentices, and which were stored in our workshop onboard. Then one day, out of the blue, came an instruction (not sure from where from but I think from somewhere in MOD) that only one toolbox was necessary and we should share one set of tools from one box between us. How can four shipwrights share one set of chisels, one plane, one saw etc? In the end, three of us had to surrender our toolboxes and tools. Complaints were made, anger expressed but to no avail. I sometimes wish I could have met the individual(s) who made such an idiotic decision; they clearly had never been to sea on a warship and appreciated how we operated, and what the boxes and tools meant to us. Even to this day some 44 year later, I still makes me angry thinking about it. However, suffice to say that the three of us who lost our tools immediately put in blanket stores requisitions for new tools and then set about making provision for their storage – an exercise I am sure was repeated on other ships too! [17]

Every good "Tiffy" took great pride in their toolboxes, whether they were Shipwright, ERA, OEA or AA. There would always be specially made or adapted tools, made by their owners for particular jobs, as well as the standard tools. These special tools were much prized and to lose a toolbox was something that was hard to bear and it is quite understandable how Mike was angry about this senseless vandalism even forty-four years later.

As is the way of things, it was not uncommon for an Apprentice to pass out and return quite soon after as an instructor and such a situation happened to Fred Davies:

After passing out from Caledonia *and doing time on* Apollo *and* Sheffield, *with* Royal Arthur *and some FMG time in between (eight weeks), I went back to* Caledonia *to instruct on the new propulsion engines of* Tyne *and* Olympus. *By this time, in 1976, the age for joining as an apprentice had been raised to an upper limit of twenty-one and at* Caledonia *some apprentices about to pass out were the same age as me, twenty-four. The "direct entries" were now also at* Caledonia, *as were the "awesome tiffs" on the "hull adqual course", who had just spent nearly all of the last four years at sea and were now working a five and a half day week like the apprentices. Many had their families in Portsmouth and Devonport and needless to say there were some extremely disgruntled Chiefs in the mess at that time. So, boosted by the additional bodies, we entered the "Cock" sports trophy and won it comfortably, much to the disgust of the apprentices. Personally, my time instructing at* Caledonia *gave me the opportunity to learn what I should have learnt the first time around as an apprentice. I remember both of my times at* Caledonia *with great affection, and friends made on each occasion remain so now. It was a very moving occasion to attend the final chapter of* Caledonia *in 1984, but after about 6pm on that day all went fuzzy! Today, Pete Bellamy (Series 61) and I, both of Exmouth Division and having served together on the* Apollo, *now work for the same company and are in contact daily, both being near to fifty years old, he is over fifty and I am under fifty. Well, we did join up a year apart.*[18]

In *Collingwood* the junior rate accommodation blocks, built to much fanfare in the period starting in 1963 and opened by Princess Margaret in 1966, were in a parlous state. They were, possibly, the worst-designed and -built blocks it has ever been the misfortune for people to live in and try to keep in a state of cleanliness suitable for the demands of captain's rounds. Even when they were new they were subject to subsidence. This caused the windows to sag and buckle, leaving large gaps for wind and rain to come in. In certain blocks this was so bad that some of the four-man messes were uninhabitable. The heads and bathrooms were situated at the centre of the building, with totally inadequate ventilation. This led to condensation, mould and bad smells. Fortunately, these blocks were condemned and pulled down in the 1990s, to the mind of many who endured this accommodation not a moment too soon.

In 1975 Mike Doyle left *Norfolk* and was drafted as an Instructor to *Caledonia*, which allowed him some much deserved time at home with his wife and while in *Caledonia* he sat and passed the examination for Chief Shipwright and as he recounted he soon learnt a valuable lesson:

I also learned an important management lesson. While acting as duty Chief one evening, a call came in to say there was a riot in the Submariners's bar. (One Polaris submarine was always refitting at Rosyth Dockyard and their crew had their own accommodation in HMS Caledonia). I was about to set off to sort out the fight in gung-ho mode, when the other Chief on duty with me – much older and more experienced than me – said "Just hold on, let them sort it out amongst themselves and we will go in and pick up the pieces" Of course he was right, if I had gone in to break things up, the likelihood was they would have turned on me as the authority figure! So when we eventually strolled over, things had settled down again and the problem had resolved itself.[19]

After two years in *Caledonia* it was time to move on again and Mike was drafted to AFD 60, known, apparently, as "Monty Pythons Floating Dock", at Faslane, the wrong side of Scotland for any further home life. But despite that Mike found the job one of the most rewarding in his naval career:

AFD 60 stood for Admiralty Floating Dock 60 which was a great big grey metal box moored out in the middle of the Gareloch at the mouth of the river Clyde. The floating dock was an integral part of the Faslane Naval base which was home to the Polaris nuclear fleet at that time. The Naval base was a large and complex arrangement of specialist facilities and workshops servicing mainly submarines – both nuclear and conventional.

AFD 60 was a massive structure consisting of a deck and two side walls and was designed lift submarines out of the water for inspection and maintenance. The dock would sink down till it was just above the water. The submarine would then enter the dock, between the side walls, and be carefully positioned over a submerged wooden cradle. The water would then be pumped out and the buoyancy of the dock would raise both the dock and the submarine, nestling in its cradle of supports, clear of the water.

To all intents and purposes AFD 60 was operated like a ship. We had a Dock Master who was a Lieutenant Commander Engineer (Hull); a Lieutenant Engineer (Hull) as his assistant; a Chief MEA (P) who controlled the raising and lowering of the dock and maintained all the pumping and ancillary machinery; and me as CMEA (H) who, with a team of four MEA(H)s: built the curved cradle from various colour coded dock blocks (a bit like a giant Lego kit); docked the submarine, and maintained all of the services on the dock – just as we would on board a sea going ship.

We lived ashore in HMS Neptune which was the large shore base establishment at Faslane with accommodation for submarine crews and base personnel (but we kept a duty crew on the dock for emergencies etc). Life on AFD 60 oscillated from being relatively peaceful and relaxed, to working long hours and at a frantic pace when a submarine required docking – especially if it was an emergency docking – which it often was.

I have reflected on my time on AFD 60 and concluded that, professionally, it was the most rewarding of my whole career in the navy. There was a real feeling of being "on the front line of the cold war" – especially where it involved the Polaris submarine fleet which were at that time, the UK's main nuclear deterrent. One of the most satisfying experiences I ever had was after my first docking. I was terrified of making a mistake in setting up the dock cradle and positioning the submarine, but then to see HMS Resolution, one of our four Polaris submarines, lifted high and dry out of the water for the first time was mind blowing. To actually see the size of that vessel out of the water and to know I played a major part in getting her there was immensely satisfying.

Although we were not part of the submarine service, we worked closely with them and they were great guys to work with – so utterly professional. AFD 60 was another "happy ship". We had a good crew who would get the job done when required. Conditions on the dock could be harsh in the winter as you were cruelly exposed out in the loch and the hours were long at times. But we tried to emulate the ethos of the submarine service in some ways by keeping things relaxed but being professional when it was required. We developed a good team spirit with away days for the crew at the base swimming pools and sports facilities where we held competitions between departments. Wherever possible we allowed the crew to accrue overtime when we were in docking mode and then to take time off when things were quiet.

Previously, AFD 60 had a poor reputation in the base as a bit of a "gulag" but with the arrival of a new Dockmaster and a new management and leadership team with myself and the CMEA (P) "Mac", a submariner with whom I developed a good working partnership, we became the place on the base where people wanted to work. One small thing we did to lighten the mood was to play Liberty Bell (theme from Monty Python's Flying Circus) the main broadcast just as a submarine entered the dock which went down a treat.[20]

At *Caledonia* in 1977 HMS *Eastbourne* was deemed unfit for sea service, but to ensure the continuation of her role as the "afloat training ship" her propellers were removed and replaced with "brake wheels". This allowed the continuation of steaming boilers in realistic conditions without actually moving anywhere.

It may be of note that there had been no Apprentices to reach flag rank since Vice Admiral Sir Hugh Thompson was promoted to Rear Admiral in 1983; however, on 10 September 1976 a young lad named John Newell joined *Fisgard* in 763 Entry. He was to have a long and distinguished career and retired as a Commodore in 2014. His start into the Royal Navy is best summarised in his own words:

My maternal grandfather joined the Royal Navy on 27 February 1917 and left on 8 October 1945 before instructing Artificers in Chatham dockyard. He had a considerable influence on me as a boy and after my mum died when I was 11, I spent a lot of time returning to England from Brussels, where we lived and either staying with him or with cousins on their farm who effectively became Foster parents. When I was given the choice of returning permanently to England to live with another relative to complete A levels or join the RN as an Artificer Apprentice I took his lead and joined the Royal Navy.

I joined HMS Fisgard on 10 September 1976 (763 Entry) from my Foster mum's farm where I had worked most summers. Pam insisted that I wore a suit for the journey to Plymouth but I managed to get manure on it before I had even left the farm.

My first impressions of HMS Fisgard were not great but soon the workshops, academics, sports and being paid to have fun made it the best boarding school around. The few memories I have of the 8 months there revolve around chanting "East side best side West side shit" (I was in Tribe Division), the static tank, being given my pay in my cap and building bridges over the roads with the bunk beds. Looking back at what went on now I suspect there was a degree of bullying with me being on the receiving end but also a witness to others getting rough treatment. I remember individuals being tied in bed and the bed turned over and me being stuffed into a kitbag with a fire hose stuffed into the end. HMS Caledonia followed for a year or so during which time I passed the AIB. I left HMS Caledonia in August 1978 with a leave pass expiring at 0800 on 13 September 1978 at BRNC Dartmouth.

Like all good ratings I turned up late in the evening on 12 September 1978 in Dartmouth and presented myself at the main gate. They had no record of me as the MOD had forgotten to pass them details of any UYs so sent me to the closest accommodation which was Drake Division. Somehow I survived the kit musters, Early Morning Activities (EMAs), Morse Code tests in Caspar John Hall and Ballroom dancing (to get out of evening rounds). Towards the end of the first term I fell out of the top bunk and broke my left elbow and had to be taken to Derriford by ambulance to have it put in plaster. There was some booze in the run up to the incident which is probably best forgotten. Anyway because of that I spent a second term at Dartmouth and missed DTS. For Fleet time I went to HMS Hermes and spent a few months in the Med followed by the East Coast of the USA.

My three years at RNEC Manadon were dominated by Diving, Riding, rugby and the academics. I was also a DJ in the "Thunderbox", the in-house nightclub. It was a great time. We were full time students on a good wage with fantastic facilities. Although I understand why the college was closed it was a very sad day for the Royal Navy and the Engineering Branch. Perhaps some of our troubles today started at that point.[21]

At this stage it would be useful to catalogue John's career before we follow it later on.

September 1976–September 1978	Royal Navy Artificer Apprenticeship
September 1978–September 1984	Initial Engineer Officer training including BSc
September 1984–February 1986	Deputy Marine Engineer Officer HMS *Sirius*
March 1986–October 1987	MSc and Initial Staff Course, Lieutenant
November 1987–November 1990	Pollution Control Equipment Desk Officer
March 1991–March 1993	Marine Engineer Officer HMS *Boxer*, Lt Cdr
June 1993–July 1994	French Staff Course
August 1994–October 1995	Joint Planning Staff
October 1995–March 1998	Marine Engineer Career Manager, Commander
March 1998–December 2000	Head of Power Distribution and Propulsion Systems
January 2001–April 2003	Marine Engineer Officer HMS *Albion*
April 2003–March 2005	Fleet Marine Engineer Officer

March 2005–July 2005

Captain Royal Navy. As Director for Guest Management for Trafalgar 200, joined the team at a pivotal point in the transition from planning to implementation. Undertook the design, and established on the ground, a management process for the approximately 4,000 visitors to be embarked for the International Fleet Review.

July 2005–July 2007

Captain Royal Navy. Assistant Director Transformation, responsible for the implementation of lean thinking in the naval bases at Portsmouth, Devonport and on the Clyde. Key activities included diagnostics in HMS Ledbury, HMS Middleton and HMS Northumberland in each of the sites to identify where the key areas of waste in surface ship maintenance were and, consequently, how cost could be removed from the business. Responsible for business case and investment appraisals to support the provision of lean external assistance at all sites. Lead on Queen Elizabeth Class Aircraft Carrier, Faslane and Rosyth aspects of the Naval Base Review.

July 2007–April 2012

Captain Royal Navy. Responsible for the support of fifty-three platforms across nineteen classes, including all minehunters, survey vessels, CLS ships, ice patrol ship and HMS Victory. Additionally responsible for MHPC, a new project in concept phase, with a projected budget of over £4bn. Led a team of sixty military and civilian personnel with the additional support of circa fifteen contractors. Annual budget circa £60m.

April 2012–September 2014

Commodore Royal Navy. Member of Director Ships Senior Executive Team. Responsible for the maintenance and support of all complex warships for the Royal Navy including upgrades and updates together with the introduction into service of the Type 45 destroyers. Responsible for the Mine-countermeasures, Hydrographic and Patrol Capability (MHPC) in concept phase. Team of 164. Annual budget circa £400m.

Perhaps this demonstrates that it is still possible to reach the highest levels of the Service from more humble beginnings and that it is still possible to have fun doing a job that you enjoy. There is also the small matter of "sprogging", which seems to have continued despite the best efforts to stamp out this pernicious practice. To continue, there are several incidents in John's career that can be related:

> Long before Manadon closed I had been off to sea to complete my Fleet Time in HMS Manchester, gone back to Manadon for the Application Course, then to sea to get my steam tickets in HMS Eastbourne and HMS Torquay. I then joined HMS Sirius as DMEO in 1984, my first real job since joining. Following the two years in HMS SIRIUS I returned to RNEC Manadon to read for an MSc in Electrical Engineering. This meant that between 1976 and 1987 I had been "under training" except for the DMEO's job.[22]

In the same entry in September 1976 was one Stephen Gosden, who found himself in the two terms at *Fisgard* accelerated stream. Steve too was destined for great things in the future as he remembered:

> I joined the Navy aged 17 in early Sep 1973, over the Torpoint Ferry and through the gates of HMS Fisgard with some 112 other Apprentices. Initially assigned with 763 class than placed in 762A I seem to remember.
>
> Joined Spicknell Division with a lively bunch and our Instructor was a Leading Seaman Jack London (funny who you can remember).
>
> **Memory joggers are:**
> Workshop training – desperately trying to get my squarish lump of filed metal into an equally squarish hole – success one way but not when you turned it 90 degrees. And then being offered another Lump to file and try again – thanks "Taff Strawford".
> Static tanks and grubby water for late night swims.
> Green and White Dance.
> Burning my ear with a soldering iron when trying to scratch my head.
> Out of the 112 of us some 100 or more declared themselves as smokers.
> Thinking I looked like a postman in my surge suit and hoping desperately for shiny buttons one day.
> We got pretty good at drill with plenty of practice!
> Making lifelong friends.
> Station Cards and runs ashore on pay day and blank weeks where you had no money.

Oh and I learnt some good basic engineering skills and knowledge.
Hoping to be an air engineer and finding myself an OEA Apprentice – turned
out to be a good decision.

HMS Collingwood *in "O" School Learning all about 4.5 inch guns/*
MRS3/fly-plane five/Seacat/Generators/pumps etc a great time although visit
to HMS Excellent for gunnery could be daunting when dealing with GIs.[23]

After this Steve went to sea in HMS *Kent* and in no time at all found
himself as a Marine Engineer, leaving guns and directors behind forever.

1975	HMS Kent: "A" turret maintainer (cleaner and painter and amplifier balancer in reality), living in 3D mess and then 3P Greenies mess a 60 man broadside mess – now that was an experience
1976	Selected for Upper Yardman sent to HMS CALEDONIA to get some A levels –. had to mix with those strange clankies
1977	Off to Dartmouth as a Midshipman
1978	HMS Fearless/HMS Ariadne/HMS Gavinton Sea training
1978	RNEC Manadon for Marine Engineering Degree (that will teach me to mix with those clankies)
1982	HMS Cleopatra – sea training Serving with Bruce Milne as MEO and Tom Elliot as DMEO both SDs – great learning experience
1983/84	Marine application and Boiler, Chief of the Watch and Marine Engineer tickets aboard HMS Torquay
1984	HMS Manchester as AMEO/DMEO, those steam tickets had to become gas tickets pretty quickly
1986	Advanced Marine Engineering Course (MSc)
1986	Dartmouth as Lt on staff teaching Leadership and Marine Engineering
1987	HMS Sheffield Standing by at Swan Hunters and then as DMEO at Sea
1989	Canada – Head of Future Marine Engineering and sea trials Officer for Halifax Class
1992-	HMS Cumberland as MEO – great Job with a great team

1994	RN Staff Course Promoted Commander
1994	HMS Cornwall and Squadron MEO to Type 22 Frigate Squadron
1996	Head of Machinery Trial Unit and ME202 in Foxhill
1999	Director of Training – HMS Sultan – Felt like I had gone a full circle at this point Promoted Captain
2001–2002	Involved in the Defence Training Review – spent a lot of my time trying to save HMS Sultan
2002–2006	British Naval Attache in Berlin – Well this was a different job to my earlier postings, but very rewarding
2006–2009	Operations and Performance Manager for Ships within the Defence Equipment and Support environment – a real challenge to keep our ships available for Fleet to use

After 36 years of a really enjoyable and rewarding career, I then retired and moved on to look after provide ship support internationally with Babcock before establishing my own marine engineering consultancy company.[24]

1976 was a good year for Apprentices, who would reach the higher echelons of the Officer Corps; another was Richard (Dick) Hobbs, who had a slightly different path to the top:[25]

1976-1977	HMS FISGARD – basic training as Artificer Apprentice
1977- 1978	HMS COLLINGWOOD – initial training as Control Electrical Artificer
1978-1979	HMS SHEFFIELD – sea training
1979- 1980	HMS COLLINGWOOD – final technical training
1980- 1982	Chatham Fleet Maintenance Group
1982-1983	Portsmouth Fleet Maintenance Group
1983-1985	HMS GLASGOW – POWEA/CPOWEA Maintainer
1985- 1987	HMS COLLINGWOOD – Phalanx CIWS Instructor
1987-1988	Post promotion training following promotion to SLT on SD list
1988-1990	HMS INTREPID – DWEO

1990-1993	Project OASIS (Lt)
1993- 1995	Outboard Project
1995- 1998	WEO HMS SOUTHAMPTON (Lt Cdr)
1998	FOST Sea Rider (Lt Cdr)
1998-2000	Reliability Centred Maintenance Team (Cdr WE – on last SD promotion signal!!)
2000-2001	SWEO to 5th Destroyer Squadron
2001-2002	MSc course Shrivenham
2002- 2005	Ship/equipment projects Abbey Wood
2005-2008	Cdr WE Maritime Capability Trials and Assurance (MCTA)
2008- 2009	WEO HMS OCEAN
2009- 2012	Surface Ship Support Alliance implementation team (Captain)
2012- 2014	Captain MCTA

He also has a few words in praise of having been an Artificer:

As a stroppy 16 year old I spent most of my first year in the RN in one "static tank" or another. Consequently, I got put into the boxing team to "funnel" my spirit!!

I believe that our training as Artificers embedded an ethos of "will-fix under any conditions" into all of us. My experiences of repairing equipments/ systems ranged from fixing missile launchers in the Straits of Hormuz during the Tanker War to mending one of the Queen's telephones on the Royal Yacht as a young Leading Hand.

I'd like to think that I took this ethos into my service as an officer; examples for me include helping to fix a Phalanx CIWS for another NATO navy and introducing additional weapon testing for deploying RN ships.[26]

Dick was able to take advantage of the amalgamation of the three officer lists, General List (GL), Supplementary List (SL) and Special Duties (SD), combined in 1998, allowing him further promotion to Captain ten years later.

Towards the end of the 1970s Mike Doyle was nearing the end of his twelve-year engagement and had decided, for better or for worse, to leave the Navy. However, he still had to go back to sea with little over a year left to serve. This, clearly, did not allow much time for resettlement and preparing for a return to civilian life. He joined HMS *Norfolk* in May 1978 prior to the ship starting a refit in Portsmouth Dockyard. This was a time of militant unions and the Dockyard was on strike. This meant that the ship was sent north for a refit, as Mike wrote:

HMS Kent was older than HMS Norfolk, built in the first phase in the mid 1960s. But in most respects she was the same layout and therefore familiar territory for me. Shortly after I joined her, we were scheduled for a refit in Portsmouth Dockyard. However, the dockyard went on strike and we therefore had a four month refit in Wallsend on the River Tyne. As it was not possible to live on board when in dry dock, the whole ship's company were decamped to B&B lodgings in Whitley Bay on the coast! It was a sight to behold in the morning as we all emerged from the B&Bs along one road to catch our buses to the dockyard.

After the refit we had our work-up at Portland as normal and then we were due to sail for the US. However, an inspection condemned one of our boilers and this trip was cancelled. Eventually we sailed for Brazil via Nigeria and exercised with the Brazilian Navy. My time on Kent was less enjoyable than Norfolk. I think part of my problem was that the CMEA (H) was essentially in a managerial, administrative and not a "hands-on" role so I was to some extent not exposed to the "excitement" of the job. For example, whilst we were at Portland for sea-training, we suffered a major defect on the anchor brake mechanism which meant the ship became non-operational. I decided what needed to be done and then my team worked through the night to repair the fault. I had a team of four competent MEA (H)s would did not need me breathing down their neck all the time. So for the duration of the repair, my role amounted to rigging a shelter for them to work in and organising sandwiches! Okay I had the pleasure of reporting to the Commander (E) that the ship was once again operational but it just felt strange to me not to be involved in a more hands on way.

I also felt that my imminent departure from the Navy was affecting me in terms of motivation and my outlook on naval life. Professionally, the trip was challenging as she was an old ship and this was her last commission so there were plenty of technical problems to resolve which thankfully, we did and we nursed her successfully through her last trip.

We arrived home around August 1979 and I handed over to my relief and left the ship. I then joined Portsmouth FMG for the remaining couple of

months. This was a depressing period for me as I was essentially a "non-person" I
helped out with ship surveys and a bit of time in the workshop until starting the
leaving process which entailed visiting different departments in HMS Nelson to
sign bits of paper and hand back items of kit. Finally, I handed back my ID card
at the main at and left the Navy with a tear in my eye.[27]

Leaving the Navy can be a daunting time and Mike was not the first to experience doubts over his decision to leave and went as far as to apply to rejoin, only being dissuaded at the last moment by the entreaties of his son to stay at home however difficult it might be in the recessionary times of the early 1980s. He did find employment in Corby, where he had returned after leaving Rosyth, and gradually made good in a local engineering company, where he eventually became the leading salesman. But the long hours and constant travelling persuaded him to move into management in a large electronics company, during which time he completed a BA and MA with the Open University. With these qualifications to start him off Mike took the plunge into academia:

I decided to move into the world of academia and in 1990 won a scholarship
to become a Teaching Fellow at Leicester Polytechnic (which in 1992 became
De Montfort University). I remained there as a lecturer and researcher in the
Business School, completing a PhD, and then retired as a Principal Lecturer in
2009.[28]

Perhaps the final words should be from Mike and a few reflections on his time in the Royal Navy and how things were changing during the 1960s and 1970s:

Putting this account of my time in the Royal Navy down on paper after all this
time, has been a useful exercise for me as it has allowed me the opportunity to
pause and reflect on what was undoubtedly a profound period in my life and one
which, I firmly believe, shaped who I became from then onwards – for better or
for worse. As I reflected on this, here are some points which came to mind about
these events during those fourteen years.

First, in my account of my time in the Navy during the late 1960s and
1970s, I have tried to be as accurate as I can, but given the time elapsed there were
always going to be gaps, for example remembering precise dates and places was

not always possible. In some cases, events have occurred but I have deliberately chosen not to include them in this account. Like life itself, there will always be mistakes we have made, things we have said or done and decisions made which are regretted later. In that sense the account has to judged as "incomplete" but sufficient to portray some sense of what life was like for me, and I am sure the wider Navy at this time.

Second, there would always be a lack of detail at times when describing what happened; and perhaps there were occasions when my recollection of events might vary with those of other parties involved at the time. And of course, events are always open to contention and dispute. That's fine by me. But what I have presented is my account the way I remember it and as such, is unique, personal to me. It is based on how I saw and experienced the events and situations described, and were therefore in a sense it constitutes "my reality".

Third, I also believe that it is important to view what I have described in a wider context which in part explains some of what occurred and why. Whilst my time as a shore based apprentice was in the late 1960s, the bulk of my time in the Navy was during the decade of the 1970s. This was an interesting decade in the sense that we were at the height of the Cold War with the then Soviet Union. However, unlike other decades before or since, the Royal Navy was hardly involved in any serious conflict in the 1970s – apart from the Troubles in Northern Ireland where the Navy had a minimal role. But even though there was no overt conflict, nevertheless, I felt there was always a tension, an awareness of "an enemy" that was "out there", e.g. when being monitored by AIG trawlers in the North Atlantic or the urgency to make sure a Polaris submarine was docked efficiently. Maybe too, the Navy of the 1970s – which was far larger and ranged much wider than our navy of today gave those of us who served, more opportunities to encounter risk and excitement; to be involved in the unexpected and unplanned for?

Fourth, technologies and ship design were changing rapidly during the 1970s and our branch of hull engineering was to some extent becoming redundant and as a consequence, the Navy was phasing it out. Indeed MEA(H)'s ceased to be trained in the early 1970s. When I undertook my apprenticeship as a shipwright artificer, it was heavily craft based in the sense that we were a branch of the Navy that "made things" from raw materials – be they planks of wood, lengths of pipe, sheets of metal. However, increasingly our day to day work into the 1970s became more concerned with diagnosis, replacing parts and preventative maintenance. It was therefore hard at times to see a long term future for the branch. For example, when I joined HMS Norfolk in 1973, I was put in charge of the main fire pumps. These were six huge capacity pumps that required regular maintenance, stripping down to replace worn parts etc. But our apprenticeship as shipwrights gave us no grounding for this at all. Luckily, I was reasonably competent in mechanical engineering and managed to teach myself how to maintain this and similar equipment to the required standard.

However, paradoxically, as my account shows, there were times when these craft skills "saved the day" (the grounded helicopter, and the admiral's boat on HMS Norfolk). I also recall reading a report by the MOD Naval Constructors on the damage ships suffered in the Falklands War. They pointed to the lack of ship repair skills in terms of plating, welding skills and the availability of appropriate equipment on ships at that time.

Fifth, at a more personal level, in this account I am also conscious that I do not dwell to long on the negative aspects of my time in the Navy but it would be wrong not to acknowledge there were a few. As I stated in the introduction, we cannot and must not deny those difficult times if we are to present ourselves with a true account of what it was like. But it was not only us who had problems and difficulties, so too did our families and a recent event brought this home to me and confirmed that my decision to leave the Navy when I did was the right one.

About a year ago my wife and I came upon a box in the attic marked "Eleanor and Mike – Personal letters" We had completely forgotten that we had both saved every single letter (yes every letter) we ever wrote to each other from the day we were first met until the time I left the Navy. Reading those letters has been an emotional experience for both of us and for me, after all those years, it gave me a new perspective on that period and revealed things that I had no inkling of.

Like all naval personnel on sea duty, in the 1970s the only method for us and our families to communicate was by letter or telephone. There was no email, mobile phone, internet, Skype etc, (I wish there had been!) So letter writing was critical to maintaining morale for us both. And not to receive a letter was like being kicked in a sensitive area. Reading our letters again I was struck how lonely we both were when we were apart but more tellingly, how hard it was for my wife with young children to bring up and a home to maintain. She reminds me of one instance when she received a postcard that I sent from St Tropez telling her how great it was her on the beach. I was bragging of course but when she received it, she was in the middle of washing dirty nappies in a bucket. She told me she burst into tears and promptly grabbed the kids and went out for the

day. Other letters tell me how difficult it was financially for us and the guilt
I felt because there was little I could do to support her and she had to make do
by scrimping and saving. And the letters also reminded us how difficult it was
trying to make contact via telephone. Having to queue for a phone box, begging
coins, getting cut off what a nightmare it was at times![29]

At this time there was further restructuring of the Weapon Engineering and Marine Engineering branches. "Engineering Branch Development" (EBD), in 1979, saw the Marine Engineers assume responsibility for electrical power generation and all its associated functions. This also resulted in a change in titles for Artificers, with those OEAs that transferred to the ME Branch being designated MEA(L) and those remaining within the WE Branch joining REAs and CEAs as WEAs.[30]

It also led to change in the training at *Caledonia* and saw the demise of metalworkers, with all Apprentices being trained as fitters and turners. This led to City and Guilds of London Institute Certificate in Skill being awarded on the successful completion of the Trade Test at the end of 9 Class and the Technician Education Council Diploma awarded on successful completion of the new EBD course. This is in addition to the academic Ordinary National Certificate (ONC) that resulted in the successful completion of Part II training.

As the 1970s drew to a close there had been little change in the everyday life of an Artificer Apprentice. The training at *Fisgard*, *Caledonia* and *Daedalus* remained a constant throughout the decade. Nothing would stay the same as the 1980s brought in some profound changes to both the training and the career structure of Artificers.

chapter ten

The Eighties and the End of HMS *Fisgard* and the Move to HMS *Raleigh*

• • •

*"That's Mr. Hinchcliffe," said Pyecroft. "He's what
is called a first-class engine-room artificer. If you
hand 'im a drum of oil an' leave 'im alone, he can
coax a stolen bicycle to do typewritin'."*[1]

The 1980s started much as the 1970s had ended, Artificer training continued as it had done since the ending of craft apprenticeships in 1968. But there was much in the 1980s that would bring about profound changes to Artificers, both in training and career prospects, that shattered the status quo and left the Artificer to ponder on his future.

However, the 1980s were a very fertile period for Apprentices joining who were bound for the higher echelons of the service in the coming decades; 1982 appears to have been a particularly productive year, as will become clear later.

Early in the decade Robert Mitchell joined Spickernell Division as part of 803 Entry. Bob will appear later when he delivers the speech at the passing out parade of the last class of WEA Artificers in HMS *Collingwood* in 2009.

In *Fisgard* in 1980 Bob remembered there being a "mosque" at the bottom of his Division's building. Mosque may be a little ambitious but there was a prayer room for those Nigerian Apprentices who were Muslim. Kitting up was carried out in *Raleigh* rather than *Fisgard*, as had been the case previously, and there was no longer any single-breasted suit. Another departure was the privilege of being able to wear "civvies" ashore after the first term. Things in *Fisgard* was still very much on the lines of a minor public school and there were still inter-divisional raids and ducking in the static tanks. Even for his sea time task book Bob still had to complete time in the High Power Section, working in the machinery spaces and paralling generators, despite this being well after EBD.[2]

At the end of the 1970s a new class of ship, the Type 42, was entering service. These ships would be entirely powered by gas turbines; steam propulsion, with all its drawbacks and problems, was to become a thing of the past. Eric Mitchell (Series 49) remembered HMS *Exeter*, the first of the Batch 2 Type 42s, starting her sea trials in 1980:

> As time progressed the "stand-by" crew grew with the addition of essential ships company, Captain J C Dreyer, officers, seamen branch etc and alongside trials began with all equipment. Prior to sea trials the ME tiffs and POMEMs were drafted to Sultan to continue training on the Type 42 simulator.
>
> Sea trials were successfully completed 13–28 February 1980 with Final Machinery Trials be completed 25–26th June. These were busy but enjoyable times as we were not in charge, learning our jobs, watching and picking the brains of the contractors commissioning engineers, as the ship was still flying the Red Ensign.
>
> One of the big changes for me was that the ME watch was not below but in the Machinery Control Room (MCR). All trust was to be placed on the dials, gauges, temperature sensors etc displayed on the panels. Trips to the Machinery Spaces was not obligatory as they were visited hourly by the appropriate "stoker", but as an old steamie I would still do "my rounds" at least three times a 4 hour watch. After taking over, during and prior to being relieved.
>
> Commander Prior accepted HMS Exeter D89 on 30th August 1980.
>
> Commissioning day was 19th September 1980 and as can be imagined it was a busy one with invited guests, families, dignitaries, shipmates of the HMS Exeter Association, etc etc. After the ceremony I was in the mess talking with Bert Pearson and guests when I was called to the MCR. There I was introduced

to Mr. John "Frank" Frances Curnow. Frank was the CERA on the heavy cruiser HMS Exeter during their South Atlantic Deployment and River Plate engagement. He had requested a visit to the machinery spaces and DMEO had brought him down to the MCR for a walk about and I had been selected for the job.

He showed a great interest in the MCR and the various positions especially the throttles and engines controls. He likened the MCR to that of an aeroplane cockpit and I assured him that, like himself, coming from a history of five steam ships I had learnt to place my trust in those panels. Sitting in the MCR was alien to the days of standing on the plates listening to, watching, feeling and even smelling the steam driven machinery at all its different power levels. I mentioned that a big bonus of being on a gas boat that Full Watch Below was usually 45 minutes prior to sailing and not 4 hours as usual on a steam driven ship.

As time was running short I showed him, from the access doors, the Forward Engine Room (Olympus), After Engine Room (Tyne & gearboxes) and After Machinery Space (2 x Diesel generators, 2 x Caird Rainor Evaporators, 2 x 1Million Btu ACPs and 2x Stones Vapour Boilers). It was a pleasure to see his face at each opening as he said "Wow, the advancement in design and technology is quite stunning and I feel quite safe knowing that we have these types of ships and the men to sail them." Back in the MCR as we shook hands he asked me "One last favour; if you ever find yourselves down south in the Falklands please could you check on the graves of those that succumbed to their wounds and we buried there." I replied that it would an honour and I would certainly carry out his request and with that he gave me his address. We parted and I returned to the Mess and advised Bert and FCMEA(P) Ian Jennings of the visit and subsequent request and promise. It then left my mind as I felt that there was little to no chance of us ever visiting that far south.[3]

How prophetic those words would turn out to be as the decade progressed. Meanwhile, there were storm clouds on the horizon. *Fisgard* was in need of a great deal of updating: the wooden huts of the 1940s were not compatible with the requirements of modern accommodation or the expectations of those likely to be attracted to join the Royal Navy as an Artificer Apprentice. Such renovations would inevitably require the expenditure of a large amount of money. At a time when the Defence Budget was under severe strain such expenditure was unlikely to be sanctioned.

Peter Bellamy (Series 61) remembered the debate about the move to *Raleigh*:

> As an instructor at HMS Fisgard 1980-82 I can remember the discussions that were taking place regarding the future move to HMS Raleigh and the required output standards from the first 12 week term before proceeding to Part II establishments. As there was to be no workshop element to train or examine the Naval General Training (NGT) and Academic elements became the focus. Without the workshop element more time could be given over to academics but it was essential to put as much of the NGT undertaken in 3 terms at HMS Fisgard into the one term in Fisgard Squadron. The Academic requirement was driven by the Part II establishments who were also gearing up to receive 2 & 3 Class apprentices. I'm not certain how the changeover was managed with regard to the Classes that passed out of HMS Fisgard in July 1983 but the plan when I left was to cancel the Spring entry of that year and Pass out two Classes instead of one.
>
> The programme and Lesson Plan was for the one term at Fisgard Squadron was the brain child of RO Lt Cdr Keith Oliver who had been the Personnel Selection Officer (PSO) at Fisgard for many years and was appointed to carry on the role in Fisgard Squadron. He became the only constant throughout the years at HMS Raleigh and through his conscientious attitude and attention to detail he oversaw each entry and adjusted the plan as required when elements were disrupted by unforeseen circumstances like weather and availability of staff. To say that the success of the move to HMS Raleigh and the future of all the artificer training at HMS Raleigh was down to this man's efforts would be an understatement.[4]

During this period John Newell continued his training at RNEC Manadon and at last had some time at sea, as he wrote:

> My three years at RNEC Manadon were dominated by Diving, Riding, rugby and the academics. I was also a DJ in the "Thunderbox", the in-house nightclub. It was a great time. We were full time students on a good wage in a University with fantastic facilities. Although I understand why the college was closed it was a very sad day for the Royal Navy and the Engineering Branch. Perhaps some of our troubles today started at that point.
>
> Long before it closed I had been off to sea to complete my Fleet Time in HMS Manchester, gone back to Manadon for the Application Course, then to sea

to get my steam tickets in HMS Eastbourne and HMS Torquay. I then joined HMS Sirius as DMEO in 1984, my first real job since joining. Following the two years in HMS SIRIUS I returned to RNEC Manadon to read for an MSc in Electrical Engineering. This meant that between 1976 and 1987 I had been "under training" except for the DMEO's job.[5]

1982 was a momentous year for Britain and for the Armed Services. The Junta in Argentina was under considerable pressure internally for changes that they were keen not to have to concede. The defence cuts announced by Sir John Nott included the withdrawal of the Antarctic survey vessel and Falklands Islands guard ship HMS *Endurance*. This clearly sent the wrong signal to the leader of the Argentine Junta, General Leopoldo Galtieri, particularly when the Argentinean scrap metal dealers started dismantling the whaling station in South Georgia and were studiously ignored by the British.

So emboldened, Galteri ordered the invasion of the Falkland Islands and South Georgia, with the first Argentinean troops landing on the islands on 2 May 1982. There could be little resistance from the token force of Royal Marines in Port Stanley. However, the Royal Marines in South Georgia did manage to shoot down two helicopters and hole a frigate before surrendering. These Royal Marines were returned to Britain soon after.

Such an invasion of sovereign British territory could not go unanswered and the First Sea Lord, Admiral Sir Henry Leach, was instrumental in persuading Margret Thatcher that a Task Force should be assembled and dispatched to retake the islands. When asked if it was possible for the islands to be retaken, his reply was that they most certainly could and further that they must otherwise Britain's voice in the world would count for nought.

A task force of over 100 ships was assembled and stored, modified and requisitioned; some ships already at sea or in ports away from Britain were sent straight towards the Falklands. One, HMS *Antrim*, was in Gibraltar and headed south instead of returning to Portsmouth. This allowed *Antrim*, together with HMS *Plymouth*, HMS *Brilliant* and RFA *Tidespring*, to steam towards South Georgia. With a replenishment stop at Ascension Island this small task force, designated CTG 317.9, commenced Operation Paraquet, the recapture of South Georgia and the ejection of Argentine forces from the island.

Special forces from the SAS were landed on Fortuna Glacier; however, two of the helicopters crashed in blizzard whiteout conditions and it was only the resolve and skill of *Antrim*'s pilot, Lieutenant Commander Ian

Stanley, that allowed all on the glacier to be rescued. For this Ian Stanley was awarded the Distinguished Service Order. There was also the small matter of the disabling of the submarine *Santa Fe* and the numerous hazardous flights undertaken by Ian Stanley and his crew during the retaking of South Georgia: an operation that was accomplished with no British casualties and only one death among the surrendering Argentineans.

That the recapture of South Georgia was accomplished with no British casualties and no damage to the ship was a testament to good planning and execution. Things would not be so easy when it came to the recapture of the Falkland Islands. This started on the night of 21 May with the landing of troops on the beaches of San Carlos Water, an area where the Argentines had not expected an attack. A bridgehead was quickly established as 4,000 troops of 3 Commando Brigade were landed; 2 Battalion Parachute Regiment landed from the roll-on-roll-off ferry *Norland*, 40 Commando Royal Marines from HMS *Fearless* and 3 Battalion Parachute Regiment from HMS *Intrepid*. Come the morning the Argentinean Air Force arrived in numbers to attack the assembled ships. This resulted in the sinking of HMS *Ardent* on 21 May and HMS *Antelope* on the 25th. Several ships were damaged, including *Antrim*, which was struck by a bomb that failed to explode, as many did in the early days of the war, and was also strafed with 30 mm cannon shells down the port side.

The cannon shells caused considerable damage to the cables that were attached to the outer bulkhead of the main passageways, making them far too vulnerable to such damage. Lessons learnt are soon forgotten. This resulted in the loss of the Seaslug missile system as a functioning system, rendering *Antrim* with only a 4.5" gun and Exocet in working order. The 4.5" gun had had a barrel change after South Georgia, a feat accomplished at sea in foul weather ready for the invasion of the 21 May. This is a testament to the skill and fortitude of the Artificers and seamen involved as it was the first time this had been accomplished at sea.

The damage to the cabling on the port side also resulted in the loss of the port interconnector cable between the forward and after switchboards. To overcome this the CMEA(L) devised a plan to utilise some shore cables, which he had prudently squirrelled away, to connect the forward and after switchboards via the forward and after shore supply boxes. This proved a solution, though, of course, not the ideal solution, that lasted until repaired in Portsmouth Dockyard some months later.

Chris Parry, *Antrim*'s Flight Observer, remembered this incident:

The ME Department has done a clever thing today. The cannon shells in our port side did substantial damage to our electrical cables and, after a though survey, our ME's have got power running again by improvising. When we were in Gibraltar, they thought that one of the shore power cables might come in handy for a rainy day, so it was promptly lifted and hidden onboard. It has now been pressed into service as a temporary high-power cable running down the port side.[6]

When *Ardent* was attacked in San Carlos Water there was considerable damage and many casualties. Among them was MEA(M)1 Ken Enticknap, who was in charge of the After Damage Control Party. He was slightly injured by the first bomb but continued to fight the fires around him. After the next bombs he and two others were the only members of his team still alive. It is worth repeating his citation at this stage:

On May 21st 1982 HMS Ardent *was on station in San Carlos Water, East Falkland Island, providing a defensive cover against air attack by Argentine forces as land forces equipment and supplies were being put ashore. The ship was first straddled by two bombs with little damage caused, but a subsequent aircraft in the same wave hit the ship port aft, destroying the Seacat Launcher.*

HMS Ardent *was then attacked by eight aircraft resulting in eight further hits and very severe damage. The Damage Control Parties, working in exposed positions suffered the most serious casualties. There was widespread flooding of major spaces and a list developed.*

Marine Engineering Artificer (M) 1st Class Enticknap was in charge of the After Damage Control Party. Although the area was wrecked by the first bomb hits and he slightly injured, he led his team successfully in firefighting and damage control. Then in the second wave of attacks, further bombs hit his team, killing all except two of his men. Now seriously injured MEA(M)1 Enticknap continued to fight the fire with one other man until a further bomb felled him, trapping him in the wreckage. Despite his own serious injuries MEA(M)1 Enticknap showed dedication to duty under constant enemy attack in the best traditions of the service in placing the safety of other lives above his own.[7]

Ken was awarded the Queens Gallantry Medal and later in his career was promoted to the Officer Corps, retiring as a Commander.

At this point, as the war ends, there is closure for some who came before, the visitor to *Exeter*. Frank Curnow, who had served as a CERA in the wartime cruiser *Exeter*, received a letter from Eric Mitchell telling him about the wartime graves:

Whilst we were busy doing our bit in the WI a certain Argentinean General was rattling his sabre. Margaret Thatcher did her bit and the rest is history. A part of that history includes HMS Exeter's involvement.

We completed our duties in the WI and sped off south to Ascension where we took on stores, equipment mods etc before taking on fuel from British Esk which was heading North and had members of Sheffield and Coventry onboard. Our HODs were fully briefed by those survivors and we continued south. All our manmade fibre clothing was consigned to our lockers and only natural fibre clothing was to be worn and we had been furnished with Army overalls.

After the surrender our Captain requested permission for Exeter to be the first to enter the Inner Harbour at Port Stanley, given the link between Port Stanley and our predecessor. Permission was granted and late June we were in the Inner Harbour looking at Public Jetty where RFA Sir Galahad had been berthed. It was quite eerie having to cross her to get ashore onto Public Jetty knowing what had happened to her and those soldiers. A Church Service had been organised and all those that could be spared went, via liberty boat and Sir Galahad to the service. The church was on the crossroad at the end of Public Jetty, across the road on the right. After the service, Bert and I took the opportunity to go across the Public Jetty Road to the Cemetery.

We had to navigate hoards of Johnson outboard engines of all sizes, neatly stowed on stands and vehicles, to the Cemetery entrance gate which faced the harbour. On reaching the gate I turned to Bert and said "Well here we are Bert. Who'd have thought it?"

It was with pride and pleasure that I wrote, later that night, to Frank Curnow, to let him know that the six Exeter shipmates that died of their wounds whilst at Port Stanley were being well looked after. The local populace were maintaining the graves to a high standard, the grass was neatly trimmed and all headstones were clean. The grave head markers, designed and carved by PO Harold Head Pitman, of the Exeter ships company had been replaced with British War Graves Commission Headstones suitably engraved and all the graves were neat and tidy and well maintained.[8]

While Ken survived, several Artificers were not so lucky. Those who lost their lives in this conflict are listed below.

Lt. Cdr Gordon Batt	C015622P	800 Squadron
ACWEA John Caddy	D075562M	HMS *Coventry*
MEA(M) Paul Callus	D145600D	HMS *Coventry*
WEA Anthony Eggington	D076798T	HMS *Sheffield*
Lt Rodney Heath	C025065S	HMS *Coventry*
MEA Alexander James	D098624T	HMS *Fearless*
AEA Kelvin McCallum	D121589B	HMS *Glamorgan*
MEA Geoffrey Stockwell	D154502T	HMS *Coventry*
WEA David Strickland	D138928M	HMS *Coventry*
WEA Kevin Sullivan	D082300A	HMS *Sheffield*
WEA Phillip White	D154510D	HMS *Coventry*
WEA App Ian Williams	D178859U	HMS *Coventry*

Amongst all these surface ships it would be as well to remember those of the Silent Service who also went "Down South". There were six submarines deployed: *Splendid, Spartan, Courageous, Conqueror, Valiant* and the conventional submarine *Onyx*, all of whom provided sterling support to the task force.

How many felt about the forthcoming conflict is summed up in the following passage:

As HMS Conqueror's *crew sailed towards South Georgia, they too reflected on the implications of what was to come. "I thought about it on the way down there" said* Conqueror's *Chief Engine Room Artificer, Edward Hogben, "I mean, when you do patrols up north the Russians would deter you from staying there by dropping various bits of armament at you. That was to get you to go away, I thought, this time these buggers want to kill us. But, if I go, I shall be going in good company and we'll all go together. Once you've got over that bit, I found it relatively simple to just get on with life. There's no point screaming and making a fool of yourself. That would be embarrassing. So, you know, life was normal as it can be.*[9]"

As a final entry regarding the Falklands War it is worth noting an address that Rear Admiral Mike Simpson (Keppel 1944) gave at the HMS *Fisgard* passing out parade in April 1982 as the task force headed south:

Captain and Mrs. Hamilton Price, Officers and Ratings of HMS Fisgard, Ladies and Gentlemen firstly may I say what a pleasure it is to be here today, and to see so many parents witnessing their son's Passing-out Parade?

Secondly I would like to commend you for your appearance and bearing on divisions – they were just as outstanding as I expected them to be.

I am also very proud to be back in Fisgard. A very long time ago I was sitting out there somewhere, in a passing out ceremony, but unfortunately I don't remember who made the address, or what he said. So I suppose with hind sight I either didn't hear or understand the advice given, and if I did, at your age I probably didn't believe it anyway. So I don't intend to give you much advice – except – treat your chosen profession seriously. You are training to join the technician branch of the navy – the branch which keeps everything working – ships, submarines, aircraft and the weapons that they carry. There is no compromise, second best is not good enough, and the standard which will eventually be required from you will be uncompromisingly high – this will not only apply to routine maintenance and repair of systems under normal conditions, using existing spares and schedules it also applies to keeping things going under occasionally appalling conditions when the only assets available will be your technical knowledge and skill of hand. This will call for technical judgment and enterprise which may eventually determine the safety of the ship. This is why artificers are trained for four years. One year to cope with the ordinary, plus three years to cope with the extraordinary.

This demand for resourcefulness and ingenuity reminds me of an apprentice in my class here many years ago (and a well known Fleet Chief – I won't mention his name) who because of some injustice, developed a pathological hatred for his Divisional Chief who happened to be a Chief Stoker: some sort of revenge was obviously necessary and so he decided to liquidate the chief's major asset – his pusser's red bike – very difficult to come by in those days. One evening he took the bike from outside the chiefs' mess and spent the rest of the night cutting it up into very small pieces, all to class next morning with bulging pockets, he broadcast little red pieces all down the main road, and the chief stoker's bike disappeared for ever. Naturally the work of a mechanical apprentice – a greenie would have probably wired it up to the mains!

As far as your future career in the navy is concerned take what the Navy has to offer, which is probably much more than you realise. All the opportunities are there, ready and waiting.

To conclude, the past month has produced profound events which involve us all. First we were told that we didn't need a large surface fleet, which meant the navy would be cut. To be followed almost immediately by the dispatch of almost every available naval ship and aircraft to the south Atlantic on a wartime footing, although we at home are still at peace. At this very moment about 12,000 of our comrades are steaming into a situation which could result in a major naval battle, with all that that entails. Pray God it doesn't happen, but if it does, I have no doubt about the result, although we must face the fact that the large distance from home may not make it either easy or painless and there will be a price to be paid.

In such an engagement artificers will play their key role as maintainers of some of the most sophisticated maritime warfare systems ever to have been seen at sea. This key role will be underwritten by what the navy has taught apprentices like you over the years, and will continue to teach others into the future, and this is indeed one of the sources of the Royal Navy's strength.

This occasion has given me great pleasure and I hope it has to the other guests. Thank you, and good luck to you all in the future[10]

These are prescient words indeed and highlight the strengths and abilities necessary to become a good Artificer.

Back at *Fisgard* there were Apprentices joining who would leave a mark in the higher echelons of the Service. First in September 1981 in 813 Entry Matthew Bolton joined *Fisgard* and in 1982 there were several newly arrived Apprentices bound for senior rank, Peter Towell (823 Entry), Mark Cameron (823 Entry) and Mike Rose (823 Entry), showing 823 Entry to be full of potential.

In the early 1980s Matt Bolton remembered joining *Fisgard* and Bennett Division. He was in the accelerated class spending only two terms in *Fisgard*:

When I joined the Royal Navy on 4 September 1981 there was a rail strike. This meant new Fisgard recruits were collected by bus from numerous locations across the country and transported to Torpoint. I had been on a Youth Club camp in the Lake District and my parents had to take me to Lancaster to wave me off. I was just 16 and half years old.

It was a hot September; Tainted Love by Soft Cell was No.1 in the charts. My early recollections were being assembled in the gym to sign the Official Secrets Act and for various briefs, which even included how to clean your teeth properly! We were all male of course, as this long preceded WRNS at sea. The parade ground seemed huge, with the ominous "Factory" looming large over the far end, its brick chimneys reaching into the sky. The accommodation blocks ran up each side, 3 Divisions on the East (Lane, Frew and Tribe) and 3 to the west (Bennett, Griffin and Spickernell), all linked by a long corridor. I was allocated to Bennett Division and all New Entry recruits were accommodated in alphabetical order in a single dormitory. For the next 8 months my home would be a steel framed bed, a wardrobe and a chest of drawers (secured with a steel locker bar). We were all required to visit the barber, which for me meant a "Bennett Special" – No. 2 all over! We were issued with our uniform, which included a green canvas belt and puttees to be worn with blue No.8 working dress and "Compo" Boots. Best uniform was also issued, Fore and Aft Rig of course as we were on track to be Senior Ratings in a few years' time. The suit had black buttons and we would not get to wear gold buttons until later. The first few days would be spent marking our kit, using wooded letter blocks and black or white paint, or sewing on labels and name tapes, learning how to iron and starch everything into "ship's book" size and cleaning and bulling footware. I had been a Sea Cadet but had been warned not to tell anyone but as I was so good at bulling boots I could do other peoples' in return for them doing my sewing or ironing; when challenged I explained I had been taught by my Dad who was a policeman (not untrue) hence I acquired the nickname PC Plod or Plod/Ploddy for short. We all quickly acquired nicknames, an early indication of Naval culture to come. Kit musters would become a major feature of the first few weeks; sitting on the steps of the accommodation block to spit and polish parade boots, all seemed a bit surreal and somewhat serene – the calm before the storm!

We soon learned the hierarchy of the place; of course we had our Divisional Senior Rate (a Petty Officer) and Divisional Officer, but there were also Leading and PO Apprentices in each Division and a Chief Apprentice (the Head Boy). The Leading Apps and PO Apps were to be respected and revered, some were bullies. We were woken in the morning by bugle call or bosuns call and after breakfast we headed off to our instruction with calls of "Move Out" from the Leading Apps. The first 4/6 weeks was New Entry, so mostly, PT, Drill, Kit Musters and R&IT (Resource and Initiative Training). As Artificer Apprentices we would be rapidly promoted to Petty Officer and would be Leading Hands before completing training, hence character and leadership was also an important part of our development. Two tests would be visits to Scraesdon Fort and Cardinham. It was normal to spend a year at Fisgard, at this stage we were all Artificer Apprentices and the training was common irrespective of our future specialisation, Marine, Weapon or Air Engineering. This would be determined by an interview with the Personnel Selection Officer; Air Engineering was by far the most popular choice but the most limited in numbers. I declared an interest in gas turbines (thinking it might make me an air engineer), I was however streamed Marine Engineer. We also all sat an exam (maths, science, English), during New Entry, those that were successful would skip the first term's engineering training and Pass Out after 2 terms; hence Accelerated and colloquially known as "A Boys", thus my entry was designated 813a (the September entry of 1981, accelerated). We were all petty bright kids as the academic entry requirement was 5 GCE O Levels at Grade C or above (or CSE Grade 1), including maths, English and a science.

By today's standards, New Entry might be considered quite brutal; it was not uncommon to be woken in the middle of the night and ordered to do bunny hops around the parade ground or to be ordered to run through the static tanks (numerous rectangular concrete open vessels positioned around the camp to store water for firefighting purposes – needless to say the water was not fresh!). Physical Training was undertaken most days and involved rope climbing (by numbers), vaulting and circuit training. It was conducted in white tee shirt, shorts, socks and "daps"; the inspection beforehand was so severe that unless your kit was spotlessly clean, ironed to perfection (including starched shorts so stiff they would stand up on their own and you wouldn't dare put on until the last minute for fear of creasing them and any rain meant a very quick dash to the changing room) and if anyone even has the slightest twist in one of their laces it would result in the whole class being beasted with extra punishing exercises. We grew to dislike the PT staff, and often felt that they were being especially hard on the Apprentices as they would very quickly become Senior Ratings (it was not unknown for non-artificer ratings to spit after the word "Tiff"). I do remember LPT "Ginge" Nelson, who was a particularly tough instructor. He went to war in 1982 and lost his life in HMS ARDENT along with AB(S) Sean Hayward, with whom I had been in Sea Cadets.[11]

A look at Matt's career shows how he progressed from the humble beginnings at *Fisgard*:

September 1981	Apprentice Art App HMS *Fisgard* RN Artificer Basic Training Awarded Naval Knowledge Prize
May 1982	Apprentice MEA App HMS *Caledonia*/HMS *Eastbourne*/ HMS *Collingwood* Marine Engineering Apprenticeship Awarded HMS Eastbourne Best Apprentice
May 1985	LMEA/POMEA HMS Ariadne Operation and Maintenance of Steam Propulsion and Auxiliary Machinery
November 1986	POMEA CFM Portsmouth Fleet Maintenance Support
February 1987	POMEA HMS Manchester Operation and Maintenance of Gas Turbine Propulsion Machinery and Electrical Power and Distribution Systems. Selected for promotion to officer
April 1988	Officer Under Training (OUT) Midshipman BRNC Dartmouth Officer Basic Training
September 1988	Mid/Sub Lieutenant RNEC Manadon Engineering Degree training 1st Year Design Prize, 2nd Year IMarE/RINA Prize for best results, 3rd Year Prize for best exam results and IMechE Project Prize
September 1991	Sub Lieutenant HMS Active Fleet Training
April 1992	Sub Lieutenant RNEC Manadon Systems Engineering and Management Training
January 1993	Assistant MEO Sub Lieutenant HMS Beaver Preparation for MEQ
August 1993	Deputy MEO Lieutenant HMS Broadsword 2 i/c Marine Engineering Dept.
September 1995	Higher Academic Training Lieutenant UCL MSc in Marine Engineering

October 1996	Electrical Propulsion Future projects Lieutenant Ships Support Agency. Electrical Propulsion specialist advice. Propulsion motor development. Secretary to NATO Sub Group
October 1999	Head of Controls and Diagnostics Lieutenant/Lieutenant Commander HMS *Sultan*. Lecturer control engineering & signature reduction. Control and diagnostic section manager
January 2001	Marine Engineer Officer Lieutenant Commander HMS *Newcastle*. Head of Marine Engineering Department
January 2003	Technical Manager Lieutenant Commander Defence Procurement Agency Marine Systems Development
October 2005	Availability Manager & Operating Authority Lieutenant Commander Fleet HQ Administrative authority for Major Warships
February 2008	Diesel Engine Group Leader Commander Defence Equipment & Support Support to all maritime defence diesel engines and outboard motors
February 2010	Head of Fleet Time Engineering Commander BAE Systems Secondment Planning, management and execution of engineering support to all Portsmouth-based warships, worldwide
September 2012	Head of Surface Ship Operating Safety Group Commander Navy Command Headquarters. Led the development and application of policy and process to fulfil duty holder responsibilities and ensure effective safety management is enabled across the surface ship community

March 2014	Staff Marine Engineer Officer Commander Portsmouth Flotilla. Responsible and accountable to Commodore Portsmouth Flotilla for the assurance of engineering practices and standards across forty-nine ships of the Royal Navy, ranging from patrol boats to the new aircraft carriers; as coach and mentor to Marine Engineer Officers and their departments and providing advice and guidance to Commanding Officers
June 2016	Deputy Assistant Chief of Staff (Engineering Support) Captain Navy Command Headquarters. Responsible for development and publication of naval engineering strategy, maritime engineering doctrine, policy and strategic operational planning

Captain Matt Bolton is currently (2018) Deputy Assistant Chief of Staff-Engineering Support in Whale Island, Captain Peter Towell is currently (2018) Captain of *Sultan*, Captain Mike Rose is currently (2018) Defence Engineering Champion in Abbey Wood and Commodore Mark Cameron is currently (2018) Head of Training, Education, Skills and Resettlement and Commemorations and Ceremonial in the Ministry of Defence in Whitehall.

Here are a few details and thoughts from these ex-Apprentices.

Captain Mike Rose joined the Royal Navy in 1982 as an Artificer apprentice. After initial training at HMS Fisgard, *he then specialised in Marine Engineering at HMS* Caledonia; *a three year period which were to prove his true formative years; be it as a "slave to the lathe" during a comprehensive city and guilds programme, learning to camp out on Rannoch Moor in every season as part of leadership training or learning the rudiments of watchkeeping at sea; it was the full package and as such an apprenticeship with a difference. "Caley" sadly closed as a training establishment in Dec 95 and therefore with four months to go the class of "822" shifted to HMS* Sultan, *the new spiritual home of the "MEA" to complete their training in the rank of leading hand and be the first "tiffs" to pass out of HMS* Sultan *in Apr 86. He then applied his trade at sea in*

HMS Arethusa *attaining a boiler ticket and professional qualification resulting in promotion to Petty Officer 12 months later. The highs for that year were manifold ranging from promotion to learning the art of the "lower deck" through the lens of the stokers mess; a craft that should not be underestimated where he made mates for life and comprehended the backbone of the department which was to serve him well throughout his career as an Officer. The low was the loss of a great mate, LMEA Scouse Tracey who like all in "822", was undertaking his professional training in 1986 having passed out of HMS* Sultan. *He was to lose his life that year in a main machinery space fire in HMS* Plymouth *two valve isolation became the norm that year and so his legacy lives on.*

After a period of consolidation ashore in Rosyth Fleet Engineering Centre, POMEA Rose returned to sea in HMS Edinburgh *for what was to become the shortest draft of his career (6 weeks) during which time he passed his AIB and walked through the gates of BRNC Dartmouth in April 88 handing over his "hooks" for a set of midshipman tabs – now that was a shock having overseen a section at the age of 22 to now back in basic training. It was to be the start of a special journey for which he feels extremely humbled and fortunate. On reading for a degree at RNEC Manadon from 1988-1991, he then pursued application training before undertaking his first engineer officer's role in HMS* Newcastle *as the DMEO. He went on to undertake several other sea assignments ranging from MEO IN HMS Sutherland to being a sea rider as DSMEO to COMDEVFLOT with his last one being in HMS* Albion *as Cdr(E) where he saw operations in 2011 during the Arab Spring, before then placing the ship into Extended Readiness in 2012. In between his sea appointments he has undertaken positions in engineering support, acquisition and HR, interspersed with RN sponsored academic development. This included reading for an MSc in engineering at the University College London and then some years later for an MA in strategic studies at the Joint Services Staff and Command College, Shrivenham. Promoted to Captain in February 15 he was assigned into the inaugural role of Defence Engineering Champion Team leader. Here he has assumed responsibility for bringing a clarity of purpose and coherence to the multitude of engineering skills initiatives and activities currently underway across the Ministry of Defence, set against the strategic backdrop of a National skills shortage. So what keeps him going – in essence it is his roots because you never forget; perhaps epitomised when he joined HMS* Albion *as Cdr(E) in 2010 during which time he was invited to leaving drinks for a WO2 Martin who had been a Junior MEM in the stokers mess of HMS Arethusa, 1986 alongside a certain LMEA Rose. The now Cdr(E) whispered to WO2 Martin, "Pincher who would have put money on you and me doing this".*

In essence the Engineering Branch is the "beating heart" in the delivery of operational capability with the then Artificer and now Engineer Technician at the very centre of it all. "No ET – no sail" it is as simple as that.

To have been a "tiff" and served amongst them is very special indeed – it states that "it shaped my entire career in the RN".

Turning to the domestic side of his life he is married to Michele a school teacher with two teenage sons Hamish and Alexander, living in Cornwall where he can often be seen trying to tackle the North Cornish surf by board or kayak – badly.[12]

Mark Cameron decided on a career as a Weapons Engineer:

Mark Cameron was born in Sherborne, Dorset in January 1966 and educated at Sturminster Newton High School. He joined the Royal Navy in September 1982, initially training as a Weapon Engineering Artificer. Following advancement to Petty Officer and selection for promotion via the Upper Yardman Scheme, he joined BRNC Dartmouth in January 1988, moving onwards later that year to RNEC Manadon to read for an Honours Degree in Engineering. He completed the Weapon Engineer Application Course in May 1993 at which point he joined HMS Beaver as the Weapon Section Officer/Deputy Weapon Engineer Officer.

Moving from sea in 1995, he was appointed as the Sensor Systems Instructor within the Type 22 Training Group of HMS Collingwood. This was followed by a period as the personal Military Assistant to Director Ships Weapon Engineering at MOD Abbey Wood/Foxhill. During this time, he also read for a Masters Degree in Defence Administration through the RMCS Shrivenham/Cranfield University Executive Programme. Promoted to Lieutenant Commander in April 2000, he returned to sea as the Weapon Engineer Officer of HMS Cornwall.

After a 2-year period as the Weapon Engineer Officers' Career Manager, he was promoted to Commander in May 2005. Onward appointed to the staff of Flag Officer Training & Recruiting, he was responsible for the training element of the overall Fleet Transformation Programme. A move to MOD Main Building as the Capability Sponsor for Surface Ship Integrated Combat Systems (2007-09) was followed by a return to the frontline as the Staff Weapon Engineer Officer to COMPORFLOT (2009/10). Subsequent appointments were both quite short and comprised a 10-month period as Military Assistant to DE&S Director Ships and a return to Navy Command HQ as the Career Manager for Commander Engineers. He was promoted Captain in November 2012 on appointment to the role of Captain Naval Recruiting (during which time he became a Chartered Manager and Fellow of the CMI), followed by a second short OF5 tour as DACOS(Career Management) from Feb 17. His leadership, transformation and recapitalisation of Naval Recruiting was recognised with the award of an OBE in the 2017 Birthday Honours list. He joined MOD Head Office as Hd-TESR/C&C in Feb 18 on promotion to Commodore.

Married to Michele, they have 2 grown-up children, Charley (born 1995) and Dan (1997). With the family home in Hill Head near Stubbington on the Hampshire Coast, he is now rediscovering how to use his spare time, having devoted the last 20+ years to supporting his children's sporting pursuits. [13]

Peter Towell was trained as a Marine Engineer:

Peter James Towell, educated at Winterton Comprehensive School North Lincolnshire, joined the Royal Navy in 1982 as an Artificer Apprentice. Having enjoyed training in HM Ships Fisgard, Caledonia, Fearless and Collingwood he completed his apprenticeship at HMS Sultan in July 1986. Sea service followed in HMS Glasgow, with promotion to Chief Petty Officer in 1989. He returned to HMS Sultan for specialist training before returning to sea in HMS Edinburgh from 1992–95. He was commissioned as a Special Duties Officer in 1995 at Greenwich Naval College then undertook additional technical training in HMS Sultan. Subsequently appointed to sea he served as DMEO in HMS YORK 1996–98. Shore appointments followed with the engineering staff of the Flag Officer Surface Flotilla and as a course manager at HMS Sultan. Promoted to Lieutenant Commander in 2001 he returned to sea in HMS ARK ROYAL as the Senior Engineer, then served on COMOPS' staff as DFOMO2 and subsequently attended the Advanced Command and Staff Course (ACSC), from which he graduated in 2006 with an MA in Defence Studies.

Promoted to Commander on completion of ACSC he joined the Defence Logistics Organisation maritime financial planning team, which during his tenure became part of Fleet Resources and Plans. To complement his financial work he studied for an MBA and graduated from Cranfield University in January 2009. In February that year he was appointed to the Destroyers Project Team, initially as the Platform Systems Manager and subsequently as the Requirements Manager where he was deeply involved in the acceptance into service of the first of class, HMS Daring. In May 2010 he was assigned as SMEO to COMDEVFLOT, a challenging and rewarding role. This was followed in August 2012 by a move to West Battery as the Engineering (General Service) Branch Manager. In that role he oversaw the genesis and early delivery phase of Project Faraday, for which he was appointed an OBE. He was selected for promotion to Captain in 2013 and assigned to COMPORFLOT as Captain Engineering in March 2014. Captain Towell has the privilege of returning to HMS Sultan as the Commanding Officer from 26 July 2016.[14]

Bill Oliphant is another Apprentice from this period to reach senior rank. but in a different perspective in reaching senior rank from an Apprentice. He took a different route, as a Logistics Officer, and is currently (2018) Captain of Portsmouth Naval Base and shortly to leave the Service and take up the post of general secretary of the Royal Naval Association. He joined in September 1982 in 823A Class. Bill decided when he was selected for officer training that his weak mathematics would make the route through RNEC Manadon too much of a challenge and instead opted to join the Supply Department:

Bill Oliphant joined the Royal Navy in 1982 as an Artificer Apprentice and was commissioned in 1986. Early appointments included assignments in the amphibious assault ships FEARLESS and INTREPID, the carrier INVINCIBLE and the destroyers EDINBURGH and GLASGOW. These complimented shore appointments in the Clyde Submarine Base, on FOSNNI's staff at the Maritime HQ in Pitreavie, Scotland and on the staff of HQ British Forces Cyprus.

He was the Logistics Officer of HMS GRAFTON during the Kosovo crisis in 1999 where GRAFTON supported the FS FOCH Task Group in the Adriatic. He attended Initial Staff Course in 98 and the Advanced Command and Staff Course in 00/01, completing an MA in Defence Studies during the later. A fascinating appointment in UK's deployable Joint Force HQ followed where he was involved in the planning and execution of the initial operation in Afghanistan to remove the Taliban from power after the 9/11 attacks and later the 2003 invasion of Iraq.

Promoted to Commander in 2004, he returned to amphibious operations as the senior logistician on the staff of Commander Amphibious Task Group and took part in amphibious exercises in climates as varied as Northern Norway and West Africa and a Non-combatant Evacuation Operation of Lebanon during unrest there in summer 2006. Later that year he was assigned as the COS of the UK Joint Force Logistic Component which included a 6 month tour in Afghanistan.

After a period as the Royal Navy Logistics Branch Career Manager and in the MOD as the Assistance Chief of Defence Staff (Logistic Operations) lead on International Engagement, he was promoted to Captain and attended the NATO Defence College's Senior Course in Rome. His most recent appointment was in JFC Naples, Italy where he was the J3/5 Section Head and the lead for NATO's Assurance Measures in E Europe. He assumed the role of Captain of the Base (COB) Portsmouth in October 2016.

He lives in Southsea, is married to Anne and has 2 girls: Emily (1994) and Katie (1997). His interests include history, rugby, tired old cars and adventures![15]

Bill's time as an Apprentice followed the normal route for one bright enough to join the two-term accelerated entry and he left *Fisgard* early in 1983 to move onto Part Two training and he remembered his time as an Artificer Apprentice with pride:

On 28th September 2018, I was afforded the very great privilege of taking the salute at the Passing Out Parade at HMS RALEIGH. It was my last day in uniform having started at HMS FISGARD 36 years earlier in 832 entry. For me it couldn't really have been a better way to finish my time and during my address I was able to say if anyone wanted to swop uniforms with me right now, I would gladly do it all over again… Oh, and by the way, I get to wipe 30 years off the slate!

Earlier that day, I had been given a tour of the New Entry blocks and of course it brought back memories of Bennett Division in 1982. My PO App on joining was a wiry wee Scotsman, Mark "Jock" or "Johno" Johnstone who was full of mischief and good humour – we are still in touch. If you can imagine a blend of Sgt Mackay from "Porridge" and Windsor Davies from "It ain't half hot Mum!" then you have a fairly decent minds eye picture of Johno. He was to be our guide and mentor for One Class and, frankly, we had dipped in. I had been brought up on a diet of relatives' dits of their square bashing during their National Service so to be honest I was expecting new entry to be fairly brutal.

One of the stories from an elderly relative who had been taken POW by the Japanese always made me chuckle. They had been mustered for a roll call one morning and the Camp Commandant was issuing a bollocking after some misdemeanour or other. In his best English he announced, "You prisoners think I know fuck nothing. But, I can tell you, I know fuck all!"

The new entry mess was very regimented; bed, locker, bed, locker… and these long thin messes lent themselves to standing at the ends of the beds while Johno would march up and down berating us. "You're a bunch of wankers. What are you?"

"A bunch of wankers PO App"

"I didn't hear that."

"A BUNCH OF WANKERS PO APP."

This psychological stuff I could take all day, indeed, it made me laugh but I do seem to recall doing endless press-ups as Johno would catch me with my hands in my pockets – again! "Down for five Oliphant!" was a regular call. At one stage Johno even threatened me with sewing up my pockets. When I think back with all the bulling of shoes (which, I confess, I never really mastered) and ironing of kit (which I was much better at), I really don't know how I had time to have my hands in my pockets at all.

I got round my ineptitude for bulling by being the messdeck chief ironer, my speciality being the white PT shorts which by the time they were ready were like card and had creases so sharp you could almost shave with them. The daft thing was that the changing rooms in the Talbot Hall where we did PT were downstairs so we all would nip up the stairs in our undies before slipping into the starch-stiff shorts at the top step and then waddle like constipated penguins to where we would stand for LPT Taff Evans' kit inspection. He was a guinea a minute but I wouldn't have wanted to get on his wrong side. For some reason, I always stood at the LH end of the front rank for the inspection and I would always fill my lungs to max capacity before his eyes shifted to me for the inspection. I wasn't thinking about making myself look bigger but rather it was a technique to ensure there were no wrinkles in the T-shirt. Taff wouldn't miss an opportunity to pull my leg. "Smart as a guardsman Oliphant." And then as he was walking round the side of me he would say under his breath, "Railway guardsman that is." On another occasion he said, "Built like a brick shit-house Oliphant." and then the grounder, "pity you smell like one too!" So we all got through Taff's inspections and magically, having done the rounds, my boots would reappear late on Friday night gleaming and ready for Saturday's Divisions.

There were only 52 passing out of RALEIGH in September, a relatively small number compared to an intake of 300 or so boys who joined on the same day with me and were processed into our Divisions. The layout of FISGARD lent itself to rivalries between messes, between Divs and, of course, between East and West sides. Late one evening during the New Entry phase the seniors had organised a mass East v West pillow fight. It must have been quite a spectacle with 150 boys lined up on each side of the Parade Ground awaiting the signal to engage. One of the Chief Apps was on the dias, the flag was dropped, the order to charge was given and we thundered off to meet our deadly East Side foes mid Parade Ground and dish out some sporting blows with the pillow. The battle was in full swing when, after a few minutes, there was a loud whistle followed by an almost purple Duty SR shouting, "STAND STILL!" We did exactly that and just for a moment you could hear a pin drop. A second later someone broke ranks and made for the blocks followed immediately by the rest of us. I would suggest that within a minute, all of us were undressed and back in our beds hearts beating and tittering away. I know I certainly was. Nothing came of it, not at our level anyway, but I often think about that poor young Engineer OOD coming out with his Duty SR to investigate the noise and turning the corner to find a pitch battle in progress on his watch. Without putting too fine a point on it, he must have nearly shat himself!

Needless to say, new entry wasn't quite as tricky as a Japanese POW camp but I was glad of the mental preparation anyway. My mother recounts a telephone call when I reported that it was great, "a bit like Scout Camp and we're getting paid for it too" – which doesn't necessarily say much for the regime our Scout camps were run on. I was also able to report how good the food was although I came to realise that my mother was no great chef. I recall some of my messmates grumbling about the food and I could only respond that they must be joking. There were always three or more main choices and a similar number of accompanying vegetables and, invariably, a hot duff to finish. What was not to like?!

One evening after a particularly enjoyable meal, I thought that it was only right and proper that I should show my gratitude by telling the Duty PO Chef how much I had enjoyed it. If you recall, in those days, the PO Chef would stand outside the servery and was the first line of approach should there be a catering issue. I seem to recall that on this occasion, it was a particularly hairy-arsed PO wearing his cap and standing with arms folded over his not insignificant belly defying anyone to challenge the quality of his team's offering. It didn't even dawn *on me that a young baby Tiff thanking him for a lovely meal would catch him off guard; but it certainly did. He just stood there then, regaining his composure, he looked me up and down, motioned to the exit with a thumb and whispered under his breath, "Piss off, Sunshine!" I took the advice, and was amused to reflect later that he had clearly assumed that I was taking the mick. If only he'd known that I would never have had the bottle to do that – not in week two anyway!*[16]

Bill seems to have a knack of getting into scrapes and the next story shows another mishap with those in the senior classes:

However, possibly emboldened by this, an opportunity did present itself shortly afterwards for some deliberate mick taking action. Maybe in week 3 or so, we were paid a morale visit by the Bennett Chief App John "Nobby" Clark. This was definitely the softer edge after Johno's constant attentions, inspections and marches through static tanks. The good cop to Johno's bad cop. There was interest in whether any of us had girlfriends (I think we'd say partners these days) and maybe about half a dozen of us responded positively. Then the question came about did we have any photographs. I still had my hand up but when the Chief App and PO App got round to me I said that she had given it to me and it was private. When encouraged to show it I had to explain that it was private because she wasn't wearing anything in the photo. At this news I was positively ordered to expose it and despite my protestations I reluctantly revealed from my wallet my photograph of my naked girlfriend – when she was a 6-month old baby! Well, as you can imagine, I was doing press-ups for the rest of the night but at least I was doing them with a smile on my face.[17]

It seems that his capacity to get into unfortunate incidents did not improve either with age or seniority, as these two tales from Bill illustrate:

Reflecting on some of these FISGARD experiences it strikes me that the fun, shenanigans and scrapes have continued throughout my career. When I was promoted Captain I was assigned to JFC Naples. I deployed ahead of my wife and for a short time was living in transit accom in a block with singly officers. The block was in a suburb of Naples which had a bit of a reputation and I was very much aware of the undercurrent of organised crime. I was on the top floor of a five storey apartment block, coombed ceiling and nice little individual balconies on each of the windows, all of them fitted with steel shutters. As an army man would say, a crime level combat indicator if ever there was one. Although it was February it was still sunny and quite warm during the day so I had already sat out in the sun and couldn't help but notice that the guttering was made of a rather flimsy plastic. At night it was still warm so I slept with my internal french windows open and my outer steel shutters closed. Anyway, a few nights later at about 3am – couldn't bring myself to write 0300 as that lends a degree of precision which certainly wasn't there – I thought I heard a car coming into the gated compound where the block was. I then waited for the noise of the roller garage door opening into the basement. It didn't come. Strange. Who would leave their car outside and possibly get it stolen? Should I get up and have a look? While I was still contemplating pulling back the covers and leaving the warmth of my bed I then thought I could smell smoke. I was up in a shot, instinct kicking in immediately. Security was one thing but safety completely another.

I noticed that the door to the rest of the apartment was closed. The smoke must be coming from outside. I opened the steel shutters and sniffed the air. Nothing. Wonder if it's anything to do with that car that came in? Better have a look. I walked the two yards outside to look over the balcony and again nothing. It was then that I heard a very distinctive and disturbing loud click very close behind me. I span round. It was a complete nightmare. There wasn't a gunman standing there with his pistol pointed at me… no… it was much worse. The steel shutter had swung back on its hinges and had locked shut behind me.

So, picture the scene, there I am locked outside my apartment on a balcony at three in the morning and, wait for it, I'm in the complete bollocky buff! If I'd stopped to think, I would have imagined Johno saying, "Stand on your locker and repeat 10 times at the top of your voice, 'I am a complete prick!'" As it happens, I found myself clawing at the door as if somehow that was going to open it. Clearly that wasn't going to work, after all, they were designed to keep people out. I knew the guttering was nowhere near being able to take a man's weight and the drop to the flat below had no purchase points so would only be contemplated in absolute extremis. The temperature was in the teens so I knew I wasn't going to die but I was beginning to resign myself to a fairly miserable night outside followed by the embarrassment the following morning of having to call for help presumably to an elderly Italian woman living opposite who was always out on her balcony early in the morning. And, to make things worse, at that stage my Italian was so poor, I don't think I could even order a pizza! Problematico!

In desperation, I remember that the entrance to the flat was via an external staircase on the other side of the building. Maybe there was an escape route that way? It would mean climbing over the roof but it was worth a recce. It was then that I discovered my salvation – I had left my Velux window into my bathroom cracked open. There then ensued the naked cat crawl of the newly promoted and newly joined Capt O across the roof. I prised open the window and carefully lowered myself in – that catch right in the middle looked like it could do some lasting and painful damage – and dropped the 7 feet or so to the bathroom floor. The landing would have made LPT Evans proud, bending my knees to absorb the shock and then, realising I had made it, punching the air with wild delight. I probably ought to have kept the story to myself but, frankly, it was just too ridiculous not to share. It soon got round and when I was introduced to people some would ask if I was the Captain who locked himself out, naked! Already renown, but hardly for the right reason.

As the senior RN matelot in Naples I had the joy of presiding over the Trafalgar Night dinners which, in Napoli, were fairly grand affairs with about 170 folk including wives and sweethearts and a large contingent from US 6th Fleet also based in Naples. Sadly, the first year was a bit of a let down with the visiting RN admiral boring us all half to death.

I got to know some of my US colleagues pretty well. Close enough for them to tell me that I needed to do better next year. "When we come to a Royal Navy function we expect to be entertained!" Goodness, the pressure was on. Who did I know in the Navy Board who was charismatic? Well, I knew the 1st Sea Lord, Adm Zambellas from my time at COMATG when he was the Commander so I thought I would start there. I checked his movements with his outer office and was pleasantly surprised to find that he was planning to be in Venice for an international sea power symposium at about that time. I quickly dashed off a letter to ask if he might be available and, within the hour, I had a response from London… he was coming!

Wind the clock on seven months to the day of the dinner and I met him off the plane in Naples. "Word got back to me that it was a shit show last year Bill, we'll need to ginger things up a bit for the audience. Are you planning to use the material from Norway?"

"Oh yes Sir, I certainly am."

"What are you going to say?"

"I'm just going to tell them the truth Sir. It was February in northern Norway and we were short of the usual LPD for a command platform as the

available one was away chasing pirates off Somalia. We'd set up our HQ ashore near Narvik but the Royal Marines, bless them, thought that it would be a good idea to get the matelots to do a mini arctic survival course – duty of care and all that. We had three nights out on the ground; the first two were relatively civilised under canvas with arctic sleeping bags. On the third night however we built an emergency shelter and, just to spice things up a bit, they took our sleeping bags away. Well, as you can imagine, it was the longest and the coldest night ever with temperatures down to about -20C. Baltic didn't describe it. It must have been about three in the morning when I heard the immortal words from the Commodore, "Bill, I haven't had to order this of a naval officer before but, could you move a bit closer?!"

We laughed, "Great, that's how I remember it Bill but, as I said, we need to entertain them so why don't you say, "I haven't had to order this of a naval officer before but, could you move your arse a bit closer?"

"Roger Sir!!!!!"

Wind the clock forward again to that evening and we're at the dinner, "I am delighted to introduce the First Sea Lord, Admiral George Zambellas. I should say I know the Admiral quite well having served together previously, in fact, I confess, we've slept together!" I paused for effect – good that's tickled them a bit – and continued the story. When I delivered the line about moving my arse a bit closer it certainly had the desired effect – with the audience that is(!) although I could see in the eyes of a few Americans seated close to me that there was an element of shock that I had the audacity to tell such an irreverent story. Little did they know that it was the great man himself who had put me up to it.

Finally I said, "Before I hand over to the First Sea Lord to verify this account and to propose the toast to the Immortal Memory, Sir, I think there should remain an element of decorum about this and it should remain between us who was big spoon and who was little spoon!"

Anyway, it was a great night and the Admiral didn't disappoint after the staged warm up act… pun intended!

So, a while later I found myself in Portsmouth as Captain of the Base and feeling very honoured that I had been asked to come back and prepare the Naval Base for the arrival of HMS QUEEN ELIZABETH in August 2017. What was also great was that I was also working with a number of ex-Tiffs all of whom had similarly clambered up their respective greasy poles. Alan Dorricott, who as a Chief in the FISGARD workshops introduced me to a hacksaw and a

*10" bastard file, and was now running BAE Systems engineering at Portsmouth,
Jon Bullock was Cdr E in PORFLOT and, by the time I finished, John Pearson
who was effectively running the entire BEA Systems operation at the Base. All
FISGARD men, good and true.*

*Now, as the General Secretary of the RNA, I am fortunate enough to still
remain in the Naval family. If I have any regrets at all it would be that I
never actually made it to the Senior Rates mess having been picked up as an
Upper Yardy at CALEDONIA and went through as an LMEA. No complaints
though, especially with the food! Oh, and I now know how to break in through
metal shutters – amazing what can be done with a wire coat hanger!*[18]

In the light of the fecundity of this period to produce officers who have
done well must be included Andy Donaldson, who also joined 823 Class
in Spickernell Division. His early memories of *Fisgard* started at one of
the earliest evolutions for the newly entered Apprentice, the first Service
haircut. It appears the barber did not pay sufficient attention to his craft and
with the first application of the clippers managed to score a completely bald
stripe through the middle of Andy's hair from back to front, to provide an
instant reverse Mohican. This, of course, caused much amusement among
his peers and a certain notoriety from the staff, the WO GI introduced an
"off caps, bow head" to numbers to highlight his temporary discomfort.
However, this haircut was naturally only transitory, though it provided
enough unwanted publicity for the barber that Andy had free haircuts for
the rest of his time in *Fisgard*.

He also remembered the awful state of the accommodation building
in *Collingwood*, so little had changed in that respect and it would be some
years yet before they were demolished and more suitable building were
produced. The old Fisher Section in *Collingwood* that was the home of all
the Artificer Apprentices had by now given way to a new regime in which
the Apprentices arriving from *Fisgard* would now join "T School" for their
training before going to sea.

Andy was commissioned as a Charge Chief and remembered on one
ship that the wardroom owned a pet parrot called Jenny. This parrot walked
everywhere so its wings were more for decoration than utility. This parrot
had a crush on the navigator and when the navigator came in off leave to
update his charts before BOST the parrot perched on his shoulder. This was
fine until the navigator went on the bridge wing for a smoke; Jenny thought

this was a great time to make a bid for freedom and launched herself off the shoulder. Unfortunately the wings failed and the parrot plummeted into the harbour. The navigator rushed down to the dockside and launched himself into the harbour in a vain attempt to rescue the parrot, who was by this time dead. This leap into the harbour was seen and the alarm raised. This caused the police boat and SAR helicopter to be sent to aid a rescue of the unfortunate man in the water. When the truth was discovered there were questions to be answered, particularly as this episode had caused an aircraft carrier to miss its tidal slot to sail. The story made *The Sun*, where the navigator was feted as a hero in trying to save the parrot and *The Sun* provided a replacement parrot.[19]

There were further changes to Artificer ethos when in 1982 the long-standing rate of Mechanician, first introduced by Jackie Fisher in 1903, was abolished and existing mechanicians were subsumed as Artificers. In the same period the old titles of Artificers, based on a numeric progression that had started in 1903 with the introduction of Boy Artificers, gave way to a more up-to-date nomenclature. To this end 3rd Class Artificers became LMEA/LWEA etc., 2nd Class became POMEA etc., 1st Class became CPOMEA etc. and Chief Artificer took the splendid title of Charge Chief Artificer.[20] The date of issue of this DCI(RN) was not lost on many Artificers and perhaps heralded the future.

There was still exped training and the Factory still loomed large in any Apprentice's life, though the amount of craft skill was still declining after the end of craft apprenticeships in favour of a more academic structure, as Matt recalled:

Our first R&IT test was to Scraesdon Fort where we camped in the grounds and conducted an assault course of high ropes (single and double leopard) and jumping in and out of the old fort windows. Sleep would be interrupted by gunfire and thunder flashes and we were warned not to leave our tents unless we wanted to be captured by Royal Marines (probably not true, but it worked). I enjoyed it, but not everyone did.

We also had our first introduction to craft skills (fitting and turning) in the "factory" (workshops) which started with chiselling a mild steel block. Like many others, I had never worked with metal before (I had done some woodwork at school but did not continue it to O Level, opting for Technical Drawing instead). Hence, this was challenging, physical work that soon resulted in blistered and calloused hands. We would move on to hacksaw and filing and our first introduction to fitting. We were allowed to keep what we made if it was good enough and I still have my Tee Block to this day.[21]

As a final reminiscence of the final days of *Fisgard* Matt Bolton had some interesting words on the general day-to-day workings for young Apprentices:

Kit musters would continue but with the benefit of top tips from the senior classes of how to iron and fold to millimetre accuracy, how to starch sheets and pillow cases, how use pieces of cardboard and to buy extra kit so you didn't have to wear what you had carefully folded. There were regular inspections, and one inspecting officer was so displeased he ordered all our kit to be thrown out of the windows after which we were ordered to march over it; needless to say it all had to be washed, dried, ironed and re-mustered in 24 hours. Thankfully we did have good washing and drying facilities; however they were not intended for lashing people into their kitbag and sometimes leaving them in the drying room! And if anyone's personal hygiene was not up to scratch they would be hosed down and scrubbed with a yard broom – it might sound like bullying, and probably was, but we didn't really see it like that. Expectations of cleanliness were extremely high resulting in the allocation of duties and tasks, which might be polishing the "spit kid" (an aluminium bowl traditionally used for spitting tobacco into but used for gash (rubbish)) or "Pipes & Rads" – cleaning the pipes and radiators that ran along both lengths of the block and included using a toothbrush to remove and dust from the carpet under the pipes.

Divisions took place on the parade ground on alternate days during the week and there was full uniform divisions every week. When fallen in on the parade ground the divisions would be facing the Factory and with the chimneys in full view they were fair game. There must have been 7 of them because someone climbed and painted "Bennett" on them, only to be overpainted a couple of weeks later with "Griffin". Our Division got into a lot of trouble for painting Bennett, but it was also us that painted Griffin, which resulted in our closest rivals on the West Side getting into big trouble too! There was also rivalry with HMS RALEIGH across the road, the New Entry establishment for non-artificer ratings (the majority) – inevitably there were sports competitions between the 2 establishments, but there also night raids and the Fisgard apprentices one night managed to acquire one of Raleigh's Whalers from the river and bring it back to Fisgard! Fisgard also had its own volunteer band to provide the marching and incidental music. As I had learnt to play the cornet in the Barrow Steelworks Band, I joined; the commitment to attend all practices and parades came with the privilege of a "Blue Card" meaning exemption from other duties. We also carried station cards, which were left at the main gate before going ashore, but of course there was no shore leave during New Entry and then for the first term shore leave was restricted to uniform only (which usually meant talking a bag of civilian clothes and getting changed on the Torpoint Ferry). All "libertymen" were inspected before they were allowed to leave the camp. We were all encouraged to write letters home and receiving them was always an important boost; there were no mobile phones of course, but there were 2 red phone boxes adjacent to the Main Gate for which we saved our 2 and 10 pence pieces, usually having to queue and often not getting to the front before the spare time was up and no 'phone call home could be made.

Things got much easier after New Entry and the Passing In Parade, the first time we would see our families and after which the first time we were allowed out of the camp. As first termers we would remain at the bottom of the food chain until the next New Entry arrived at the start of the next term. So it would not be uncommon to be woken in the night by the senior apprentices (on their return from a run ashore), to be tipped out of bed (where the whole bed would be tipped on its side) and if the whole class or division had been ashore, it would be normal to find all beds, chests of drawers and wardrobes, piled up in the centre of the dormitory on return. There was also much rivalry between the West and East Side divisions, mostly through sporting competitions. Getting promoted to the second and third term brought more privileges, slightly more space and the opportunity to personalise it. The Leading and PO Apprentices arranged their furniture to create much larger personal space according to their authority. Many used their new found wealth to buy "boogey" boxes, one even had a full music system and regularly filled the dormitory with Status Quo 12 Gold Bars. For the first few weeks we were paid in cash, fortnightly, into our removed berets and for many years our pay statements were handwritten, with corrections made in red ink for additions and subtractions. My initial rate of pay (4–30 Sep 81) was £6.07 per day and I was charged £1.94 per day for food and accommodation. We also had a TV Room and a full-sized snooker table, with which many apprentices became quite adept. In addition to the many hours of Craft skills training there were also lessons and exams in maths, mechanical engineering (ME), electrical engineering (LE), current affairs (CA), Workshop Processes and Communication (WPC) and naval knowledge (NK – for which I *was to win a prize). So many evenings were taken up with study and revision on top of keeping kit up to standard.*

The second foray into R&IT was to Cardinham, camping on the edge of an old open mine pit and next to steep "slag heaps" that inevitably we were required to run up and down. Cardinham was also home to a long assault course, which included walls, ropes and a submerged tunnel. Unfortunately, most of had just had our inoculations before going and the stagnant water and mud encountered at Cardinham resulted in many infections. This was not good planning, but we all survived and have the scars to prove it. It was very cold at Cardinham and wet overalls had to be left outside the tent overnight only to find that by the morning they had frozen into rigid sheets of ice – not pleasant.

Finally, we would Pass Out of HMS Fisgard, having been assigned to a specialisation and to move on to our Part 2 training establishments for another 3 years training – HMS Caledonia for Marine Engineers, HMS Collingwood for Weapon Engineers and HMS Daedalus for Air Engineers. A very proud day, FISGARD had taken in young men and boys, given them a level of fitness, resilience, self-reliance and an introduction to technical knowledge and skill that would set the foundation for membership of an elite engineering corps.[22]

Another young man who joined *Fisgard* in 821 Class was Ian Dickinson, who remembered his first ever duty after the passing in parade:

Joined Fisgard as 821 Lane Division and after passing in my first ever duty was early morning on the main gate. Absolutely crapping it in case I got it wrong the first car in was a very familiar red mini van. Didn't even stop it and waved it straight though. 5 secs later the guard room window was flung open by the duty killick screaming something about checking all id's. He finished up by saying, "You probably don't even know who that was".

I replied very confidently "Yes I do. It was my Dad". (He was Div Chief of Spickernell). The window closed.[23]

Without doubt the most momentous event of the 1980s was the closure of *Fisgard*, when initial training of Apprentices moved across the road to HMS *Raleigh*. This was the end of the separate regime of Apprentice training that had started in 1903 at Chatham, through *Indus* at Torpoint, *Fisgard* in Portsmouth, *Tenedos*, the temporary Second World War establishments and finally HMS *Fisgard* as RNATE Torpoint from 1940 until 1883. This was clearly a decision based on financial considerations with no recourse to nostalgia.

In August 1983 there was a final Open Day at *Fisgard*, which allowed many old boys to visit the establishment for the last time as a commissioned ship. Sydney Wakeham (Keppel 1944) wrote about it later:

On Saturday 13th August 1983 a Fisgard Finale Open Day took place prior to the establishment closing down later that year.

Various events took place during the afternoon and early evening. There were exhibitions demonstrating the Artificers' skills over the years and the one thousand ex-boys who attended enjoyed meeting old friends and recalling the escapades that have become part of Fisgard folklore.

Then, on a bright sunny evening (who says it always rains in Guzz?), following a display of Guard Drill by apprentices, all of the ex-apprentices present were invited to take part in a last march past. There were a few GIs stationed on the edges of the parade ground to encourage us to assemble and gradually, egged on by wives and families, a very large contingent massed in the South-West corner. With a little persuasion and advice from the GIs the ex-Tiffies of each entry year formed up in "platoons" headed by the sole representative of the 1916 intake and gradually growing in size until the entries of the 1940s, who mustered large groups of marchers. My own year (1944), was well represented by more than sixty former members of Blake, Anson, Jervis and Keppel Divisions who formed up in three rather ragged lines. The Fisgard Apprentices Band was playing splendid martial music and eventually the order was given "Ex-Artificer Apprentices – Quick March".

The mob started shuffling forward, turned left to march up the east side and, on reaching the top of the parade ground, was ordered by the Chief GI to turn left into line. There were about fifty yards to go to the saluting dais and initially the long lines of Ex-Boys advanced in the old style "Tiffies' shuffle." Then suddenly there was a change. No one could say what caused it. No words were spoken but when the first motley platoon of Ex-Boys was about thirty yards from the dais an odd feeling must have come over those marching for suddenly, heads went back, arms swung rigidly, the strides improved and the four hundred or so marchers became united. It was as if everyone felt the importance of this historic occasion and immediately became a "Band of Brothers" marching with pride. I can remember my back hairs standing on end and an emotional feeling as, in our turn we smartly responded to the order "Eyes right".

We halted at the far end of the parade ground and were dispersed. I met up
with my wife who was dabbing her eyes with a handkerchief, as were other ladies
nearby. They had all noticed the change to the lines as each platoon approached
the rostrum and said how lumps came to their throats as they sensed the pride
being displayed by those taking part in the Last March Past.[24]

The numbers of ex-Apprentices that attended and the timescale they covered is testament to the affection that is felt for *Fisgard* and the training, comradeship and sense of belonging to an elite band that being there engendered.

The final class to enter *Fisgard* joined at the beginning of 1983 as 831 Entry, with 832 Entry joining *Raleigh* in May 1983. One minor point of disappointment felt by 831 was they wore black buttons, whereas 832 wore gilt buttons from their day of entry. Another bone of contention was the change to the length of basic training, which had been three terms at *Fisgard* for many years. This was now reduced to one term in Fisgard Squadron, after which time the Apprentices would move on to *Collingwood*, *Sultan* and *Daedalus*. So after 43 years 831 Entry passed out of *Fisgard* in December 1983, ending an era that had seen thousands of young men moulded into the elite of the lower deck.

Pete Bellamy had some reflections on how he saw the changes:

Fisgard Squadron Staff consisted of an Apprentices Training Officer (ATO),
PSO, Six Instructor Officers that doubled as Divisional Officer or vice versa,
Squadron Warrant Officer (FSWO), two Chief Petty Officers who managed the
accommodation blocks, six Petty Officer Mechanics as Divisional Instructors and
one civilian secretary who worked mainly for the PSO. In general the Instructor
Officers would contain at least two SD Officers that had joined as Artificers and
the SWO was an WOMEA appointment. This at least gave the new entries
someone with first-hand knowledge to ask career questions about life as an
artificer. What was lost was the continuity of having senior apprentices to teach
the ropes to the new arrivals and get normal routines established early. This left
the instructors with an uphill task at every new term and especially the August
entry which was always six full divisions of 30+.

The first four weeks were much the same as it had been at HMS Fisgard with;
haircut, Scraesdon Fort, fitness test, swimming test, assault course, Drill exam,
kit musters, medical and injections and firing range. All these were designed for

the Navy to assess the apprentices for NGT and their ability to accept discipline and have the ability to continue through training. It also, purposely, put the new entries under stress and gave them the opportunity to assess their own ability to stand up to the pressure and if necessary volunteer to leave under the Premature Voluntary Release scheme with no penalty. Once the New Entry period was over the focus was on academics and the NGT element became more about leadership than withstanding the pressure although leadership was tested under difficult circumstances during Cardinham Exped. Class Leaders changed on a weekly basis to give as many apprentices as possible the experience of responsibility and organisation.

During my time as FSWO recruiting for the Armed Forces became very difficult as the governments "Education, education, education" policy was implemented and nearly all 16 year olds were going on to sixth form and university, subsequently the Recruiting Officers were finding it difficult to fulfil all the training places available. It is my opinion that the recruiting standards were managed and many of the artificer recruits were below the standard required. This led to a situation whereby over 25% of apprentices were failing on NGT and Academics grounds during the first term and discharged unsuitable for artificer training. At this point CinCNAV Home directed that Fisgard Squadron failures were to be capped at 19% on academic grounds stating that it would be up to the Part II establishments to consider extra academic training for those not reaching the required levels. At the end of some terms we were passing out apprentices that had failed two of the three academic exams. Fisgard Squadron presented CinCNAV Home the analogy of fuel supplies to a gas turbine on a Naval Vessel; all the fuel supplied to a ship has to be course and finely filtered before separation to remove the particle and elements that can seriously damage the engine. By restricting the failure rate was like removing the course filter that would allow larger particles through to the finer filter a separators that were operating in the Part II establishments causing them to be clogged or damaged or in the worst case allowing the missed particles into the Fleet and thus damaging the fine-tuned engine. All this was ignored and the standards were lowered.[25]

To highlight the changes in the training regime the following résumé was published in 1983:

Up to May 1983

Part I New Entry Training in HMS FISGARD Weeks 1–4

Part II Training in HMS FISGARD from Week 5 onwards

Part III Training in HMS CALEDONIA, COLLINGWOOD or DAEDALUS

The normal course, in HMS FISGARD, lasted for 3 terms of 15 weeks each. Some Apprentices, appropriately qualified on entry and doing well in a Grading Examination during their first week here, were selected as Accelerators and passed through HMS FISGARD in 2 terms.

The Naval Department Part I Examination (ND I) was taken towards the end of the second term; the Part II Examination (ND II) at the end of the third term. Accelerators were exempt ND I in most subjects. These examinations were part of the qualifying process for award of The Technician Education Council (TEC) Diploma awarded on completion of the full 4 year apprenticeship.

The normal foundation course in HMS FISGARD was broken down as follows:

Naval General Training 38%

Technical Education 44%

Craft Skill 18%

The terminology of Technical Education and Craft Skill are self explanatory. Naval General Training (NGT) included an element of naval general knowledge e.g. Firefighting, First Aid, Hygiene, Naval Heritage, Internal Security and Upkeep of Kit, but was primarily concerned with the character development and leadership training of Apprentices.

After May 1983

The first entry of the new training scheme (150 apprentices) joined HMS RALEIGH in May for a 14 week Initial Training term in the "FISGARD SQUADRON", set up for the purpose. This term is split about 50:50 between academic subjects and Naval General Training. There is no craft at this stage. Apprentices are categorised ME, WE and AE during their first term before moving on the Artificer Training Establishments of HMS SULTAN, COLLINGWOOD and DAEDALUS where the whole apprenticeship will now be concentrated. As before there will be 3 apprentice entries per year into HMS RALEIGH with a forecast annual requirement of 550 apprentices. The present and last 2 classes in HMS FISGARD will pass out as normal in August and December 83. The last ME class to pass out to HMS CALEDONIA will do so in January 84. ME apprentice training thereon progressively switches to HMS SULTAN.[26]

As can be seen from the last paragraph of this synopsis of training, there was also another almighty upheaval for Apprentices to endure. In 1985 HMS *Caledonia* was scheduled for closure, with ME training moving to *Sultan*. The last class of MEAs joined *Caledonia* in January 1984. At the same time the harbour training ships *Eastbourne* and *Duncan* were paid off to go to scrap. On 4 August 1984 a "final" reunion was held in *Caledonia* and the Commanding Officer, Captain A.E. Sturgeon, wrote the foreword for this reunion:

WELCOME BACK TO CALEDONIA.

Many of you will have travelled far and wide to be with us here today and we are delighted to see you all. I am sure that everyone has been brought together by the spirit of comradeship and friendliness that HMS Caledonia *has developed over the years. Although we do not finally transfer training to HMS* Sultan *until next year, we have decided to hold this final reunion today so that you can see us running at full steam. No doubt you will see many changes in the place since you were last here. However, a large portion of the old buildings still remain and, with them, the character of Calley lives on. The syllabus has changed considerably over the years, but we still attempt to give the apprentices a first class training covering a wide range of academic, technical and craft skills. The ability of the MEA has never been in doubt and we produce a most competent and professional Artificer who is well respected in the Fleet. Today you will have the opportunity to see how they are trained and the skills they have developed. But, most important of all, you will be able to meet old friends and remember the "Good Old Days". Please feel free to go anywhere and ask any questions. My staff are here to help and are only too willing to assist. I hope you have a very happy and enjoyable day.*

The reunion was attended by several hundred ex apprentices and others who had travelled from all corners of the UK and from all over the world, especially from Canada, New Zealand, and America. The staff and trainees provided an action packed day:

Programme

Saturday 4th August 1984

1300 Main Gate open to Visitors

1345 Divisions fall in on Boiler House Lawn

1400 VIPs arrive to witness Divisions

Chaplain of the Fleet: The Venerable N D Jones QHC

Ex Apprentices:

Rear Admiral H L O Thompson

Rear Admiral J Burgess MVO

Rear Admiral M H Griffin CB

Rear Admiral J C Warsop CB

Former Captains of HMS Caledonia:

Vice Admiral Sir George Raper KCB

Rear Admiral D N Callaghan CB

Captain R H P Elvin

Captain W G M Burn

Captain C C Loxton

Captain S G Morgan CBE MVO

1500 Static Displays open

1530 Tea

1615 Activity Displays on Boiler House Lawn

1730 Main Bars open

1915 March Past of Ex-Caledonians (including the

ex-apprentice Rear Admirals!)

Ceremonial Sunset on Boiler House Lawn

2000 Main Bars open

2015 Buffet Supper for visitors in Main Dining Hall

2300 Bars close!

The salute was taken by Vice Admiral Sir George Raper as all the ex-apprentices, including the Rear Admirals, marched past in their original divisions. Sir George selected Rear Admiral Warsop's division (Howe '43) to be "sent round again!" Off the parade ground the guests were given guided tours and demonstrations of equipment, gymnastics etc. In the evening old friendships were renewed and the years rolled away.[27]

In the years from its inception in 1937 over 20,000 Artificer Apprentices passed out of *Caledonia*, from the first, Roy (George) Penny, who joined the floating *Caledonia* in Rosyth Dockyard in 1937, to the last Apprentice, J.R. Walton, to pass through the gates of *Caledonia*, the shore establishment, in 1985. So, on 17 December 1985 the Royal Naval Engineering School shut its gates for the last time, the flag was lowered and an era ended. The flag is now in the Marine Engineering Museum in *Sultan*. And with the closure of *Caledonia* the eighty-two years of separate training establishments came to an end.

When the Apprentices of Classes 822, 823 and 831 arrived at *Sultan* there had to be a rapid assimilation into this large and diverse establishment, however there were plenty of ex-Apprentices to soften the blow of being in such a large impersonal establishment where Apprentices were only one of many undergoing training, as Peter Collings, an ERA of Series 5, and an instructor in *Sultan* at the time of the last *Caledonia* Apprentices, recalled:

I was instructing "foreign navy apprentices" at HMS Sultan *in December 1985 when my boss told me that the last three classes from* Caledonia *were arriving in* Sultan *in the New Year to continue their training, instead of dwindling down to one class in the huge establishment in Rosyth. So, from teaching foreign apprentices how to weld and shape metal, with all the associated language problems, I looked forward to teaching the same to apprentices who were in the same position as I had been some thirty-three years before.*

On the 9th January 1986 about one hundred and seventy-four apprentices were spread over HMS Sultan *in different workshops, depending on their trades.*

Gone were the ERA Apps, OA Apps, and Shipwright Apps. These were now all known as MEAs with the designation (L) for purely electrical, (ML) for mainly mechanical but some high power electrical (generators etc.), (EL) for electrical and control systems, weapons etc.

Class 822 (ie they joined in the second term of 1982) comprised L1, ML2, ML3 and EL1. Class 823 (the third term of 1982) comprised EL2 and M33. There was also a class 831 known as A and B. A bit confusing but they were all Caledonia *apprentices.*

I tried to obtain information from them about their life in the dormitories and workshops at Caledonia *but I soon found that it was me who was telling them about "fagging", "dormitory musters", and the "class distinction" between senior and junior apprentices. So when my boss came into our workshop, looked down to the end and saw my class gathered around me, I was probably telling them how on hearing the shout, "Boy," I used to rush from the dormitory and report to the Senior Apprentices' dormitory – not how an oxy/acetylene burner worked!*[28]

With the closure of *Fisgard* and Apprentices spending their first term in *Raleigh* there was further consolidation of training, which remained extant until 1993:

Between 1983 and 1993, all Artificer Apprentices spent their first term in the Fisgard Squadron undergoing initial training and specialisation selection. They then transferred to their respective Part 2 specialist training school, Air Artificers to Daedalus, Electrical and Radio Electrical Artificers (Air) and Control and Ordnance Electrical Artificers to Collingwood and Marine Engineering Artificers (P) and (H) to Sultan.

During the next four terms of their training, apprentices concentrated on an in-depth study of the technical subjects relevant to their specialisation. They also received some craft training in the workshop.

In their sixth term, whilst Air Artificer Apprentices enjoyed their first taste of (air) field on-job training at one of the RN Air Stations, MEA, CEA OEA and REA apprentices received practical on board training in the Harbour Training Ships berthed off Elson jetty in Portsmouth harbour, (close to where the Fisgard hulks were berthed from 1908 to 1931). The apprentices lived onboard and played the role of a normal crew. MEAs were trained to operate ship's auxiliary and propulsion machinery, each MEA Apprentice being expected to earn his Auxiliary Machinery Certificate. CEA and OEA Apprentices learnt to test and tune, operate and maintain ships' weapons electrical, hydraulic and electronic equipment. This valuable practical pre-sea training was followed in the next term by a draft to a seagoing ship where apprentices were able to put their training into use. They were also introduced to life in the real Navy, and at a relatively young age, the delights of foreign travel.

The final phase of their training, (carried out back in the Specialist School), was similar for all Artificer Apprentices, and mainly comprised training modules in modern technologies relevant to their specialisation. On successful completion of their final craft test job, apprentices were awarded a City and Guilds Craft certificate and were advanced to Acting Leading Artificer, (formerly Artificer 5th Class and later Artificer 3rd Class)

In 1988, the balance of training between craft and academic/technical instruction again swung towards the latter with the transfer of one term from the workshop to the classroom. At the same time, for economic reasons, use of the Harbour Training Ships ceased.[29]

In the aftermath of the Falklands conflict there was a very unfortunate accident onboard HMS *Fife*, while deployed to the Falkland Islands in 1984. It was still a lively area to be in and ships were kept at constant readiness. This included having live missiles loaded onto the Seacat launchers. On Saturday, 28 January 1984, a young WEA Apprentice, Jonathan Mills, was tasked to carry out routine maintenance on the missile. During this testing the missile rocket motor ignited and the unfortunate Jonathan was caught in the motor efflux. He was rushed to hospital in Port Stanley; this involved a helicopter journey of 150 miles to Stanley, where he was met by ambulance and taken to the military hospital there.

His parents were informed and arrangements were made to fly them to Port Stanley via Ascension Island. As was the nature of the journey at the time, the flight took over thirty hours. Unfortunately, Jonathan died some hours before his parents arrived. He was eighteen years old. In the aftermath, the MP for Arundel, Michael Marshall, in whose constituency Jonathan's parents lived, asked in Parliament about the accident and the arrangements to fly Jonathan's parents to be at their son's bedside. He raised three issues:

As to the concerns I wish to put to the Minister, I wish to specify these into three brief areas. First, there were problems of communication and travel after news was received of Jonathan Mills' severe injuries. Having visited the Falklands myself, I am aware of the major problems posed in trying to get communications between Port Stanley, the Royal Navy in Portsmouth and other parts of the United Kingdom. I also appreciate the logistical difficulties in arranging swift travel to the Falkland islands via Ascension island. The tragedy in this case was heightened by the fact that by the time Mr. and Mrs. Mills reached Port Stanley, their son had died some hours earlier. From the full account that they have given me, and in which, incidentally, they express the view that every possible kindness and consideration was shown to them from the time they left this country until the time they returned, I am nevertheless worried about the fact that their Falklands visit was arranged at their own suggestion when news of their son's medical condition proved sparse and difficult to obtain. I put it to the Minister: would it not be appropriate in such cases for an immediate option to be given to next of kin for such a visit?

Second, I have to say that. I am further concerned about what appears to be a complete lack of written formal advice to families in such cases. It was only as a result of detailed questions, which Mr. and Mrs. Mills submitted to me, and which I put to my noble Friend, that such basic information as the processes for registering death, the issue of a death certificate and arrangements with the coroner in Oxford were made known to me by a letter from my noble Friend dated 1 March, a month after the death of Jonathan Mills. It should surely be standard practice in a situation such as this for guidance notes to be made available to families at the earliest possible moment. It would also have been helpful, and, I believe, more sensitive, to have arranged for some form of personal caller to make contact with Mr. and Mrs. Mills, rather than the repeated use of the telephone by a number of differing contacts and telephone callers.

Thirdly, the period awaiting further advice has caused anxiety of an even more profound kind. I refer to the rumours which perhaps inevitably come with uncertainty, in this case to the effect that the Seacat missile and launching system, which had been in service for many years, are inherently unstable. Such suggestions were put to Mr. and Mrs. Mills, riot by those serving in the Falklands, but by other naval families including, I am bound to report, some with direct Royal Navy experience. The anxieties of Mr. and Mrs. Mills in recent weeks can well be imagined, and, while some judgment must be reserved until the naval inquiry is complete, I believe that the Minister and I have an opportunity tonight to try to set at rest the minds of not only Mr. and Mrs. Mills, but also of other naval families by a re-statement of established facts relating to this missile system.[30]

John Lee, the Under-Secretary of State for Defence Procurement, replied:

I am sure that the House will join me in expressing to the parents of Jonathan Mills our profound sorrow at the tragic death of their son. He is reported as having been a cheerful, lively young man, and popular on board his ship HMS Fife, where he will be greatly missed. It must be a terrible shock for parents to lose such a fine young son in an accident in a faraway place, and a terrible experience to know that he was lying seriously ill in a place where they could not get quickly to his bedside.[31]

He went on to say that all the questions raised would be addressed by the full inquiry into the incident and to this end he detailed the help and assistance given to Mr and Mrs Mills:

A decision was made to fly out Mr. and Mrs. Mills. Whether the decision should have been made earlier is a matter we will be looking into. They left Brize Norton early on 31 January and arrived at Stanley at 1500 hours local time on 1 February. Sadly, Jonathan had died while they were flying there.

Mr. and Mrs. Mills were met at Stanley by Jonathan's divisional officer and the chaplain from the ship, who accompanied them during their two-day stay in the Falklands. They were also attended by the chief petty officer who had been landed to be with Jonathan, and the commanding officer of HMS Fife released him to fly home with them to provide comfort.

On their return to England the commodore of HMS Nelson wrote personally to Mr. and Mrs. Mills and offered his assistance. He appointed an officer to assist them, particularly with any problems connected with their son's estate, and the chaplain of HMS Collingwood—where Jonathan had recently served—made several visits to the family to provide comfort and offer help. Sadly, at such a time of loss it can never be enough.

When my Department has studied the reports we shall know whether all that could reasonably be done was done. What I have said should, I believe, show the House that the Royal Navy does take trouble to look after its families. If the final analysis shows anything wrong, I believe that it will not be through failure to care.[32]

The results of any inquiries do not seem to be in the public domain. An obituary to this unfortunate young man appeared in the *Navy News* for March 1984 in Britain and in the *Penguin News*, the Falkland Islands news magazine, of 27 February 1984.

Returning now to John Newell, we find him employed in Foxhill near Bath in a job ideally suited to a young Lieutenant with an electrical MSc, as he remembered:

Three years in Foxhill, Bath, followed the MSc, working on the pollution desk, the job being known as "SHITO to the Fleet". The obvious job for someone with an electrical MSc, however I can't be too rude about the appointers as I later became one of them. The main project I was responsible for was to get a sewage treatment plant that worked at sea. The aim was to replicate the system ashore which effectively treats the sewage then separates the solids from the "clear" liquid in a hopper. Hoppers do not work at sea so we had to find a filter. If you wind forward to today with the use of ceramic filters it all sounds so easy but back then nothing worked. We tried cyclone separators, filters, screens and centrifuges. Standing next to the centrifuge in our 40' ISO container at HMS SULTAN into which was pumped 180 peoples' worth of poo, it suddenly threw a large fountain of the stuff all over us. It was not a pleasant drive back from Portsmouth to Bath in the hire car![53]

The Appointers move in mysterious ways to ensure the talents of all are best employed, but as John later became an Appointer himself he found out at first hand the difficulties there are fitting people into jobs as they would wish.

On 1 October 1986 Nick Cross arrived at Fisgard Squadron in Shervil Division, one amongst an intake of about 240. His initial reaction was that he hated it in Fisgard Squadron; he was totally bewildered and in a new and alien environment. Even from Dorset he remembered the train journey being long and convoluted, meeting up with some other lads on the train, and more at the station, and having what seemed to be an interminable bus trip through Plymouth. He seems to think that though he was eighteen his upbringing had been somewhat sheltered compared to his peers; he found standing up in front of the class, taking charge and giving orders were particularly difficult. Looking back, he knows he wasn't fit enough and was in no way prepared for these first weeks at *Raleigh* and he believes he only just scraped through this phase of his training. Perhaps the turning point was an incident with some of the mechanic trainees, who decided to move the Apprentice class gear around in the gym changing room. This naturally provoked retaliation, as this class foolishly changed in the same room. Parade boots were stamped on and beret badges turned upside down. Later that day Nick's class were marched back to the gym, where the PO PTI demanded to know who had been responsible, PTIs having no sense of humour, and Nick held his hand up and believed that this is where he grew up at last, but still remembered either being spat at or saluted as one wearing a peaked hat.

Things were very much better once he arrived at *Collingwood*. An early incident happened early during an induction week where the class was programmed in to go to the "bop" on the Saturday night. An Apprentice, who for the sake of modesty must remain nameless, to help out a friend who had trapped, escorted the girl's friend home. The result of the ensuing romantic liaison was not what the young lad expected and resulted some weeks later with the necessity to visit a certain clinic within the sick bay at *Nelson*. This visit had to be conducted in no. 1 uniform so everyone in the sick bay knew where you were going. The consultant, as a matter of course, asked the young man if he had any idea from whom he had contracted the affliction. He replied yes: "Sorry, sir, she is sitting outside." The doctor looked surprised and asked what he meant. "She is the Wren receptionist," to which the doctor replied, "Leave that with me."

Nick played in the volunteer band, which brought with it the much-prized "blue station card", which excused the owner from many of the camp duties. The backbone of the band was Artificers because of the length of time they spent in *Collingwood*. This does not mean things were easy: there were many gigs to perform for eight or nine weeks, which took up many weekends.

One of the Apprentices in a couple of classes ahead of him was on crutches with his leg in a cast from hip to ankle. This was the result of an accident following a Sunday DTS in the Bugle in Fareham. At closing time on a raw and frosty November day he managed to get into trouble with the local police for "urinating in a public place". This resulted in him having to appear at the captain's table for the consequential naval penalties following an appearance in a civil court.

The Captain could understand the need for the young Apprentice to relieve himself after the lunchtime imbibing, but the Captain was at a loss to understand how he broke his leg doing it. The Apprentice replied that as he was relieving himself someone shouted at him and as he turned to see who it was he fell off the bus shelter. The Captain managed a straight face while he stood him over; once the Apprentice had left the room everyone dissolved into laughter.

After two years in "T" School Nick was due to join *Ark Royal*, however a friend heard that HMS *Hermione* was due to deploy to the Gulf, which seemed a far better option; having approached the Apprentice Training Officer this was duly arranged and off they went to the Gulf for the Armilla Patrol and the runs ashore this allowed. He returned to Plymouth on his twenty-first birthday to enjoy it at anchor by the breakwater and came back to *Collingwood* for specialist training, after which he went to HMS *Campbeltown* as the Seawolf tracker maintainer for just over two years.

Campbeltown he remembered as a "party" ship and a happy one and he made a good impression on his superiors, which made life that much easier.

He remembered that due to unexpected overnight snow on the day he was due to sit his Chief's Board, which instead of the usual three or four hours his was "done and dusted" in an hour and a quarter. His boss would not allow him to pick up acting rate until his due date, however his DO got it backdated for the three months so nothing was lost.

Nick returned to *Campbeltown* after two years in *Collingwood* and was instrumental in a comprehensive upgrade of the Seawolf tracker system. There followed two years in Abbey Wood and a return to sea in *Cornwall*. He left *Cornwall* on selection for Charge Chief and was then selected to go to Dartmouth. As Nick had already completed an OU degree he was selected to join the E (IS) (Engineering (Information Systems)) Branch, which led to an MSc and no sea billets. However, the branch was short-lived and he returned to the WE fold, but with no DWEO experience, which put him at a considerable disadvantage compared to his peers.

He felt, looking back, that apart from the initial shock of *Raleigh* his time as an Artificer was rich and rewarding and an experience that stood him in good stead in his career in the wardroom and a career he would be happy for his son to follow.

It may be wondered how the esprit de coeur that had maintained the sense of humour of Apprentices over the years endured the transition to *Raleigh*. That it continued is illustrated by an episode remembered by Peter Bellamy (Series 61), who was the Fisgard Squadron Warrant Officer in the late 1980s:

When I was serving at Fisgard Squadron the Training Commander, Tim Peach, sent the Raleigh cannons from the main gate to armourers for refurbishment and without consulting me or my boss organised for the Fisgard cannons to replace them for the duration of the work, up to a year. I fought hard to stop the movement but Commander Peach would not listen and eventually a lorry with a Hiab crane came to take our cannons away. At Both Watches the next morning I assured the assembled apprentices that in my day we would have organised a night raid and retrieved the cannons back to their proper position. sure enough the next morning the cannons were back on the plinths outside our Squadron. The Training Commander took two weeks to reorganise the transport and the cannons were returned to the Main Gate. The apprentices waited until the night before they were due to leave Raleigh to perform the disappearing act again; thus ensuring that the cannons were back in place when the next entry of Tiffs arrived. I also served at HMS Fisgard as a New Entry and Workshop Instructor and it was one of the most rewarding jobs I fulfilled.[34]

One area of Artificer recruitment receives very little coverage and that is the entry of direct entry Artificers. These were men who had completed an apprenticeship in a civilian company and then decided to join the Royal Navy. This method of recruitment was, of course, the way the original ERAs were recruited and continued even after the introduction of the Boy Artificer.

It has been in and out of favour over the years and has recently had a renaissance with the introduction of direct entry Petty Officer Engineering Technicians, who may join up to forty years of age. This may be something of an admission that the Artificer concept was scrapped prematurely, but that is not likely to be an admission made any time soon.

It has come to light recently that John Harrison, who joined as a direct entry OA in 1938 and served in HMS *Belfast* during the Second World War, is still going strong at 104 years old. He recently attended the eightieth anniversary of the launch of *Belfast* and attended, with his son, the Artificer 150 dinner. A game old chap indeed.

Among those who joined as DE Artificers was Steve Drayton, who joined *Fisgard* in 1982. He had served an apprenticeship with Chrysler and wanted to join the Royal Marines when he was twenty-two years old, however he was persuaded that he would be better off as an Artificer and after going to *Sultan* for a week's aptitude tests some weeks later he joined *Fisgard* as a Probationary MEA3 for one term with nine others in a separate division. He then spent a year being navalised in *Sultan* and three months in *Collingwood*. He then went to sea in HMS *Achilles* as a Probationary Acting MEA2, where he gained his Boiler Watchkeeping and Switchboard Operators certificates. After this time he joined the mainstream of Artificer advancement through to CPO.

Selected for Portsmouth Field Gun Crew in 1988, he then joined HMS *Intrepid* and completed three tours between 1988 and 1998, interspersed with instructional duties at HMS *Sultan* and two more seasons at Command Field Gun. He was selected for Charge Chief in 1997 while on HMS *Fearless* conducting Operation Ocean Wave. In 2001 he joined HMS *Illustrious*, achieving a Flag Officer Sea Training Commendation, and was involved in Operation Veritas, the initial operation into Afghanistan. Promoted to Warrant Officer in 2003, he has held senior positions within the Marine Engineering Branch, including the Marine Engineering Warrant Officer on the RN flagship HMS *Ark Royal*, Fleet Time Project Manager, Officer in Charge of Naval Engineering Falkland Islands, Assistant Staff Marine Engineering Officer to COMPORFLOT and Engineering Requirement Manager for Director Naval Personnel. Due to retire from the service in 2014, he was extended, joining the Integrated Change Programme, implementing recommendations from the Levine Report and designing and writing the annual support contract between Navy Command and the DE&S.

While this was one way of entering ready-trained craftsmen to the Royal Navy, it was not a resounding success and the last direct entries joined in 1983. This may have something to do with the dwindling pool of trained time-served craftsmen in civilian life from which to draw personnel. However, Steven is still serving in *Sultan*, as a Warrant Officer in the post of Engineering Technician Career Course Manager, having been extended in his service longer than was the norm fifteen years earlier. Does that say anything about the calibre of training at present?[35]

The Captain's remarks in the *Fisgard Magazine* of 1981 give a flavour of the numbers involved over one particular year:

> *I believe our performance at HMS FISGARD continues to be impressive. We have sent on 178 Apprentices to HMS CALEDONIA, 156 to HMS COLLINGWOOD and 81 to HMS DAEDALUS. 48 DEAs passed on to HMS SULTAN, 7 to HMS COLLINGWOOD and 1 to HMS DAEDALUS. Many have been recategorised into other branches of the Navy, too many decided to take their optional discharge before giving themselves a chance to appreciate fully the value and quality of a Naval Apprenticeship, and a number fell by the wayside. Mathematics continues to be a bugbear for many, and with the variation that seems to prevail in maths teaching nationally, I feel for them![36]*

In 1989 Jonathan Pearce joined *Raleigh* in 893 Class and was in Harcus Division. He spent the normal time in *Raleigh* and then joined *Collingwood* as a WE Apprentice in December 1989. He spent some time in *Collingwood* before joining *Campbeltown* in 1992. After several ships, *Battleaxe* and

Cardiff, he was commissioned in 2001. He served as DWEO in *Grafton* and then as a Lieutenant Commander brought HMS *Defender* out of build. After time in North Battery in Whale Island, he was the General Service Appointer for General Service engineering ratings, including Fleet Air Arm and submariners, a total of just short of 10,000 bodies.

He then spent time in the MOD and, as he said, "I saw my self go a little bit right of arc into Media Ops and PR for eighteen months".[37] This included seven months in Afghanistan, a WE officer in the middle of the desert being quite a duck out of water. But he saw how both the Royal Marines and the army worked in that environment and the RAF spanning the whole period. Jonathan is now, as a Commander, in charge of all WE training within *Collingwood* and he now sees training going full circle, not in terms of craft training but the necessity for skilled diagnostic technicians. One thing about Jonathan's recollections was the fondness with which he remembered his time as an Artificer, and the camaraderie of those with whom he served during his time as an Artificer.[38]

chapter eleven

The Nineties, Equal Opportunities and Lost Identity

• • •

And men, taught wisdom from the past,
In friendship joined their hands;
Hung the sword in the hall, the spear on the wall,
And ploughed the willing lands:
And sang—"Hurrah for Tubal Cain!
Our staunch good friend is he;
And for the ploughshare and the plough,
To him our praise shall be.
But while oppression lifts its head,
Or a tyrant would be lord;
Though we may thank him for the plough,
We'll not forget the sword!"[1]

The 1990s started off with a radical departure in recruitment of Artificer Apprentices. With the first girls in the WRNS (Wrens) to go to sea in HMS *Brilliant* in October 1990, there opened up a whole new area of female participation in the operation of the fleet. It was therefore decided that girls would be allowed to join as Artificer Apprentices and in September of 1990 seventeen girls were among the 200 prospective Artificers who joined *Raleigh* in 903 Entry.

While serving as the Fisgard Squadron Warrant Officer, Pete Bellamy oversaw the first Wren Artificers:

Also during my time at Fisgard Squadron the first entry of Wren Artificers entered the Fleet. The changes took some getting used. The Wrens lived in a separate mess deck but were scattered throughout the divisions which meant that not all the division were messed together. We had to employ one female Instructor Officer and one female Petty Officer Instructor, these were allocated different divisions and looked after the male and female apprentices within it but also they had authority over the Wrens Mess. At this time we had arguments from the male apprentices who wanted to grow their hair into a bun and have earrings; the Navy had its stock answer to this involving Society and History but the Petty Officer Instructors told the men as soon as they had their reproductive organs removed they would stay as they were! There was also a different fitness standard for the Wrens and I complained at length about this. Even though I accepted there is different physiology in the genders, the physical standard required was always explained as that required to move quickly around a ship and be able to escape in the case of an emergency; this standard is surely the same for both sexes. For instance the Wrens were required to run a mile and a half in twelve minutes, at the age of forty I could walk that and very often went with them on the test to prove it. Some of the wrens who joined had never run for a bus let alone a mile and a half. That said the vast majority were of a high standard and most of the first entry passed out of HMS Raleigh.

Princess Anne came to take the salute at the first Wrens Passing Out Parade and Prize Giving so throughout that term not only did we have to cope with an entirely new aspect of training but we also had to prepare for a Royal visit. As can be imagined this involved a serious amount of painting and rehearsal. The final rehearsal included all the Senior Officers from Raleigh with one of the HR Wren Officers acting as Princess Anne. As FSWO I was to escort the Princess throughout the tour of the Academic Block and introduce her to the prize winners and their parents. Within the Academic Block ATO was to give a PowerPoint presentation on Apprentice Training within Fisgard Squadron and he was keen that this would be his presentation alone and have no influence from the Senior Officers who may wish to change some aspects or take ownership. To this end ATO came to an agreement with the Training Commander that this part of the rehearsal could be bypassed as he trusted that ATO would produce the goods. However, on completion of the rehearsal, ATO requested that I meet

him in the Presentation Room where he would run through the lecture to check
timings and for me to comment on how I thought it might be accepted by the
Royal visitor. I quickly arranged for the PO Wren to lend me one of her skirts
and some lipstick and after donning these and stuffing the front of my shirt
entered the Presentation Room to watch ATO perform. He fell about laughing
and admitted that he will have that image in his mind as Princess Anne came
in. It became a bone of contention between us after the event that I spent most of
the day with Princess Anne and appeared on the television and most of the local
press whereas he only saw her for the presentation. He got his own back when I
left though; he found one of the official photographs of the Princess meeting one
of the prize-winners and down the left edge my nose is just in shot. He had this
picture framed with the caption "FSWO Meets Princess Anne" with an arrow
pointing at my nose [Pete is renowned for his prominent hooter].[2]

Among these girls was Dawn Jennings, who joined Griffin Division in
903 Class. She recalled that the ethos of the old *Fisgard*, which trumpeted
the superiority of the Artificer, was alive and well in Fisgard Squadron.
However, there was a reciprocal to this where the other trainees in *Raleigh*
were encouraged to disparage Artificers as elitist snobs. However, those
with this attitude had little or no experience of the Royal Navy and little
to base this attitude on other than the prejudices of their instructors, who
were all non-Artificers and this may indicate a certain jealousy of the swift
promotion of the Artificer Branch.

Now, of course, the old ritual of three class in *Fisgard* using one class as
sprogs was long gone, with Apprentices staying only one term in Fisgard
Squadron, but this can in no way be seen as a bad thing considering the
continuation of the *Fisgard* ethos. Further to this Dawn remembered having
to be dressed to a better standard than the other trainees and those failing to
meet the necessary standard would not go ashore.

Dawn had already completed three years of an Apprenticeship in civilian
life, but found that it was the change to a military environment that was
the biggest challenge. She particularly remembered being accommodated
in what was then known as Dauntless Squadron, where all the other female
recruits were accommodated; she recalled the two senior rating females in
Dauntless Squadron, who shall remain nameless, were less than sympathetic
to female Artificer Apprentices and did little to mentor the young girls of
Fisgard Squadron. One other problem arose as to what title should be given

to the girls. With the Service's love of acronyms it had to be something short but indicative; female Artificer was a non-starter as it shortened to FART, and Wren Artificer, again, WART was not suggestive of a skilled engineer. In the end MEA Apprentice seemed the safest option.

Dawn also remembered that in the first year of girls joining there was a perceived requirement of twenty-five girls. Dawn remembered thinking that twenty-five from the whole country would involve very fierce completion. In fact, there were only seventeen girls, of whom thirteen passed out to go on to *Sultan* and *Collingwood*. In *Sultan* the girls were accommodated in a male block but had the top floor to themselves.

One interesting aside Dawn remembered is their passing out parade, which was inspected by Princess Anne. Having not got all her kit in one go there was a problem with marking her name in her second tricorn, there being no marker paint available. Using Tiffy ingenuity she thought that dap whitener would suffice to get through the remaining kit musters. This, of course, was bound to have repercussions later on. Sure enough, on the day of the passing out parade there was a persistent and pernicious shower of rain that soaked the whole parade and all on it. It also had the unfortunate effect of leaving Dawn's name imprinted, backwards, on her forehead in white dap whitener for all to see as her hat blew off during the march past: how a bright idea at the time can come back and bite you.[3]

Also joining as an Artificer Apprentice that day was Derek Nadine, who had a sharp recollection of his time in *Raleigh*:

The 3rd of Sept was an auspicious day to join the RN as an Artificer Apprentice, exactly 51yrs since the outbreak of WW2. It was 37yrs give or take a week since Dad joined Series 22, when I too joined Fisgard (albeit Squadron, not HMS) with some 230 lads and lasses for 903 Entry.

Yes, lasses…

Unbeknown to me, the 3rd of Sept 1990 marked a series of many firsts for the RN as a whole. The first date that all WRNS joined up as "Sea going WRNS". No longer opting for a preference to go to Sea. From this point forward, they would all go to Sea. Including the first entry of Wren Artificers, with blue cap badges. Rifle drill had to be perfected. First of all by the Parade Staff, for today was also the introduction of the SA-80 Assault Rifle. Shorter in length than the SLR by some 9 inches, it proved a worthy adversary to the Gunnery Officer Lt Death (pronounced De-arth, as in De-mantle-piece) and his long-gaitered

GIs in training. Wow be-tide any man (or woman) who called them Missile-Men... and yes, at this point they couldn't slope arms for toffee!

The first few days were a bit of a blur, though as an ex-Sea Cadet, I think I found the transition a bit easier than most... except the lads from Brunei who waltzed it. Meet your classmates, followed by a hair-cut, whether you needed one or not. And a Photo for your ID Card. Being 19 yrs of age and Top Gun all the rage, I sported a rather trendy Flat-top. The Barber apologised for skimming the edges off and charging me £2.30 for the privilege. He followed this up by skinning the long haired Heavy metal dude behind me. Like any craftsman, the barber stopped halfway to admire his handiwork in the mirror. Half the lad's scalp was skinned to a nozzer's No2 all over. The other half a long haired metal head, with hair down to his waist, complete with the requisite black T-shirt. This raised a wry dry smile from Hippy-Tick-Tock (you know who you are!) and he definitely got his monies worth! Draw your kit from stores, matched pair of No 1s and No 2s, (what's the difference to an Artificer Apprentice?) and No 8's. Blanket stackers guffawing as they try to get you to accept hats too big, or trousers too small. Ironing (they had to teach you to iron!?!), followed by stamping your dog tags and marking your kit. Next, how to lay out for a Kit muster – everything was to be A4, the size of your General Naval Knowledge (GNK) Handbook. BR1939 was now a thing of the past (Good job too as I'd never get my shirts pressed to the size of that Handbook!)

Right lads, get your arse down the Ghadaffi and get yourselves some black boot polish, a yellow cloth, some starch, a couple of coat hangers, some suit covers and some NAFFI Blue. They must've sold a ship load of the stuff that day. Lord knows where the girls got to, I hear they were down in Dauntless Block. So much for mixed training!

I spent the first of many evenings showing the lads how to bull boots and shape Berets (well I had been a Sea Cadet since I was 12!). Using a BT Card I rang the girl back home and with a pen & paper, wrote a letter home to mum & dad.

How to Salute, Square bashing, Assault course, PT, schooling (BTEC Level 1) was generally how the first week went. It was around this time I had a cunning plan. Like everyone else who joined up that year, I'd signed up for 22 yrs. Just how many sets of kit would I go through in that time?

The first Kit muster was a stressful time. EVERYONE wanted to iron. The truth was there was just not enough ironing boards to go around. The top of your kit locker just had to do, with a towel on top. And that saved time because *your towel had to be ironed too. Just how else were you supposed to get that towel down to A4 size too? Up again at O my God it's early, bedsheet ironed, bed blocks made, kit laid out. Boots bulled as best they could, ready for POs inspection. Round he came, quietly and meticulously working his way around your kit, all laid out on your bed and Pussers case. In some cases, not for long! Oh God will my kit be on the floor? Or worse, we watched as some poor soul in the block opposite has his gear dumped out from the first floor window. I hope that won't be me.*

Divisions. We fell in by classes under the Clock in the Square. Tallest on the flanks, shortest in the centre. It paid to be short, as the middle was where the girls were at;-) Out comes the Warrant Officer "Are we happy?" "Over the Moon!" A quick "Morning Chaps" from the DO & out we marched with the Class Lead, from Fisgard Sqn to the Parade Ground. I can hear the RM Band, but where are they? I don't know – PIPE DOWN, EYES FRONT. Eft, ight, eft, ight, eft, ight, eft (why can't he pronounce em?). Class Halt! Left Turn! (Cue giggles and a quiet Shuddup) About Turn! Stand at Ease! There follows rounds of various Attention/Stand at Ease until the Inspecting officer comes around "So, how are you enjoying your time in the UK?" he enquired. "Not me Sir, I'm from Southport." Every week, the same question from a different officer. The only one to never ask me that was at my Passing Out Parade. Cue more music, still no Band. Wait ages for the front row classes to march off, then the 2nd row... then the 3rd... still more music, still no band. Off we go and I can clearly see why we we've been left till last. "Round again!" Oh, the Bootie Band, they're in the Dalek!

Money, don't get too excited! You get paid £10.86, per day, every day. No matter if you were sunning yourself in Barbados, or stuck in a foxhole, £10.86, per man (or woman) per day. Less Food and allowance, less your first kit issue, which yes, you paid for. Because you are all Artificer Apprentices and new to all this money, your pay will be reduced to £150 for the first month. All monies would be payable to a Bank or Building Society of your choosing. Just to make you financially aware, no bias intended, we have a briefing by our friends at the onsite Lloyds Bank who are going to brief you on the benefits of having a Bank Account and the reasons for staying in credit. In they trot, 3 lovely ladies appeared before our eyes. One of every hair colour you could then imagine. Not one appeared to be over 25, curves in all the right places and boy did they dress to impress. Right lads, take two forms and pass them on. The first one is for you to open a Lloyds Bank Account with which you can take the second form and have your pay put into. "Er Miss, I already have a Building Society Account, can I just fill in those details on the second form?" Simple question really… across the room she sauntered, stopped next to me, bent at the waist and shimmered "and why would you NOT open a Lloyds Bank account?" "Well I don't need 2 current accounts, and I already have one". Glancing upwards I could see her colleague was already on her way. She too stopped by and proceeded to bend at the waist. One Brunette and one Blonde beautifully trained in the art of persuasion. "It takes 10 days to clear a cheque in a building society but only 5 days in a Bank" I stood by my guns expecting the red-head to come over. Alas that trick never worked. And so I left with Pay due to enter my building society account, and they left with one less commission.

Chiefs Kit muster was a breeze. I told others of my plans but no-one followed. I bulled my boots the night before though I didn't stay up all hours. Come to think of it, I didn't get up before call of hands. Everyone was in a panic. Chief was apparently known for casting your kit aside if he didn't like it. (How did we know, none of us were there last Term?). I set up my kit, cardboard formers in my socks, new hand towel stamped and folded to A4. All squared off and ready in minutes. Up came the Chief and took one look at my Parade Boots, bulled stem to stern. He picked one up and turned it over, took one look at the mirrored sole and placed it back in place "Very good" and off he popped.

How did I do it? Dead easy – I signed up for 22yrs, in which time I expected to go through many pairs of shoes, boots and trousers. In fact I expected everything to wear out at least once, so for the stuff I expect to wear often, why not visit slops and buy a spare set now and put it away for a rainy day… like Chiefs Kit Muster!

Part way through the 14 weeks we seemed to get the hang of square-bashing. Rifle drill had finally been perfected by the drill staff so I guess it was our turn to learn. No 8s and Puttees were rig of the day and so we reported to the armoury for our shiny new bang sticks. Endless bouts of rifle drill ensued with such gusto that we seemed to be practicing almost every day. One particular day we were all quite terrible and the GI exclaimed he could never form an effing Royal Guard with this bunch of misfits. Er, did he just say Royal?!?

The cat was out the bag and next morning we were informed that HRH Princess Anne as Commandant of The Women's Royal Naval Service would be the Inspecting officer at our Passing Out Parade. She was to be there primarily to witness the Passing Out of the first Wren Artificers (and I guess the first batch of sea going WRNS). For this we were sworn to secrecy & reminded of one of the many papers we had signed on day 1 (we did?). Not a soul was to know of her movements and we were again reminded that it was not that long since that her uncle had been murdered in an Irish Lough. Of course the down side to HRH's planned arrival, was that this required a Royal Guard of 96 men (& women), all skilled in the art of Rifle Drill. That night I rang home, we could say we had a VIP coming, but not to say who it was. So how come Pusser had already written to mum & dad, in fact all mum & dads telling them that HRH was on her way? Yes mum and dad were planning to come to our Passing Out Parade, as was my sister Anne, namesake of HRH.

Lord knows how, Bass Division were selected with a few other classes to form the Tiffy Guard of 48, with Square Rig nozzers forming the other half (I guess the GI was right after all!). We practiced till we were blue in the face with extra drill sessions with & without the Dalek cancelling out other fun activities such as Rifle shooting (I never did get the chance to try out for my marksman's badge).

The big day came and the Guard were milling around in the drill sheds, watching as everyone else formed up. In the rain. I guess it's the Guard's prerogative, last out, first in. Out we marched, Dressed out, slowly. And waited. Out came HRH onto the Dias. General Salute was given, the band played then shoulder arms. Up she walks past the front stopping to one or two. Off again past most of the back row and stops again, front and centre. "So how are you enjoying your naval training?" I could've kissed her! Good on you Mam (as in Jam, not Ma'am as in Barm) ⌧ she stopped & chatted for a while. So that confirmed it, I was skin AND essence!

Why did I always get asked the same question you ask? Well I guess it's an easy mistake to make... Sometime after Dad left the Mob, he first worked in Saudi, then got a job in Gresik, Indonesia, where he met and married a local Chinese lady. They married and came home to England. Sometime after which, the new Mrs Nadin became somewhat ill. Dad being Dad & knowing nowt about scablifting, especially the specialist variety, took her off to the local school of Tropical medicine. The short version is, I was misdiagnosed by an ERA as a Tropical disease. Cue one lad, half Chinese, all grown up (skin!), one family holiday, dark tan from 2 months in the Tropics, dressed in No 2s, lid on, peak cap down mixed in with 230 other Tiffys. Somewhere within, were 8 lads from Brunei. Oh the Brunei lads. They were not just lads, but damn smart ones too. Their boots gave them away... and their smiles. Despite their diminutive size, it turns out they were all Sergeants in the Sultan of Brunei's Army, here to train as MEAs at Sultan.[4]

Derek also remembered his time in *Collingwood*, though he rued the fact that he was unable to pursue a life in the Fleet Air Arm:

They're a lying bunch down at the recruiting office, either that or truly incompetent! "What Branch would you like?" "Fleet Air Arm" says I. "Right you are, we need loads, so first you'll go to Raleigh for 14 wks, then you'll go straight to Daedalus for the next few years"... so how come I got asked again at Raleigh what Branch would I like – FAA, "ah well, we only need 11 from this entry. So what Branch would you like?" Again I pondered and whilst having a penchant for sleep and things that go bang – "Weapons please!" I need not have worried!

Once again I found myself on a Train to the South of England, alighting at Fareham I got a taxi to the Wooden Gatehouse and walked right in. Kit bag over my shoulder and my Pusser's case in my other hand, this would be my home of the next 2 years. Armada Block (not the Gatehouse), 3ʳᵈ Floor (top), 4 men to a room, overlooking the Parade Ground. So best we ALL open our curtains for Divisions! It was unusual for 4 lads from a new Entry to get a room together. Not really a room, it was 1 long series of windows facing the Parade Ground, 2 walls dividing you from the adjoining rooms, a sink and a curtain segregating you from the passageway, running almost the length of the room. 4 beds, 4 wardrobe type lockers and if you were lucky, bedside lockers. If you were very lucky, a table and 4 chairs. Alas, we were not that lucky! Opposite your room, there were the communal areas. Showers, metal sinks, washing machines (they didn't work!), heads and 2 baths! Transiting out the other door there were more rooms on the other side, including the TV room. One lucky fella got a 1 man cabin. For this, he had to be responsible for the whole floor, its day to day cleanliness including rounds. Somehow this was never allocated to a new boy like us.

It turned out that 4 blocks were allocated to Baby Tiffy's – Armada, Jutland, Trafalgar & Nile(?). Built in the 60's they were cold in the winter and too hot in summer. One block (Nile?) was always in refurb, useful for finding a locker that closed, or a middle shelf for your bedside locker. Forget looking for a newer bed, they were all dated the year dad joined up with a Pussers arrow to prove it – 1954. After a week, the saggy bed springs compensated for by way of a spare Fig 11 Target.

In Jan 1991, HMS Collingwood *was still the home of the RN Weapon Engineering School. Although other Shore Establishments were closing, we were yet to see trainees from any other Branches. Collingwood had recently undergone a period of rebuilding with Atlantic Block popping up at the Main Gate end of the Parade Ground, Tiffy Blocks on the other. Looking out from Armada Block, the Drill sheds were to the right, with POs and Chiefs/WOs Messes beyond, with the cinema behind that. To the left were the 3 schools, T School (Technical), A School and M School. All recently built in brick, with the covered way behind. On the other side of the Covered way were Naffi shops and the very things we were here to learn, Weapon Systems. Sadly White City had been in the process of being demolished when I visited as a Cadet in the mid 80's. Behind the schools lay quite a few football fields, the gym, an Olympic pool and squash courts with a small bore range running along the underside of the pool. Next to this was the Colly Club/Naffi Bar, where Bop Tarts would appear a couple of times a week, looking to meet up with a sailor or two. Away from the Parade Ground there were other areas to explore in our limited time off. The Southern Club, with pay to use washers & dryers (was this why the ones in the blocks didn't work?) and a bar. Jack Blair, Trendy Menswear had a shop, though we seldom went in. Too much ole civvy dress from the 80's for my liking. Senior Rates loved it! The Rugby club (with a much better bar!). Other buildings were used by the dive club and for Volunteer band practice. The Car Club just beyond might come in useful, if I had a car.*

903 Entry were Split into two classes, Alpha & Bravo. I think I was in Bravo. Other classmates were "Apples" Appleton, Brett "Chicken"… Nobby Clarke, Durand Gunn, Lee Ford, Brett "Felix" Meese, Ian "Moly" Molineux, Paul Ray, Matt Sawtell, Philip Blakely-Smyth, Kieron Waterworth, Peter "Scouse/Shiner" Wright, Karen Phillips

As a baby Tiffy, Classrooms filled our days with strange and varied formulas, getting ever closer to that BTEC Ordinary National Diploma in Electrical/Electronics: –

E = MC²

Power = Current x Resistance

Threat = Capability + Intent

Workshops was a welcome distraction. Fitting was an odd experience, if you weren't sawing, you were filing and if you weren't filing you were sawing. Eventually to a finer or lesser degree, then bluing and filing, then filing and bluing. Turning was good (at least I had used a lathe at High School) but this was to another level. I could never recall milling, though I guess we all did. Offset turning, knurling, drilling and other things I never knew you could do on a lathe till I got here, though like my classmates, I soon got the hang of these.

I seem to recall Paul was very good at his Test Pieces. I always seemed to be just behind him in speed, though just ahead in accuracy. Between us we usually came 1ˢᵗ or second in most pieces which is possibly why I still have them all, except pipework. As usual Paul and I had finished ahead of the rest so we both set about polishing our pipes… alas we were so far ahead of the rest, I ended up polishing right through it, to which Chief said "Excellent – bin!" So that was the end of that.

Projects – Electronics & Test Equipment was just that, build a Digital Multi-Meter (DMM) from sheet metal up. Design the PCB, etch it, drill the holes, mount the DIL Sockets and components, wire it up, test it and final assembly. Just don't test the power sockets in your mess with them. Yes they broke them. No, mine still works.[5]

Amongst the other girls who joined in 903 Class was Karen Phillips, who joined straight from school having completed her A levels. She recalled a certain animosity in *Raleigh*, which she believes was exacerbated because of her sex. She followed the usual pattern, with one term at *Raleigh*, two years at *Collingwood* and then a year at sea, serving in HMS *Manchester*, which she loved. Karen was lucky enough as one of the top four WDOs to spend four months in Hong Kong, she then returned to *Collingwood* as an LWEA. After further time in *Collingwood* Karen returned to spend more time in *Manchester*. She had further time at sea in HMS *Westminster* as the 4.5" gun maintainer, a job some thought unsuitable for a girl because of the physical nature of the work. Karen proved them wrong and thrived. One thing that sticks in her memory is being invited as an after-dinner speaker at Roedean Girls School, which had hosted electrical training for the Navy during the war. Unfortunately after a car crash Karen was medically discharged with a back injury and so ended her time in uniform, though she continues in *Collingwood* in a civilian training role.

On 2 September 1991 Jef Webster joined *Raleigh* in 913 Entry and remembered his time in Fisgard Squadron:

Joined 02 Sep 1991. Collected from train station, taken by bus to the Torpoint ferry, across the ferry then to HMS Raleigh. Being the third intake of 1991 we were 913 entry.

Approximately 240 people joined including 16 females and 8 Saudi nationals. We were split into 8 divisions of around 30 people and accommodated in two accommodation blocks (plus the WRNS were in another block). Basic training lasted 14 weeks. The first 7 weeks was Phase 1 training, the next 7 weeks was Phase 2 training. Phase 1 wore orange epaulettes, Phase 2 wore Grey epaulettes. Non-artificer recruits used to spit on the floor near 'tiffs. Anecdotally I heard several stories as to why this was. None of them seemed to make much sense to me.

Instructors

When at HMS Raleigh we were taken to a large room. Standing around the room were 8 Petty Officer's who we discovered were to be our Divisional PO and instructors through basic training. I looked at them all. They looked fairly serious apart from one slightly shorter and stockier one who seemed more jolly. Another dark haired one looked a bit quiet, almost nervous. As names were called out and instructors allocated I saw the jolly man leave with his class but the quiet, nervous looking one remained. I found myself hoping I wasn't in his division but as it turned out, I was.

Petty Officer AEM Liam Grimes was our appointed instructor for basic training. What had I thought? Quiet? Nervous? This was the single biggest misjudgement I've ever made (and trust me I've made a few bad judgements in my time resulting in black eyes, time in cells and even court appearances!). PO Grimes took us to our accommodation and settled us in then over the next 14 weeks bollocked us, trashed our mess, beasted us to within an inch of our lives, and ran us ragged all over the base. He also taught us to look after ourselves, to become independent. We learned how to iron, how to wash, how to shave. He taught us the value of friendship and loyalty. He inspired us and made our class into the people they became. He is an absolute legend and this will stay with me forever.

Divisions

Burgess (me)
Bass
Thompson
Harcus
Shervil
Griffin
Simpson
Warsop

Our collection of 4 buildings was called Fisgard Squadron and comprised two accommodation blocks and one classroom block (Grenville block). The fourth building accommodated the WRNS on the top floor with the first floor housing the "barrack guard". These were non-artificer recruits who had finished basic training and were used as barrack guard for a week. We saw little of these people.

Routine (approximate, I can't really recall accurately)
Mon–Friday 0600 CTH, 0700 cleaning stations, 0800-1600 core training, 1800 evening scran, 1900 cleaning stations, 2000 evening rounds, 2230 pipe down.
Saturday 0800–1200 Miscellaneous often including parade ground/guard training.
Sunday 1000–1100 Church

The schedule at Raleigh was tight, deliberately so. Trying to get from PT to the classroom to lunch, to the obstacle course to a church lecture to the classroom again all took precision. One day we had to go to the church for a lecture after we had been on the assault course. We had to get from the assault course in our overalls all muddy and sweaty back to the accommodation to get cleaned up and showered, sort our dirty kit out and then march to the church. Looking back this was a tall order and I wonder if it was a deliberately unachievable one. We were late for the padre but that's ok isn't it? He'd understand wouldn't he? I mean he had the equivalent rank of Commander and he was a Royal Marines padre but he'd be ok with it, he was our friend wasn't he?

When we got to his church brief he said we were late, told us off and said that would be the end of it. Clearly that wasn't the end of it. He had contacted our instructor probably "just to let him know". When we got back to the mess PO Grimes was fuming in his own flushed, quiet and very scary manner. His cold, Irish voice firmly and slowly stated "Div shirts, black shorts, own socks, own trainers, hockey pitch GO!!!!!!" We knew what was coming and when we got to the hockey pitch we weren't wrong. An hour later we were destroyed.

The padre had done us a favour; I had a nice hour in the dogs outside in the fresh air with my mates, my fitness level improved, and I learned never to trust a word those bastards said ever again.

Duties
Each division took turns at being the duty division. The class leader sorted the duty roster.

Block sentries for each of the 3 buildings. Duty involved sitting at a desk at the front lobby from secure until lights out. This was a very dull duty.

Automat. Duty involved sitting in the automat making sure nobody misbehaved and ditched their gash etc. This was a popular duty as you got to sit in the social hub of Raleigh. As class leader you would put whoever was next class leader down for Automat duty, that way when he took over you had his duty in the Automat.

Cleaning stations. The class leader appointed the cleaning stations. The kit wash room was the worst cleaning station due to all of the bright-work and the high likelihood that one division had been on the assault course or something that day. The ironing room was the easiest as it was never dirty or untidy, you could generally just turn up in there, close the door and spin a few dits rather than doing any cleaning. As with the Automat duty, the class leader would ensure he got the ironing room when it was his turn.

Lessons were in Electrical Engineering Science (LES), Mechanical Engineering Science (MES), maths and Naval General Training (NGT). During the 14 weeks we sat 3 sets of exams, Alphas, Bravos and Charlies. Failing any would result in dismissal or (if you were a good egg) re-categorisation into another branch (e.g. WEM, AEM, medic etc).

Mess life

There were around 30 beds all laid out in alphabetical order. As a "Webster" I was between a guy called Dave Stringer and another called Wilson. Wilson didn't last long so my new neighbour was Paul Wright. We also had a Saudi national in our division, Sal Al O Tabe. The Saudis were going through our basic training and later artificer training to become senior Saudi CPOs. Dave Stringer went on to have a full and successful submarine career as a Marine Engineering Artificer, Shiner became a Weapon Engineering Officer.

We each had a bed and a chest of drawers. Nothing was allowed to be dirty in your drawers. Every day our instructor would inspect our mess. Each week we had formal rounds with beds made specially and almost artistically, counterpane diagonally across the bed, ties laid out like anchors etc. Each week for rounds all drawers had to be left open except your locked personal drawer.

Cleanliness was ingrained into us as it should be for men living in close proximity for their career. PO Grimes gave us all a direct order on our first day. He ordered us all to shower at least twice a day for the rest of our career. He asked us if we understood the order which we did. He explained that failure to follow *that legal and direct order was an offence under the Naval Discipline Act for which punishment was severe. I did not break that order for the duration of my career.*

We were not allowed out of Fisgard Squadron for the first couple of weeks. A small NAAFI contingent came to the squadron and set out a small table of items we would most likely need to buy. This included toiletries, cleaning kit etc.

The slightest misdemeanours saw the whole class punished in a cycle which became known as a shit sandwich. Every time we were built up we were then brought back down to earth with a crash before being built back up again. I lost track of how many times our mess was totally trashed. Sometimes it would just be one individual who had done something wrong only to get back to the mess to find all of his drawers tipped out upside down on the floor, all his ironed and folded kit would be strewn all over the place. If your bed corners weren't quite right you'd find your bed upside down when you got back. If we'd done something wrong in general then the whole mess would be trashed. We'd get in to see everything upside down and thrown all over the place. Our instructor would then come in and give us a right bollocking for the place being in shit state. Most of the time I have no idea what we'd done to deserve any of it.

But the rest of the time life was good and social. As time went on PO Grimes suggested we all chip in to buy ourselves a radio. We put £10 each in and bought a ghetto blaster with a CD player. The leftover money we used for some CDs. We could then sit and polish our kit whilst listening to the radio and spinning some dits. Life could be good.

PO Grimes had told us all that gambling was illegal in the RN and no form of gambling would ever be tolerated. He also told us that as a division we were to stick together – either everyone did something or no one did. One evening he offered up a challenge that he bet we could not solve. Our class leader Craig "Chunky" Chambers said he'd accept the challenge but as Liam said, all or nothing. Most of us were up for it and Chunky convinced the rest. Liam made a bet with us all at £1 a head (almost £30 total) that we couldn't solve it and we took him up on it. As he reminded us all, "gambling is illegal and this never happened". We all agreed. Liam gave us a list of numbers: 12, 22, 23, 25, 32, 39, 40, 41, 55. We had to work out the odd-one out.

Chunky seemed to be our self-appointed code cracker and after ages he came up with the answer. He went to fetch PO Grimes to the Mess. Liam arrived and gathered us all around. Chunky presented his findings. It was the wrong answer. PO Grimes laughed as he told us that the correct answer was in fact 25. Apparently, the number 25 is the only dish in his local Chinese takeaway that you don't order with egg fried rice because it comes with egg fried rice. "And don't forget" he said in his northern Irish accent as he scanned the room pointing at us all "gambling in the RN is illegal and this never fucking happened". He took his winnings and left.

We subsequently also lost a bet with him that he could down a pint of Guinness in 5 seconds.

But we loved it. Suddenly there was an element of trust between us and our instructor. We'd broken the navy law together with our gambling and betting. We had shared something and whilst this achievement may seem almost incomprehensible to anyone outside the military the boost it gave you to be at one with your instructor was incredible. It wasn't us and him anymore, we were all of one company.

Kit musters

Through the 14 weeks we had a number of kit musters. Passing each kit muster resulted in award of privileges. The first was being allowed to go to the Automat in the evening. Next was being allowed ashore. Final one was being allowed on ELWE half way through basic training.

Going ashore

When we were finally allowed ashore we could only go out on Liberty Boats at specific times, miss the boat and you had to wait for the next one. The Carbille pub was the nearest and normally rammed full of those in basic training. As Artificers had the longest basic training it tended to only be 'tiffs in there. Alternatively we used to get the bus to Torpoint for a run ashore or across into Plymouth for a night out. We were not allowed down Union Street as basic trainees. Torpoint's highlight was the Harbour Lights (aka the Royal Navy School of Dancing) but we still had to be back onboard by 2230, just when we expect the place started to liven up!

On Saturday my division would go to our chosen pub "The Abbey" in Plymouth. This pub was chosen by our instructor who accompanied us. We would go into town at secure (1200) and the pub would put a few sandwiches on for us. We weren't allowed to buy drinks in a round but only individually. This made sure everyone drank at their own pace and it seemed to work well. Later that evening we would head back to the Harbour Lights in Torpoint. We had to make sure our cleaning stations were covered back at Raleigh and that they were correctly reported. There was always someone who didn't want to go out *and as time went on we worked out a routine that they covered it by cleaning and reporting several areas for us and the duty instructors seemed fine with that.*

Outward Bound

During basic training we had two little ventures out. The first was to Scraesden fort just up the road. Here we camped within the confines of the fort grounds, ran an assault course, got woken up in the middle of the night to go on a night navex running around Torpoint in the dark, and some practical leadership type tasks (PLTs).

The second was to Cardinham. Here we camped for a couple of days. There were 4 large sandy hills which we had the pleasure of running up and down several times. We ran it once as a squadron and when we got back the squadron WO asked who couldn't do it again. Those foolish enough to put their hands up were immediately sent to run it again. Once they had set off the rest of us were ordered to run it as well and beat all of them back again. We also ran it in teams carrying a log as part of a 1.5 mile assault course. AND if you failed to shave properly or had dirty mess tins you could run it as an individual, taking the mess tins with you.

Other activities at Cardinham included orienteering and a long walk over the moors.

Adventure Training

As a bit of a "well done" and an introduction to Adventure Training we had an AT day towards the end of course. The idea of AT was to encourage self development and teamwork through the controlled exposure to risk and hazard. Activities ranged from rock climbing or horse riding to laser quest. I chose horse riding whilst most of my class went to laser quest. I'd done a lot of hill walking before I joined up and I loved the outdoors. The trek took us across the moors all morning, pub lunch, then back across the moors in the afternoon. The afternoon included bringing the horses up to the gallop which with the wind in my hair flying over the ground was exhilarating. The horses knew what they were doing and where to go but I still felt in charge. It was a beautiful part of the country and I don't particularly recall wondering how the laser quest was going.

Streaming

At the end of basic training we were streamed ME or WE. AE was not an option for our entry as the training was being altered at HMS Daedalus. Collingwood and Sultan's 'tiffs courses followed suit in due course.

MT Training

The very last part of our basic training was spent in the blocks across the road from Raleigh in what was the original HMS Fisgard. Here we learned how to handle a rifle, the SA-80. We learned how it worked, how to strip and clean it and of course how to shoot it.

Passing Out

We passed out with our families watching and that night got to stay in a hotel. Our passing out parade was accompanied by the Royal Marines band playing, an honour I hadn't really appreciated until later in life, at the time I just thought that's what the marines did – play instruments.

One of our 8 divisions had been selected to be guard for the passing out and it wasn't ours. We had worked hard on our guard drill and we were good at it but we weren't selected. Our instructor told us that whilst it might be seen as an honour to do guard for your passing out it also meant less time spent with your family because of the drawing of extra kit, rifle etc. He was of course correct and none of the families particularly cared if we were in the guard or not.

This was also the first time we got to stay out late and see what happened in the Harbour Lights after 2230 only to find the answer was "nothing much".

Attrition

Of the 240 who joined quite a few PVR'd when they found out that AE was not open to us. Of the rest many failed along the way to make the grade. In total approximately 120 of us passed out split roughly 50/50 between Sultan and Collingwood. Of those who failed during basic training some were discharged outside (those who weren't really suited to the military) whilst others were offered the chance to re-cat into a different job/branch (those who were suited to the military but could not handle the demands of the technical training). Many chose to go AEM.[6]

Another to join Fisgard Squadron in 1991 was Ian Cook. He originally joined as an MEM in 1988 and qualified to join the Submarine Service. After three years in the submarine *Conqueror* he went to *Raleigh*, when *Conqueror* paid off in Plymouth, and sat examinations and interviews to recategorise as an Artificer Apprentice and shortly after started new entry training in Fisgard Squadron; he is thus probably the only Artificer Apprentice to go through Apprentice training wearing the Submarine Service "Dolphins".[7]

Helen Robson arrived at *Raleigh* on 4 May 1992 and joined Fisgard Squadron in Shervil Division as one of only nine girls from an entry of 125. Helen had already completed an apprenticeship with GEC Avionics. This allowed her to be fast-tracked to sea after thirteen weeks at *Collingwood* rather than the usual two years. This meant that when Helen completed her further training in "A" School she was rated Probationary Acting Petty Officer Wren WEA, something of a mouthful for anybody. This did cause some friction with those males who had also completed civilian apprenticeships and were not afforded the same accelerated advancement.[8]

She also remembered the Rubber Road in *Collingwood* being a hive of activity, teeming with people at stand easy and lunchtime; there were three teaboats all vying for trade, whereas now everyone has their own kettle, microwave and all mod cons; this together with the reduced numbers means that now only one teaboat remains. Helen still pines for the past, the effort that was required to become an Artificer, obtain an HNC and qualify for advancement, and has never considered herself an Engineering Technician.[9]

There were further changes to Apprentice training during the 1990s. In 1994 after their one term at *Raleigh* Apprentices spent only one term at *Sultan* and *Collingwood*, during which time they would receive the same training as MEMs and OMs. After this second term they would go to sea for a complete year, being employed as an MEM or OM, rather than as of yore as a more highly skilled Apprentice. This also heralded a change to the selection and training of Mechanicians from Mechanics; from January 1994 Mechanicians would no longer exist and would henceforth be known as Artificer Candidates. This is encapsulated in the following extract.

From ERA to MEA, with the exception of a few title changes, the fundamental training and employment of the Artificer changed little for several decades. Engineering Branch Development (EBD) in 1979 saw the Marine Engineering Branch take responsibility for electrical power generation and distribution systems. The early 1980s saw the phased relocation of Artificer training to HMS Sultan, whilst the introduction of gas turbines and microprocessor control caused some changes to training and the way of doing business at sea. These changes were all taken well in the stride of the ever-flexible Artificer. The most recent change for the branch is as a result of a 1990 review of employment and training as part of Marine Engineering Branch Development (MEBD). The review team found that in a number of areas training was failing to meet the needs of employment, and there was considerable scope for adjusting the balance of employment between Artificer and Mechanic. More emphasis has been put on the Artificer's primary role as a diagnostician, technician and manager and less on the traditional role of craftsman, a large proportion of craft training having been transferred to the mechanics. With these aims in mind the initial training undertaken at HMS Sultan has undergone fundamental changes and the Artificer Apprentice and Candidate Courses have been combined into a single Marine Engineering Artificer Qualifying Course (MEAQC).

After initial training in HMS Raleigh of one term, apprentices join HMS Sultan for a second term where they are trained to the same standard as a Marine Engineering Mechanic (MEM, formally "Stoker") after initial career courses.

This prepares them for one of the biggest changes to their training, a full year at sea where they consolidate their technical training, gain a better understanding of the Marine Engineering Department and, most important of all, get a taste of life at sea. Half of the MEAs fill complement MEM billets and half go into the training margin; all are employed on routine watchkeeping, maintenance, whole-ship responsibilities and communal tasks. They also complete technical and academic "task books" prior to a final selection board and their return to HMS Sultan.

Those Mechanics selected for "Artificer Candidate" (formally Mechanicians) work through a distance learning package to prepare them for the MEAQC. Before the apprentices return from seatraining the mechanics come to HMS Sultan for a series of short Enabling Courses to compensate for several years away from a classroom. Apprentices and Candidates are then fully integrated for the remaining thirty months of training, beginning with a year of academic studies. This is the first time that the classroom ability of the young apprentice and the experience of the stokers have been brought together. So far the scheme has worked very well with each group gaining from the experience and ability of the other. After the "academics", trainees split into three streams for more specialist courses. The "new" General Service Artificer is not streamed, but receives training mainly biased towards electrical and controls technology, whilst the Submarine Service has decided to retain the original ME/EL division. Successful completion of the course earns the award of a BTEC National Diploma in Engineering. Completion of the MEAQC prepares the Artificer for his – or her – first sea draft, after which they can expect to return to HMS Sultan for further technical and professional courses throughout their careers. Whilst the learning curve may not be as steep, it never levels out!

314

All these changes have been necessary to meet the requirements of the "customer", the Fleet at sea, and to prepare for the next generation of highly sophisticated warships.[10]

It can be seen from this extract that the modern apprenticeship bears little resemblance to the old craft apprenticeship in force prior to 1968 and has little in common with sending the Apprentice to sea with several years of training and experience, albeit not seagoing experience but an in-depth knowledge of the design and function of the machinery he would be expected to operate and maintain. It also, of course, saw the demise of another rating, the Mechanician, which had been in existence since Jackie Fisher in 1903 and was always the butt of Tiffy humour as being a "Mickey Mouse" Artificer, but was in fact a skilled and valued brother to the Artificer.

Meanwhile in the 1990s John Newell's career continued to prosper:

Probably the highlight of my time at sea was my two years as MEO in HMS BOXER. The first year was spent in the Mediterranean conducting CACs trials with much of the next year deployed on ORIENT 92. A fantastic ship with fantastic people.

I had been asking for the French Staff Course in Paris for some time so in the summer of 1993, Jane and I moved to an apartment in Neuilly sur Seine for me to undertake the 1 year course. On my return to the UK I went to the Joint Planning Staff, the precursor to PJHQ J8 (now J5). The next year or so was spent planning joint operations with the French and Americans. My boss was a parachute regiment half Colonel and his boss a Royal Marine Colonel. Fitness was a key part of their day's routine which was a bit of a shock.

I then became the Appointer for all ME Officers below the rank of Commander. A great job in many ways but you soon learned that you cannot please everyone all of the time. It is amazing how many people who have volunteered for foreign jobs turn the post down when it is offered to them because they have just got a new cat/dog/wife.

As head of the electrical power generation and distribution section in DGME at Foxhill, Bath, I finally started to use my electrical knowledge (and worked with the author). The team wrote the SOTRs for the ESTD site and equipment and helped run the competition. We were also heavily involved in the selection of IFEP for future Naval Platforms.[11]

There were changes afoot in the weapon engineering world; this started with the closure of HMS *Mercury*, the home of the Communications Branch. Training was moved to *Collingwood* and changed the nature of this establishment from a purely electrical training establishment into the Maritime Warfare School it now is.

Some of these changes in the WE world come out of Jef's memories of *Collingwood* after he left *Raleigh*:

I was a WE so was sent to HMS Collingwood. This was split into 3 schools. MT-School Mechanic Training School was where the WEMs undertook their 3 month technical training course.

> *T-School Technical School is where Apprentices undertook the first 2 years of their technical training course. After these 2 years the Apprentice went to sea for a year.*

> *Suitably apt mechanics (LWEMs and POWEMs) also completed T-School but in separate classes. These were referred to by the old name of Mechs (short for Mechanicians). Their correct title was Artificer Candidates but they were always known as Mechs and they were on Mechs course.*

> *A-School: After a year at sea Artificers returned as killicks (LWEA) and entered Application School. At this point Artificers and Mechs were in mixed classes. A-School lasted approximately 9 months depending on specialisation.*

T-School (1992-1993)

We arrived on 02/12/1991, three weeks before Christmas Leave and were allocated into a class, division and messdeck. We did 2 weeks of MT, re-learning how to handle the SA-80 but this time learning all about the rules of engagement for armed guards. This was to be our duty for the next couple of years. At the end of this 2 weeks and as the term didn't start until after the New Year, we were sent to join the Buffer's Party for a week and learn how to handle a broom.

> *There were 5 classes slit up into 913A, B, C, D and E. I was in 913B. These 5 classes were split over the 3 divisions, 913B was in Philips Division.*

Accommodation

We were allocated a division and a mess, I was in Trafalgar Block, 2nd floor "H" Mess or "T2H". Our 4-man messes were of mixed seniority with some apprentices having been there nearly 2 years. I was sharing a mess with two

912's so they were the second entry of 1991 approximately 4 months ahead of me. The 'tiffs accommodation was in 4 blocks:

Trafalgar

Armada

Jutland

Barfleur

These blocks housed 'tiff classes from the last 2 years (901 to 912, plus now 913). The 893, 892 and 891 classes were at sea.

The messes were for 4 man and we each had a bed, wardrobe with drawers within and a boot locker. There was a sink in the mess. The messes were divided from the outside corridor by a curtain rather than a wall and a door. The corridor outside was very narrow and low. In the centre of the building separating each row of messes were the showers and the bathrooms with accesses each side. The easiest was to cross from one side of your floor to the other was through the heads.

I hadn't known but the layout and style of the accommodation was akin to a ship with the low deckheads and narrow bulkheads. Identical corridors made it very easy to become disorientated if you went to the toilet then accidentally went out the wrong side of the building to the messes the opposite side. I lost count of the number of times I pulled the curtain back on a mess that wasn't mine to find a load of lads just staring at me wondering what I wanted, after all it was polite to knock before simply entering someone else's mess.

I still don't know if the style of the accommodation was to make transition to sea easier or not but if it was then the idea was genius and should have been continued when the accommodation was replaced.

Cleaning was mandatory but there were no evening rounds for us, we were phase 3 trainees after all. The senior class would produce a cleaning roster and they would be excused cleaning. The accommodation was inspected weekly during the working day. The WEMs accommodation was formally inspected every night and we heard the "standby for evening rounds pipe" every night.

Routine

0700	Skirmishing classes.
0800	Muster in the T-School quadrangle.
	Class inspected by Class Leader.
	Class reported correct to senior divisional Apprentice.
	Division reported to senior T-School apprentice, who in turn

reported to the T-School CPO.

T-School CPO (or sometimes the WO) would read out any parish notices.

0830	*Fall out, go to classes or march to workshops.*
1000	*Stand Easy.*
1025	*Rubber Road Skirmishing classes.*
1030	*Out Pipes.*
1200	*Lunch.*
1315	*Muster in the T-School quadrangle.*
1330	*Fall out, go to classes or march to workshops.*
1420	*Stand Easy.*
1430	*Out Pipes.*
1630	*Secure (1515 on Friday).*

Every Tuesday was sports afternoon.

Once a week (Thursday) our DO would come to the muster and inspect us.

Divisions (Parade Ground)

Monday	*MT School Divisions.*
Tuesday	*T-School Divisions.*
Wednesday	*A-School Divisions.*
Thursday	*Collingwood Divisions (all schools).*

Dog Watch Activities

Wednesday Dog Watch Sport (circuit on the parade ground, squad run to PT centre, games).

Thursday   Dog Watch Lecture (various visiting lecturers etc).

Skirmishing

Each class was in a roster to undertake skirmishing of an area of classrooms or sweep the Rubber Road. T-School and A-School skirmishing was simply a bimble around looking for any gash before retiring to breakfast. Rubber Road skirmishing was done at the end of morning standeasy. As a class we would be supervised by a killick and a PO from an A-School class. We'd draw brushes from the Marlborough Building buffer and starting at one end sweep the full length of the building (approx 200 meters).

MT School accommodation comprised 4 blocks, Saintes, Nile, Finistaire, Frobisher. WEMs had to wear putties and march from their accommodation everywhere, they were Phase 2 trainees after all. All the bolshy spitting at 'tiffs in HMS Raleigh seemed to have died a massive death at Collingwood and we were treated far better than the WEMs as we were now in Phase 3. They had to stand evening rounds every night, we didn't. In fact Collingwood was like a holiday camp compared to Raleigh.

Duties

We were the armed sentries outside of working hours all week from secure to turn-to.

The duty month ran on a 4-week cycle

1. *Tuesday-Friday-Sunday*
2. *Thursday*
3. *Wednesday-Saturday*
4. *Monday*

With that many apprentices the duty roster was run 3-months on, 3 months off.

The barrack guard duty watch comprised around 20 people and we had to sign for our duties in the Manpower Allocation Office (MACCO) the day before. The list in the MACCO was generally about 40 people long and if you weren't in the top 30 the chances were you would get a stand-off so weren't required for duty. Failing to sign for your duty meant you were piped to the MACCO and no matter where you were on that list you would be guaranteed to be duty.

The duty watch muster took place near the UPO at 1245 each day, 0800 on Saturday and 0900 on Sunday. Every day there was a duty watch warning read out that you heard so often you could eventually remember it all. The duty POs who read it out kept so few duties they really thought they were passing on vital information. Highlights were "You are warned that you are duty for the next 24 hours or until relieved by tomorrow's duty watch" and "You are to remain onboard for the period of your duty and listen out for pipes. An excuse you did not hear the pipe will not be tolerated". A totally redundant line was still in there "anyone requiring webbing is to draw it from the main gate on completion of this muster" which nobody ever knew what it was about.

We were allocated rounds times, 2 hour stints throughout the night.

T wo patrols would be out at any one time, each patrol comprising either 2 apprentices or one apprentice/one killick. There were also "Green Flashes", these were WEMs who had been selected for 'tiffs course but not picked their killicks rate up yet so they wore a small green stripe on their epaulette.

The duty roster did not take anything into account and it was quite possible that you would be out patrolling between 0200–0400 when you had a complicated exam to sit the following morning.

When duty we were accommodated in part of Marlborough building. There was a TV room and upstairs accommodation comprising beds (without bedding) and nothing else. You would take your own pillow and a blanket with you. We remained dressed throughout the period of duty as we were the Reaction Force. Occasionally we augmented the main gate and slept in the beds down there. It wasn't unusual for the main gate staff to forget an apprentice was asleep out the back and they'd wake up about 10am that morning having been reported as absent from the morning muster.

Patrols had to report to the main gate where they were given a radio, weapon and route card to complete in the first hour normally, about 40 minutes. You'd then go back to the gate, be unloaded and have a brew. Then repeat the above for the second stint. Initially the main gate was run by a PO who was sound. Later on they put LREGs on the gate and these tended to be arseholes. A tall, spotty, loud, dark haired one called Taff gave me a right bollocking for making myself a brew using "his" victuals. I told him we'd been told we could use the main gate victuals by the CPO GI to which Taff replied that he didn't give a f*** because the CPO GI wasn't there. He didn't seem to give a shit that we'd been freezing our tits off walking round outside whilst he sat there watching TV.

One night an apprentice patrol had been asked to undertake a perimeter fence patrol and make a note of any perimeter lights that were defective. Because he was a typical cynical smug Reggie "Taff" was thinking that this was to make sure they did the route properly. When they returned from their 1 ½ hour walk around the entire perimeter fence "Taff" took the list off them and ditched it. He ditched it because he thought the list would be shared to other patrols who could get their heads down in the squash court rather than do the patrol, such was his pathetic view of human nature. The next day he got a right bollocking from the Collingwood Buffer who had wanted that information so he could attend to the defective lights the XO had been complaining about. Nice one "Taff".

Another LREG called Ash used to leave us waiting outside for ages to be unloaded whilst he was on the phone to his Mrs. He eventually got a Warrant reading for stealing the mail so I didn't see much of him after he'd been busted back to AB(R).

Some people got blue cards. This was for pool lifeguard, Collingwood Club Committee, Collingwood Band and Sea Cadets instructors.

Course Content

Like before we did LES, MES, maths and also DPS (Defence & Political Studies). There were phase tests throughout each lesson and term.

After a couple of terms we spent an entire term in workshops. This included a week of GEM (General Engineering Maintenance) where we learned how to identify bearings (roller/ball/caged/thrust/journal), and how to grease them. We also learned how to shim a motor-generator using a DTI, something I never had to do ever ever again.

A further 2 weeks were spent in Allied Trades learning how to bend metal and how to braise repair some pipework. A week of tech drawing was another part of workshops. Next was the actual workshops themselves. This was around 4 weeks of drilling, sawing and filing some metal to make a small desk vice. Afterwards a couple of weeks was spent on a lathe turning down a piece of metal into a piece of metal with left- and right-hand threads, knurling and a brass internally-threaded nut on.

Finally we spent a few weeks doing electronics including designing a circuit board layout, printing our own board, populating it with components and assembling it. We made an RC meter and a digital voltmeter in an aluminium box we had made during our allied trades phase. We also made a logic probe.

Social

Collingwood had a "bop" three times a week, Tuesday, Thursday and Saturday and this was held in the Collingwood Club. This reduced down in the end to just Wednesday. We'd often go from there into either Gosport (Emma's nightclub) or Southsea (Joanna's nightclub).

One summer they hosted a pool party. The Collingwood Club was right next to a large sun terrace outside the HMS Collingwood swimming pool in the SARC. To doors to the pool and the Colly Club were opened and beach attire was positively encouraged. This was one of the best events the Colly Club ever ran, the sun was out, everyone was diving in the pool and into the bar. Everything went well. So well that they never hosted one of those pool parties ever again.

With the further reduction in numbers of both 'tiffs and WEMs even the bop became less well attended and they started to try and boost interest with entertainment. A hypnotist was brought in, a singer, a horse racing night, Tom Conti as guest speaker etc. These events were often quite well attended but with so few people around were never going to be a huge success.

Another draw was the GX Bowling Alley across the road from Collingwood. They were offering £1 a pint for RN ID card holders and you could enjoy a pint surrounded by normal people rather than being seen as an inconvenience by the NAAFI bar staff and looked down at by the duty Colly Club Committee member.

Pubs in Fareham: Clinkers, Daniels, Crown, Cheese & Ale, Royal Oak. There was occasionally trouble in Fareham and this seemed to be targeted and involve lads in cars picking on small groups of sailors.

Pubs in Gosport: Nelson, Emmas Nightclub, Arcs Nightclub,

Pubs/clubs in Portsmouth: Albion (with Saturday afternoon disco), Park tavern, Martine's Nightclub, Mucky Duck, Peggy Sues,

Pubs/clubs in Southsea: Fanshaw's, Hong Kong Charlies, Ellie Jays, Basement, Lush, Bliss, Time & Envy, Joanna's (firm matelot favourite), Route 66, Harry Lime's Nightclub.

Weekenders

When we weren't duty (every other weekend) we would often go "up the line". Sharing a clapped out car with as many people in it as possible. All paying £20 each we would endure the 5 to 6 hour journey up t'north and the 3 hour journey back n the Sunday night. In those days pre-M3 bypass, pre-Newbury bypass and pre-M6 Toll Road we used to spend a lot of time in traffic around these choke points. Every driver had their own preferred shortcut that normally took just as long as queuing in traffic but created the impression you were getting home quicker. After a couple of terms I decided to buy my own car again and I started giving lifts. Fuel was cheap and it was quite profitable with a full car. You also had your regulars so the journey became quite good fun.

Sometimes we went elsewhere for the weekend. A group of us went to a friend's (Buck Taylor) in Chesterfield. A group came to mine in Haydock one weekend.

It was strange but despite the cost of fuel increasing over the years, the flat fee of £20 to go weekenders never changed in my time in the mob.

Tal-y-Bont

We went to Tal-y-Bont in the Brecon Beacons for a week twice during our time in T-School. This was our equivalent of Killick's Leadership course for the other branches. There was a lot of PT, a lot of walking and some leadership tasks during each week.

Sometimes a WEMs class would be there. For them I think this was a bit of a break and some AT. They were accommodated and fed in the hut.

For 'tiffs this was a leadership course. We camped down the road and ate ration packs.

Our first visit was a kind of pre-leadership course and the second week the actual leadership phase.

During the second week we camped near a scout hut. Occasionally WEMs were accommodated in the scout hut. We had heard on the grapevine that the man who lives near the scout hut was quite receptive to 'tiffs and a parlez could be struck with him. We ventured down one night to see what we could bargain. Taking a water bottle with me I knocked on the door and asked for some water. I struck up a brief conversation with him and when I dropped in that we were Artificers he relaxed a little and started to lead the conversation. He explained how he and his wife send food aid overseas and that ration pack food is perfect for it. I explained that we had lots of ration pack food but still needed to be able to eat something. And this was where we struck gold. In exchange for our ration packs and a couple of quid he would run us in his car to the nearest pub where we could have a beer and some food (and a decent shit in a proper toilet) before picking us back up again to bring us home. Winner, winner, chicken dinner.

Our final day was spent doing AT, climbing and abseiling one year and sea canoeing the next.

Sea Sense

There was a week of "sea sense" that we undertook later on in T-School which was meant to be an introduction to sailing. Normally an entry would be split into a couple of yachts who then sailed across the channel to Cherbourg. The timing of our entry meant that the yachts weren't available so we were taken to Clarence Yard in Gosport each day to learn how to sail a small 2-man laser dinghy. We were all a bit miffed by this to say the least. One day the tide was out a long way and we couldn't even put the dinghys in the water. We asked our DO Lt Cowan if we could go into town whilst we waited and he said yes. We walked into Gosport and just ended up going to the Nelson pub and sitting outside in the sun pissing it up. We were quite rinsed by the time we got back to Clarence Yard in time to get the bus back. We were very lucky that our DO had absolutely no interest as he'd slapped his notice in anyway. He told us briefly that we were irresponsible but did finish off his bollocking with "but I don't give a fuck".

Summer Duties

The role of barrack guard still needed to be fulfilled over leave and it fell to the 913 entry to cover the 3 week summer leave period each year. For this we were put into Port & Stbd watches and moved into 2 huts on Pelican Road, old accommodation. We then kept duties a couple of days on, a couple of days off etc with an ELWE or 2 thrown in. During our 1 or 2 days off between duties there was little else for us to do than go out. We had some cracking times during these summer duties going on all day sessions in Southsea at the height of summer. Retard leave for us then fell in September.

SFCs

One of the final courses we did was on static frequency changers or SFCs. This was a week learning about some actual equipment that we would see onboard. We learned the theory, maintenance and fault finding. We were instructed by a Stocky Geordie ex-command field gunner called George. He'd walk round the class flexing and glaring as we were working on the kit and he could hear when someone blew the internal fuse by the change of tone of the kit. This was normally because someone used the wrong oscilloscope probe and was immediately followed by George banging his pointing stick on the floor and booming "use a fucking ten times probe!" in a very distorted Geordie accent.

Manpower reductions

When we joined at Raleigh there were 240 people in 8 divisions. The next entry (921) was half that size and the next one half as big again. As the senior classes were leaving to go to sea we noticed that the classes following us were getting fewer as was the division and as was T-school. Perks that senior classes used to get (they didn't have to clean for rounds etc) were gone because there wasn't enough manpower. Rubber road skirmishing came round more often. This "black hole" would follow us round our entire career, not that we realised this yet.

Attrition

During T-School we had many failures. As with Raleigh if someone wasn't up to scratch they were either discharged or offered re-cat depending on preference and aptitude. 913D lost so many of its members that the class was disbanded. We took a couple of 913D into our class as we'd lost some of ours too. We'd also taken in a lad from the entry behind us (921) Darren "Desmond" Bagley, he was advanced a term because he had already done workshops with Rolls Royce before joining up.

Streams

There were 4 streams of WEs and they had a requirement in terms of numbers from our entry

CEW	*Communications, Electronic Warfare – 4 were required*
AD	*Action Data (computers, radar, sonar etc) – 8 were required*
WD	*Weapon Direction (gyros, tracking radars etc) – 16 were required (approx)*
OC	*Ordnance Control (guns, bombs etc) – 16 were required (approx)*

When I joined up I'd wanted to be CEW. I would also have been happy as an AD but competition was fierce. I'd failed a short control exam due to complacency and misplaced priorities and also had a couple of misdemeanours during the previous couple of years so wasn't exactly flavour of the month. When I went to sea I'd been streamed as WDO so would become either a WD or an OC depending on preference and aptitude during my sea time. I didn't really want to be either.

BSSC

The final thing to do was the Basic Sea Survival Course. This took a week and comprised 2.5 days of fire fighting, 1.5 days of damage control, 0.5n days of NBC (Nuclear Biological Chemical) training, and a final 0.5 day of sea survival. We were flooded out in the large Havoc training facility; we were smoked out and set fire to in the smoky-joe fire fighting trainers; we were gassed in the CS chambers to test our respirators; we were thrown into freezing water a made to swim to a liferaft. What a cracking week and at the end of it we were all deemed safe to go to sea.[12]

Some of the terms used by Jef, such as the Rubber Road, will be unfamiliar to an older generation more used to Buckley Hall, Gibraltar Road, Badger Road and the White City, so Jef has a few words in explanation:

Marlborough Building was constructed on the north side of the parade ground running the length of the parade ground. At the front are 2 floors of offices and classrooms. Coming off this are several corridors also with 2 floors of classrooms in. These all meet at the end in another single, long, continuous corridor. This has an industrial rubber floor, is wide enough to drive a car down and tall enough to drive a lorry down (if the doors were big enough to get one in). This is the "Rubber Road". The other side of the rubber road were the large equipment areas housing various equipment such as harpoon missiles, radar and sonar systems, guns etc…

The Rubber Road is where at standeasy all of the classes pour down their corridors into it for a brew. At the west end of the rubber road were all of the T-School classes, in the middle was A-School and at the east end was MT school. There were 3 NAAFI tea stalls, one for each school.

As you came back to the Rubber Road more often during your career on courses it was inevitably where you'd end up seeing old oppo's and catching up. By the time you were a CPO, if you tried walking from one end to the other it would take you the whole of standeasy as you met so many people you hadn't seen for years.[13]

The changes that were being made had several origins. The closure of some naval training establishments and their amalgamation into a homogeneous entity was driven by the need to reduce the size of the naval training estate, to save money and generate revenue from the sale of the land made free with these closures. In the case of *Collingwood* the driver was the report of the Engineering Branch Working Group Study Report published as long ago as 1975. As is the way with such far-reaching recommendations, there was a long hiatus between suggestion and implementation and it was in 1992 that a final report arising from the EBWG, the Ops/WE Interface Study appeared. It recommended that the existing Operations Branch be amalgamated with the WE Branch to form an all-encompassing Warfare Branch. There were several reasons given for this amalgamation: the increased use of automation in data processing and the much-improved reliability of modern weapon systems, which allowed for the reduction in the number of Ops Branch Junior Rates and also the number of WE Mechanic maintainers at both junior and senior rate level. This came with the assurance that such a change would lead to better career prospects for all involved.

One immediate possible problem arose from these maintainers from the WE Branch now being answerable to Warfare Officers, while the skilled Artificers would remain with the WEO. Members of the old Ops

Branch were also assimilated into this new scheme and they all became operator maintainers, with the first recruits entered in the Spring of 1993 with the new title Operator Mechanic. Their training followed a familiar pattern of eight weeks at *Raleigh* and between seven and nineteen weeks' training, depending on specialisation, followed by a time at sea in a role as an operator able to carry out the most basic maintenance.

Their career progression would see them achieve the same level of technical proficiency as the old WEM and LWEM but with a far more limited range of equipment. There were already problems appearing with advancement, there was no viable structure for an OM to advance to a WE Officer and the path to Artificer was also strewn with difficulties as the OM lacked the academic background and equipment experience to negotiate the path to Artificer Candidate, while the old WEMs and LWEMs were far better placed to achieve this route. As well as this, the OMs Divisional Officers were no longer WE and had little appreciation of the requirements for Artificer Candidate. This of course reduced the possible number of potential Artificer candidates and so reduced the numbers going forward, and this at a time when recruitment to Artificer Apprentice was also at a low level. This was clearly going to have a deleterious effect on the availability of trained Artificers in the future; as will be seen at the turn of the next century, what goes around comes around.[14]

This was also a time of major change to warship propulsion. Steam was a thing of the past and the main method of propulsion was gas turbine. However, there was a lobby in the engineering world that advocated electrical propulsion. This had been partly realised in the Type 23 frigate. This proved very successful and was a precursor of future electric platforms. This was followed by the auxiliary oilers (AO) *Wave Knight* and *Wave Ruler* and landing platform docks (LPD) *Albion* and *Bulwark*. While there had been experiments with electric propulsion going back to HMS *Adventure* in the 1920s and in the H Class Survey vessels of the 1970s, the AOs and the LPDs were the first Royal Navy ships to use full electrical propulsion integrated with the ship's service power system and to fully control AC propulsion motors with power electronics. The concept was taken a stage further with the Type 45 Destroyer, which employed an integrated full electric propulsion (IFEP) system with high-voltage motors and electronic converters. This system was also adopted for the CVFs HMS *Queen Elizabeth* and HMS *Prince of Wales*.

All this technology, new and novel to the Royal Navy, required a new breed of Artificer, with a knowledge of modern electronics and an ability to diagnose faults rather than a man with skill of hand and an ability to manufacture spares from scratch, though that skill would always be useful for a ship distant from its base and assistance. This sophistication of platform technology led directly to the new training regime that was adopted.

There were further losses on the 1990s. In 1996 HMS *Daedalus* closed and Air Engineering training moved to *Sultan* and into a purpose-built facility. The biggest loss was the change from fore and aft rig, worn by Apprentices since their inception in 1903, to square rig, making Apprentices all but indistinguishable from any other junior rating, So when 973 Entry joined Fisgard Squadron they were issued with square rig, marking the end of the peaked cap and gilt-buttoned uniform for Artificer Apprentices. They were only distinguishable from other junior ratings by their lack of branch badges and the retention of the red cap badge on their berets. Even the red beret badge was lost for a time until its return in March 2000. This change in rig, together with the amalgamation of Artificer and Mechanician training, had the side effect of mixing the two rigs in one class, where many of the Artificer candidates were already Petty Officers; this would seem to be at complete variation with the stated reason for the loss of fore and aft rig and gives the lie to the stated reason for the change.

The rather spurious reason for this – to most ex-Apprentices – dramatic and ill-conceived change to a tradition begun by Jackie Fisher, for the very purpose of distinguishing Artificer Apprentices as an elite body of highly trained and professional engineers, was that there were insufficient numbers of ratings in square rig available for ceremonial occasions. One has to wonder what scale of ceremonial was envisaged: perhaps lining the streets of London.

The Apprentice of the late 1990s was a far different animal to his predecessors:

The modern Artificer Apprentice looks very different today from those who first marched onboard HMS Sultan in 1983. The original Artificers' uniform was the fore and aft rig worn by Senior Rates with the apprentice having a red cap badge. As of January 5th 1998 the Apprentice was to wear Square Rig, the reason given was that the Navy needed to ensure that there were enough "sailors" in uniform for ceremonial occasions. The apprentices even lost their red beret badge, only to be reinstated in March 2000 – the only form of recognition of an Artificer today.

The modern Artificer now joins HMS Sultan and is combined with the Marine Engineering Mechanics (MEMs) for their Part 2 training. This module is common to both training groups' needs.

The Artificer is now recruited as a "diagnostician"; the modern needs of the Fleet do not require the skill of hand of the old Artificers. Modern computers and new methods of repair and maintenance threaten to make these skills obsolete. The apprenticeship is now rewarded with a Higher National Diploma, a clear demonstration of the commitment demanded by the Navy and achieved by the modern day Artificer. The Artificer apprenticeship is still one of the longest and most demanding of any course undertaken in any of the three services. Despite the reduction in manual skills and the loss of an identifying uniform it is often easy to pick out an Artificer. He or she is still the one with head held high, happy in the knowledge of sound engineering principals and with a standard and bearing that is second to none within the Royal Navy.[15]

Jumper Collins joined Burgess Division in 982 class and was set to follow the set pattern of going to sea after one term in *Raleigh* and one at *Sultan* but opted to join the Submarine Service, which still retained M and L specialisation and he decided on L. He remembered making a battery charger as a test job, as had been done as far back as OEA Apprentices in the late 1960s. He also remembered helping to diagnose the defect on a piece of electronic equipment but being frustrated that, having found the problem, he was unable to effect a repair as no spare components were carried.[16]

Andrew Grimes, who joined in 993 Class, remembered one lad who travelled to *Raleigh* and on learning that being in the Royal Navy meant going to sea on a ship got up and walked out and went home: clearly a lad in the wrong place and the wrong vocation. He recalled that the notion that Artificers were the crème de la crème of the lower deck was inculcated into them from the beginning, so the *Fisgard* ethos was still alive and kicking.

He joined his first ship, HMS *Argyll*, on a Saturday and on the Monday the ship sailed for a nine-month deployment. Andrew was still wondering what had happened. He first ran ashore in the Navy onto a beach in Sierra Leone, escorted there and back by the local police and Royal Marines. He must have wondered if this was the normal routine for going ashore.

As Andrew remembered, the training timeline was somewhat different from the earlier decades. As already mentioned, there was the sea time very early in the training cycle, when the Apprentices knew no more than a new MEM and could have been of limited use in the Marine Engineering Department.

Raleigh, *Ten weeks, General Naval Training, academic training.*

Sultan, Sixteen weeks, same basic marine engineering training as MEMs. Twelve months sea training, some Apprentices in MEM compliment billet, some extranummary. During this time all Apprentices were expected to complete a task book in order to qualify for LMEA as well as a board known as the "Tiff Inspectors".

Sultan two years six months further technical training, with advancement to LMEA after twelve to eighteen months and completion of HND. On completion of this training and a written and oral board and a further task book there was advancement to POMEA.

Further task books and boards were required before advancement to CPOMEA.[17]

Another lad who joined in 903 Class was Stephen Galloway-Kirkland, who remembered being "as proud as punch"[18] to join as an Artificer Apprentice. Steven was streamed ME and after the usual fifteen weeks' naval general training at *Raleigh*, where he remembered the Divisional Petty Officer for Burgess Division was an old submariner, Jan Lineker, who guided them through these early days. It was during this time that he first encountered a level of animosity from non-Artificers that seemed to include being spate at and keeping cool in the face of this provocation and not resorting to violence but perhaps just treading on the shiny bulled-up toecaps of their tormentors' parade boots when the chance arose. As with Dawn Jennings, he recalled the passing out parade as being very wet and their new no. 1 suits getting soaked and subsequently shrinking during the drying-out process at the prizegiving in *Raleigh*'s Roebuck Theatre.

He moved on to *Sultan* before Christmas 1990, where he was in Anson Division and under the guiding hand of CPO Tony Bull for the first term in *Sultan*. He recalled these early days as being made somewhat fraught by the passing out class:

The academic and initial craft stage progressed slowly, and the attrition rate seemed high. Drinking and high japes were very common, and there seemed to be a disproportionate amount of Scots under training, of which I myself am one. I remember how the passing out class would spend a week of tipping the juniors out of bed and trashing their messes, until one evening myself and a chum (who is still in the Navy now) decided to ambush the passing out class, before they trashed Fisher division which was our block. We set up with the firehose at the top of the stair well, and as soon as they came in mob handed, let them have it. Well they went berserk, but they never did catch the two of us and it was only some years later when I bumped into one in the fleet, did I confess to the job. They had no idea who done them over.[19]

While in *Sultan* the tradition of affording the benefits of Artificer training to foreign navies, at a price, continued; in this case the sailors were from Brunei. The money paid by the Sultan of Brunei, it was mooted, paid for the training of Steven's class, though that is more an inference than a fact.

Steven seems not to have spent his sea term actually at sea but was employed in the Submarine Maintenance Group in HMS *Dolphin*, working on the submarine *Opossum*, which had recently returned from the First Gulf War and required her Gulf camouflage livery of blue returned to the more normal black. This seems a strange way of employing a young Artificer Apprentice unless he was likely to join the Submarine Service, which Steven was not about to do. It was during this sea time that Steven's mother persuaded him that it would be beneficial to leave the Royal Navy and attend university, where Steven graduated with an engineering degree.

This is not the end of the story. Having graduated, Steven decided to rejoin the Royal Navy in 1997, though, for reasons that are not readily apparent but seem to follow the trend of inexplicable recruiting decisions made by the "powers that be", Steve rejoined as an MEM. While he was surely highly over-qualified for such a role, he did, of course, have the advantage in new entry training of already knowing the ropes.

chapter twelve

The Twenty-First
Century and "the End"

• • •

And by this artistic intelligence the etherial artificer creates the whole world.[1]

A t the beginning of the twenty-first century it was clear that the days of the Artificer were numbered, the loss of a formal apprenticeship discarded in favour of a more equipment-based ideology. This despite the growing enthusiasm for apprenticeships in industry. But for the early years things remained fairly static and training of Artificers continued as before. This is illustrated by the memories of Andy Bibb of his early days as an Apprentice; at the time of writing (2018) Andy is still serving as a WO1 ET (WE) in HMS *Diamond*:

Sunday 27th May 2001 and 3 of us travelled down from Fareham to Plymouth to join the 130(ish) other hopefuls waiting for the bus to Raleigh at Plymouth Train Station. I remember the journey well as it was a sunny day and the smug look given by the chap issuing us our single one way tickets in exchange for our first travel warrants must have meant he knew where we were going and what we were doing.

We travelled first on the Cardiff Central and then swapped for a Virgin Trains service down to Plymouth at Westbury (I think), something else that stuck in my mind as the service was pulled by an old Deltic Diesel Locomotive I remembered from my childhood in Yorkshire ploughing up and down the East Coast Main Line.

Having been lucky enough to have been to Raleigh before as a Reservist at HMS King Alfred, I was under no illusion as to what was in store for us, so quickly forgot any fears I might have had and found it entertaining watching my travelling companions pretty much shit themselves for 5 hours!

Once at Plymouth we were separated as Artificer Apprentices from the main throng of Warfare, Mechanics, Specs and Loggies and bussed over to Raleigh via the Torpoint Ferry, arriving early evening. With our kit dumped in the quadrangle we filed into the main Fisgard block to meet our DO's and DI's for the next 11 weeks and sign our lives away for 22 years! I was greeted by a grinning POAEM "Alfie" Hind and the sarcastic comment of "Welcome to 11 weeks of hell Mr Bibb!". Alfie had been my DI the previous year when I attended Raleigh as a reservist so I knew it was, partly, in jest at least!

Our DO's and DI's for the next 11 weeks were, for those of us in Sherval Division our DO was Lt Adam Rees, a schoolie (ETM branch now disbanded) and our DI POAEM Alfie Hind, with Simpson, Bass and Burgess having Lt Dave Hedgecox, Lt Burton and WO1MEA Pattison with PO Gill, PO Heesom and PO Sara Moseley as DI's, the block Chief being CPO Smith. 13 years later as a Warrant Officer 2 (formerly Charge Chief) I would come across a certain Lt Cdr Dave Hedgecox when we were both WE Sea Riders at FOST in Devonport and share a few good memories! He is now a Commander...

Following initial interviews by our DO's we had a welcoming speech, which I think must have given those already with cold feet the final push they needed as there were several that went straight back home that evening, quite a challenge as they had to pay their own way and for some cross most of the country! The rest of us were shown to our mess decks to find our bunks, kit bags and to get acquainted with each other. Males were separated from females with the 10-12 (I think) females in their own mess behind a locked door from the 4 main male mess decks of approx 22 each. Sherval and Simpson on the top floor with Bass and Burgess on the first floor.

The next few days were spent packing away our civvies for a few weeks, preparing our kit (I still have my kit bag, holdall, first No 1's and cap!), medical examinations, the culinary delights of Trafalgar Galley, those initial hair cuts (I have never grown mine back since with an already receding hairline when I joined) and learning about "privileges" such as not being able to leave the block to go to the NAAFI for at least the next couple of weeks, being able to use the phone booth round the back of the block and handing in valuables such as brick sized mobile phones for those that had them! Over the next few weeks privileges would be hard earned and quickly lost as we came together rising and falling as a team.[2]

Andy was a little older when he joined, being twenty-six, though he does mention he was by no means the oldest; this is very different to the age limits of the sixties and seventies and reflects the amalgamation of Artificers and Mechanicians. Andy also had the added advantage of having attended *Raleigh* as a reservist, which gave him a considerable advantage over those new to the Navy. He recalled the many hours spent ensuring his kit was maintained in first-class condition ready for a kit muster at any time:

Downtime in the block would be taken up with preparing kit, getting those creases in all the right places of our uniform ready for the next day. Attempting to keep PT rig pristine was a challenge in itself marching round the establishment with Div Bags packed full of kit as the PTI's were notorious for their exacting standards. Washing was by hand in the communal wash room with the use of 2 spinners between us all, that was until one of them was destroyed by Apprentice Trenton who thought it would be a good idea to spin his wet high leg combat boots in there after a run round the assault course and we watched it tear itself apart before our eyes. As the weeks went by a well established routine was in place with people taking charge of washing everyone's No 8's together, white shirts etc etc. With the whole establishment washing at once it wasn't unknown for St John's lake to fill up with foam from the drains, we soon found ourselves banned from biological powder so as not to upset the local marine life.

Hours would be spent sat in the passageways polishing boots and shoes into the late hours ready for the next day, I was extremely proud of the deep shine I achieved on my combat boots only to be completely gutted after our first run round the assault course pretty much wrecked the toes and they were never the same again. Many tricks were tried to get the perfect polished finish, varying from the traditional spit, hot water, melting the polish with lighters etc. Some were better than others, with the naturals taking only a few minutes to achieve a high shine, to those who just could not do it, I recall one chap who managed to polish to a high shine the entire front half of his shoe before he was stopped, it was a magnificent example of polishing but sadly had to be taken back to just the toe cap.

I recall 3 main kit musters that we had to pass, as well as the daily checks by DI's. Most of us kept some kit permanently folded and prepped, including one of the 2 pussers issue blankets, no duvets like the kids get these days! One of the punishments for poor behaviour was the rolling kit muster, if you really screwed up you ended up with a rolling kit muster which started with moving your entire bed and locker contents into the quadrangle! 3 unlucky apprentices ended up taking things a bit too far and had the honour of conducting one of these. It only happened the once![3]

The very idea of mechanical aids, such as spin dryers, for washing would have seemed like a dream to those of more mature years recalling their time in Part 1 training. Such things were beyond the wildest imaginations of young Apprentices.

During this time John Newell continued to forge ahead and he remembered the early years of the twenty-first century:

I left Bath to join HMS ALBION as SNO/MEO in January 2001. I stood by in Barrow until we finally sailed at the end of 2002. I was awarded the MBE in the 2004 New Year's Honours List for my time as SNO and being "Mr electric ship".

My time as FMEO in Fleet headquarters was largely spent arguing against the Platform Engineer Officer (PEO) concept and the demise of the Artificer. The PEO would have significantly affected the branch structure and added to the burden on the already hard-pressed engineers at sea. That idea did not gain traction but the demise of the Artificer did ultimately get adopted. One other project was to design the SCC for QEC; the design stood the test of time and is now at sea.

On promotion to Captain I helped run the Trafalgar 200 events in 2005, then started what became 9 years in Abbeywood, Bristol. I was initially in the Defence Logistics Transformation Programme, then became the MPH Team Leader and on promotion to Commodore became the Head of SS(A).[4]

Here we can see that there was opposition to the demise of the Artificer, even if ultimately to no avail. There must have been unrelenting pressure from on high to ensure that the Artificer began part of history, despite his continued relevance to the modern Royal Navy.

There remained the rivalry among Apprentices that had been a feature of life as an Apprentice from before the days of *Fisgard* but in *Raleigh* it could be widened to include any of the trainees, whatever their branch, as Andy remembered:

Mess deck co-operation was strongly encouraged and often worked well when it came to scrubbing out the heads & bathrooms etc. Rivalry was also rife and it was not uncommon for those on the top floor to engage in "friendly combat" in the evenings, I have no doubt that Bass & Burgess also had their own "relationship". 2 such notable incursions into each other's mess deck on the top floor resulted in exploding pillows in Simpson, I've still no idea to this day if they managed to clear up all the feathers before the Duty Chief came up stairs on rounds. Another sortie by Simpson into Sherval resulted in Jamie Spary getting walloped round the head (by a steaming bat in a pillow case if I remember right) at which point he became like the devil possessed, grabbed the nearest blunt object (a Henry hoover pipe) and went after his assailant with a disturbing fire in his eyes. Considering he was about 5ft nothing and about 7 stones, it still took 5 of us to wrestle him to the floor and calm him down.

Mess deck camaraderie was certainly lively, it wasn't uncommon to see objects passing by windows as they were launched from the top floor, mattresses were not uncommon. "Lamp posting" of beds was also seen as amusing twice until the mess put a stop to it as people were not finding it funny. We also had someone (Ben McCaffrey) who snored so badly he could wake the dead! On one such evening where it couldn't be tolerated any more, 6 of the mess carried him out, still snoring in his bed and left him round the corner across the hallway. Something like 2am he woke most of the mess dragging his bed back in and cursing just about anyone that offered unhelpful comments/insults in his direction.

Towards the end of our time we had worked out that the block adjacent to ours was where all the phase 1 medical downgrades were accommodated, some of the wrens took delight in showing off various articles of underwear through the windows and occasionally a flash of flesh caught the eye. There were also a fair few brushes between the blocks and again it wasn't unknown for some budding relationships to be consummated, or at least a good attempt was made before they were rumbled by either duty watch staff or cheers from the mess windows![5]

These first nine weeks in *Raleigh* culminated in the usual passing out parade, though on this occasion it was not the usual parade. This parade was attended by the four surviving Artificers who had reached flag rank: Bass, Burgess, Simpson and Sherval, after whom the Fisgard Squadron divisions were named.

After four weeks' summer leave, Andy moved on to *Collingwood* for eight weeks' Basic Engineering Principles (BEP). He remembered the accommodation being in sharp contrast to Fisgard Squadron:

> *There we had 8 weeks of BEP – Basic Engineering Principles, which was supposed to be enough to turn us into something "useful" on our first ships. This included some basic fundamental maths, circuit theory, BSSC etc. BEP was taught by an ETM, Lt Amy Alexander. I would later come across her as my WEO on HMS Daring in 2012.*
>
> *I was up on the top floor in Bryson, 5 of us sharing a mess deck, it was a stark change to Fisgard with it being essentially a small flat with kitchen, bathroom etc. All of which had to be kept immaculate to the required standards and reported every day for rounds. One of our messmates decided he wasn't going to keep his locker in a decent state and ended up with a kit muster one week, unfortunately for him when his locker was opened up it all fell out on the unsuspecting Senior Rate conducting the inspection. I don't recall what happened to him after that, but I suspect he was SNLR after some other failings.*
>
> *Our Course Manager/DO was a certain Lt Steve Rom. A character that you either liked or didn't. Ultimately he was the one who would assign us to our first ships, generally those that did well and got on with it ended up with some fairly decent first deployments, I was one of those lucky ones being sent off to join HMS Campbeltown with another, Chris Yates, via boat transfer from Falmouth!*
>
> *The journey down to Falmouth was fairly hassle free, but we ran into trouble looking for where the PAS boats ran out of! Naturally we tried the main port first but were re-directed to a small jetty further up river which was found by driving down a side road/dirt track at the other end of town. Suffice to say we made it with plenty of time and embarked upon our first ever PAS boat. My pusser's grip still bears the paint marks from where I left it against some wet yellow paint which was the standard colour of the work boats before SERCO took over and painted them all white instead.*[6]

So it would appear that there was a certain amount of nepotism when it came to allocation of ships and Andy's first impression of his new home stays with him even today, so many years later:

I'll never forget first seeing the ship in the gloomy early evening and climbing up the ladder to be met by one of the WE Charge Chief's who was getting off for compassionate reasons, it was a cheery hello and goodbye as he passed us on his way down. We were then met by the 2 LWEA's on board Mike Campbell and Stu Hotchin and taken down to 3G mess and shown lockers etc etc. Then it was our first scran onboard and settling into Ships Routine.

A few days later we were back into Plymouth, Rubble Jetty if I remember right, and the start of a 4 week DAMP (Dockyard Assisted Maintenance Period), now known as FTSP (Fleet Time Support Period). The ship had been out on trials after running aground in Norway and damaging a propeller in the process. A few months later HMS Grafton would do the same.

Over the next 7 months we had our WEA task books to complete (I've still got mine), including CBRNDC task book which resulted in a lot of work in the evenings, studying the WEG (Weapon Engineering Guide) and undergoing our WEA training programme working on all sections of the WE department as well as qualifying as a WE Roundsman. We were allocated mentors who kept a watchful eye over our progress. I don't think there was a section I didn't particularly dislike, I enjoyed working on the Sea Wolf Tracker Sections with CWEA "Pinky" Salmon and CWEA "Space" Evans. POWEM(O) Taff Elder and POWEM(R) Flash Gordon had the Seawolf Launchers, I'll never forget conducting a missile transfer at sea from the smaller forward magazine to the main magazine aft, trundling warshot missiles in their trolley's between their respective lifts down 1 deck and being told in no uncertain terms to make sure I didn't dent any of the fins! You wouldn't get away with any of that these days! I also recall climbing up the inside of the Air Weapons Lift cleaning ready for Staff Sea Check at the start of a DOST! Again not something you would get away with these days with the need for safety harnesses and several accidents involving personnel in lift wells.

The Surveillance Section was also interesting with the RT967/968, RT1007 and IFF equipment, I have memories of dragging a very large and extremely heavy new Pulse Forming Network from deep store up to the Surveillance Office when a water leak for the 968 Radar resulted in a small flood writing off the radar just after I had gone off watch, my relief opened the office door and found himself ankle deep in chilled water! I could even strip and put back together a 20mm GAMBO-1 cannon, though I got to watch a firing, was never allowed to pull the trigger myself.

Talking of firing's we also got to watch the pre-deployment Sea Wolf missile firing, again something you can't really do these days because of health and safety, but if you wanted to watch the forward system you were allowed on the Flight Deck and if you wanted to watch the aft system you had to go out to the focsle. All exciting stuff for a Baby WE Tiff.

I found the 4.5 Gun slightly unsettling (always a Pinky even then!) as I was often put in the turret to watch the firing circuit checks and always mindful of keeping out of the way of the loading arm as that thing would swing up inline with breech and back down again in the blink of an eye. I was in the turret on one occasion when the ship was in a fairly rough sea state to watch Flash Gordon bimble out of the focsle door to chat, only to watch his face turn to horror as a rather large goffer broke over the bows and if he hadn't dived into the turret just as the Gunbuster POWEA Matt Napper started to turn the mount he would have been thoroughly soaked and possibly gone overboard.

Chris Yates didn't settle in quite as well and decided he wanted to PVR so was returned to Collingwood leaving me as the only Baby WE Tiff onboard for a few months until the following spring when the next 3 Baby Tiff's arrived, one of whom with a surname of "Packer" was quickly re-named "Fudge". Unfortunately the 3 of them were allocated bunks in 3HZ, "The Zoo", the domain of Warfare and Dabbers who had an intense dislike for all things Baby Tiff. WEA Packer didn't enjoy mess deck life down there and was another to decide the Navy wasn't for him.[7]

This illustrates that even in the twenty-first century there could be animosity between Artificers and the non-technical branches. Whether this was based on a certain jealousy at the rapid advancement available to Artificers is hard to define, but it does seem to be something that has endured throughout the years, something that never bothered many Apprentices, though young Packer seems to have had a thinner skin than most and found it difficult to reconcile himself to the banter of the other mess mates, though this banter may have been of a somewhat malevolent nature.

Andy, however, had settled into life onboard. The routine onboard was for the Apprentices to spend time in all of the different WE sections and to complete the WEA task books. This involved quite a bit of work out of working hours to ensure their timely completion. It was also necessary to qualify as a WE Roundsman and, as Andy was expecting to concentrate on the "Pinky" disciplines, such equipment as the 4.5" gun he found a little unnerving and tried to stay out of the way as much as possible.

While onboard *Campbeltown* Andy had his first, but not last, taste of the Flag Officer Sea Training organisation; this is something that will happen to everyone who goes to sea and just has to be endured with a gritted smile for the weeks that it lasts. Nobody has ever liked it but it had to be done to ensure the prime fighting efficiency of the ship and its ship's company:

Campbeltown was also my first experience of OST and my first deployment. OST, or DOST as I think it was called then, started with the usual amount of cleaning and Staff Sea Check rehearsals. As I was working back aft at the start of DOST I found myself down in the bowels of the ship cleaning in the Air Weapons Magazine, which if memory serves was accessed from the WRENS mess lobby… Also I found myself cleaning up inside the lift well for the Air Weapons magazine, again something highly frowned upon these days. For Staff Sea Check my report was to SWEO at the hatch to the aft Sea Wolf Magazine.[8]

After being subjected to the rigour of sea training and the foibles of the sea riders it was time to head off on deployment; in Andy's case this involved heading out to the Middle East in what would become Operation Veritas and Operation Oracle, the supporting operations in the Gulf of Aden ready for the start of operations in Afghanistan. Andy recalled the time well:

My first foreign run was of course, Gibraltar, where I was quickly introduced to the delights of the Sports Bar, Donkey's Flip Flop, Captain's Cabin and the Mad Monk! The next day was the quickest hangover cure I've ever had, my first rock race! After that was a stopover in Cyprus, we needed parts for the gyro and ended up at anchor for a day or so until the RAF flew our stores out. I'm pretty sure I saw a U2 Spy Plane take off from RAF Akrotiri. Whilst at anchor there a few of the lads were fishing, one of them struggled with his catch, it turned out he had caught a fish, but also an angry octopus which also wanted the same fish! Eventually the octopus gave up and let go with a squirt of ink just as he was brought to the surface. After that Jim Rumbelow wanted to get a pet octopus for the mess, though that didn't happen. We also came across numeroud dolphins and flying fish which would end up on the upper deck cross passages in the bad weather.

The remainder of my time on Campbeltown took me on my first (of many) trip through Suez, most was spent on the upperdeck watching Egypt slowly pass by, the army trucks with Egyptian soldiers patrolling the roads alongside us and the missile batteries, burnt out tanks from the 6 day war etc etc. After that was the Red Sea and the run down to the Bab Al Mendeb straits. We were tasked to escort the USS Joint Venture through the straits as there was a fairly high threat level with Yemen. Being a twin hull vessel she was considerably faster than ourselves, but we managed to keep up a steady 25 knots for the short time it took us to travel through. That was my first experience of closing up to State 1 for real, with real ammunition and warshot missiles connected up! The uneventful passage took us into the Gulf of Aden and we departed company with the Joint Venture. The next few weeks saw us patrolling the Gulf were we came across a dead pilot whale which made a target for a close range weapons practice, but unfortunately for the Goalkeeper maintainer the WEO would not allow him to have a go, there would have been nothing left! The ship also conducted a boarding of a suspect vessel, deemed to be riding too high of the water and not flying an ensign or displaying an IMO registry. So the gallant boarding team went and searched a vessel which was bound for an Indian breakers yard! Our next port visit was Djibouti, my first experience of third world Africa first hand. We were relieving our sister HMS Cornwall and duly conducted our handover first day alongside with her rafted outboard of us. She for some reason departed very rapidly the next day and we found out why later as we were accused of causing damage to the Sheraton Hotel Bar. It turned out that our shipmates from the Cornwall got involved with the French Foreign Legion! A further patrol around the Horn of Africa and we arrived in Muscat, where we enjoyed the delights of the indoor Souks which had everything you could wish for from frankincense, gold, tacky gizzits, wailing alarm clocks to a barrel of fully functional WW2 vintage Lee Enfield Rifles! Some great runs ashore were had in the Jungle Bar drinking fish bowl cocktails, watching the XO having a dance off with the warfare mess and the Continental Hotel (until someone tried a Fire Exercise by setting off the fire alarms at 2am and skinny dipping in the pool resulted in the crew being asked to leave) as well as the Holiday Inn.

My final run ashore on the Campbeltown was Salalah in Oman, which tied in with a Tyne Gas Turbine change for the ship. A relatively easy process on a Type 22 but insanely more complicated on the current Type 45s. Our runs ashore were only curbed by the ban on going into town due to an Anti-Western protest going on.[9]

Andy then returned to *Collingwood* to consolidate his training and actually learn something that would turn him into an Artificer rather than the OM that he had been employed as while at sea. However, the return from the Middle East was not without incident:

> *After a highly successful 7 months on Campbeltown I returned back to Collingwood for 2 ½ years. We were pretty much the only passengers on the internal flight from Salalah to Muscat, but then had an 8 hour wait in Muscat for the BA flight home to Heathrow. I remember some altercation with the BA check in desk who wanted to charge us an extortionate amount of money for excess baggage. Lucky for us there was a senior officer with us who put them firmly in their place. We still had to pay up though and the YO who offered to put it all on her credit card found that the transaction never went through so all worked out in the end.[10]*

So in May 2002 Andy started on the two-and-a-half year-long training that would enable him to join the fleet as a fully trained and confident Artificer. However, as is the way of the world, there was a slight glitch to overcome in the early stages of his training when the firemen decided to go on strike and the Armed Forces were drafted in to provide the necessary cover while the strike lasted, Andy described what happened on his return to *Collingwood* and the start of the firemen's strike:

> *Our entry was split into 4 separate classes, 012A, 012B, 012C (mine) and 012D. A & B spent 5 months away, C & D spent 7 months away on ship. All classes were a mix of pure blood Tiffs and WEM's on Mech's course. Over the next couple of years some would be back classed into 013's or further, and one or two took the AIB at this stage and were selected and moved on at the end of course. The course consisted of Maths, Electronics Analogue and Digital, Control Theory, Radar and Sonar Theory, Gyros, Electroptics, hydraulics, tech drawing and many more. Each one would last at least 2 weeks, some up to 6 or 7. Inevitably there were the exams at the end of each module which set people on a routine of revising and then effectively "dumping" it to make room for the next. Within a few months of starting course the Fire Fighter's Strike began and the Armed Forces found themselves stood up to take over. We were notified by the course manager coming into our class room on a Wednesday afternoon and telling us he had good news and bad news. The good news was we were all on weekend leave as of then and the bad was to be back in Collingwood by 1100 on the Sunday for transport down to RNAS Culdrose for Op Fresco training!*

The remainder of the Wednesday consisted of medicals to ensure everyone was fit enough. Not all the 012C's went, I think 4 were left to continue their way on Tiff's course.

Duly turning up on the Sunday we were all bussed down to Culdrose and left there with no return journey back! We spent our first week in the theatre for lectures on Fire-fighting civvy style by the WAFU fire-fighters who taught at the RN School of Flight Deck Ops. Midway through the first week, it turned out that we could have brought our own cars down as a car park had been set aside for us. So that first weekend, pretty much the entire inventory of hirecars from Truro Avis were left at HMS Seahawk main gate for a mass bomb burst back to Pompey! Over the next couple of weeks we took it in turns to drive down, I took mine down for the final weekend.

Over the remaining 3 weeks at Culdrose we were taken through practical training on driving Green Godesses (I managed to get one to back fire in a spectacular fashion after forgetting to turn on the ignition, so after a few turns of the engine with max choke and then turning on the ignition the thing lit off with a rather loud bang! There were people falling off ladders 200m away!) using hoses up ladders, negotiating confined spaces, cutting up cars, entering burning buildings to rescue trapped people (in reality it was just Fred who was taking a break from being thrown overboard all the time to getting burnt instead.) We also learnt to use the hazard suits in the event of a chemical spill. The week we were conducting this training coincided with a visit to Culdrose by the Earl and Countess of Wessex, though we never met them.

The accommodation at Culdrose turned out to be condemned buildings and we literally only had bunks in a common room with our kit stuffed in kit bags underneath, no lockers nothing. There was uproar when the XO of Culdrose wanted to do formal rounds! To get to the fire ground was a bus journey from the accommodation site in HMS Seahawk. This involved crossing one end of the runway where a very weather beaten Buccaneer S2 sat overlooking the runway approaches.

On finishing the final week we were given our Temporary Naval Fire Station assignments, myself and Phil Blight assigned to Eastbourne which was housed in the TA Centre. There we pretty much spent the next 6 months as part of the REST crew working out of the TA Centre but sleeping in a small portacabin complex in the carpark out the back. The REST crew essentially carried all the equipment to deal with RTA as well as BA sets as back up to the main BART (BA Rescue Team) who accompanied the Green Goddesses.

In 6 months we went out 12 times. Out first "shout" was for an overturned range rover out in the country north of Eastbourne. It was a 30min drive with "blues and twos" escorted by a police motor bike. When we arrived the local retained fire station crew had extracted the casualty from the vehicle and they were in the ambulance being treated. It turned out that they had been to the dentist and was suffering with the anaesthesia. We helped get the vehicle back on its wheels and then headed back to Eastbourne in time for dinner. Other shouts included a flat fire where a candle on top of a TV had been too close to some curtains which when they moved with the breeze coming in an open window were set alight and it rapidly took hold of half of the living room! A slightly more grizzly event was a RTA where an elderly lady in a car with no airbags had headbutted the windscreen leaving part of her scalp behind! Our final shout was to a flat fire on the road to Hastings and a second team with BA was requested to assist our Green Goddess and BART team despatched half an hour previously. We overtook the Green Goddess on the A27 to Hastings, plodding along at 30mph, its top speed with a full tank of water!

We were well looked after in our Temporary Fire Station, the TA Chefs enjoyed the chance to do some decent cooking for once and the Welfare funds set up helped us with purchasing the essentials to set up "home". From our allocated budget we bought ourselves a TV, DVD player and many box sets including Band of Brothers as well as a large scalextric set which the Squaddies were none to pleased to find we had set up in their drill hall! Even more so when we tried to keep on playing with it on Drill nights! They got their own back by openly drinking in front of us on Drill Nights as we occupied the JNCO's mess during the day as our ready room. Also the differences between services was apparent on these drill nights when Officers and SNCO's would just walk in without invite! Jack would get most upset and attempt to throw such invaders out of a JR's mess deck whilst the Squaddies would be stood at ram rod attention and saluting indoors negative headgear!

There was no animosity between us and the Eastbourne Fire Station, in fact they came to pay us a visit and we had quite a social occasion with them. They would often cheer us on as we made our way out on "business".

We were also very well looked after by the locals. The Eastbourne RNA was a short walk up the road and in return for helping them redecorate their establishment we were treated to a social night up there, when off duty of course. Also a "rig run" into town in PPI Gold Fire suits resulted in VIP treatment at the night club on the end of the pier.

In between strikes, where it wasn't worth returning home, we would often take a drive to Brighton or Hastings, what better way to spend some downtime eating fish and chips in the winter rain at a British seaside!

Eventually we returned to Collingwood and were 6 months behind the rest of those who stayed put. As the last class to return we were known as 012F and were forever tainted by that brush until we completed course.[11]

It has to be said that in no other walk of life would the training of young Apprentices be interrupted for six months and then restarted as if nothing odd had happened. However, everyone who took part in Operation Fresco seems to have enjoyed the experience and it is apparent that there was no animosity between those members of the Armed Forces and the firemen they were effectively usurping.

Another young man who passed through the gates of *Raleigh* in 2002 was Darren Hawkins, who joined Fisgard Squadron in Shervil Division on 2 September. He travelled from Essex to Plymouth with "just about everything I owned", the journey taking the best part of a day. At Plymouth all those ready to travel to *Raleigh* stood around looking lost until some senior rates herded them on to a bus and off to *Raleigh*. He remembered that his entry numbered about 100, of whom there were about four or five girls. The accommodation was much as he expected but there was a duvet, the first time these had been issued. At the time that Darren was there he did not recall any animosity between the Artificers and the rest of the trainees, nor was there any interaction between them either. In fact, there seem to be no real dealings with other branches until the Apprentices went to sea.

After ten weeks in *Collingwood* it was off to sea and six months in HMS *Iron Duke* in the West Indies, but only doing the work of an OM. This was the time of Operation Fresco, the firemen's strike of 2002–2003, so Darren was lucky to avoid this, unlike Andy Bibb, who was that much further into his training. On his return to *Collingwood*, the Artificer Candidates joined them for the rest of the proper application training and there was no friction between the Apprentices and the Artificer candidates; he remembered a happy time during this period in *Collingwood*.

As an LWEA he went back to sea in HMS *Exeter* as the 909 maintainer and he stayed there for two years, during which time he was rated POWEA and completed the POs' Leadership Course, which by this time was in

Collingwood, having moved from HMS *Royal Arthur* at Corsham and latterly from Whale Island. It was necessary to complete the CPOs board to maintain the preserved promotion rights that were given to Artificers who became Engineering Technicians, but it does not seem to include the completion of the leadership course to retain these rights.[12]

In April 2003 Melanie Ward passed through the gates of *Raleigh* to join Fisgard Squadron in Simpson Division. She remembered a lovely summer with hot weather and lots of fun, mingled with a lot of hard work. She related how one weekend she was confined to bed in the sick bay. During this stay a trolley was wheeled in with a couple in a compromising position. One had a pierced tongue and there was a lot of blood about. Those who saw this were sworn to silence; naturally it was around the camp within hours. On another occasion when practising for the guard one of the other girls had a bit of a wobble; she apparently blacked out and on the way down her rifle slid from her grasp and the bayonet cut her above the eye, in what was rather too close an encounter. This caused copious bleeding and with the Navy's usual sympathy the Parade Ground Chief GI screamed at the guard to move her off the parade ground as she was bleeding all over his parade ground. After *Collingwood* she went to sea in HMS *Norfolk*, which she remembered as a very happy ship.

Melanie became pregnant and stayed ashore for this period, after serving in HMS *Edinburgh* she became pregnant again and was drafted to HMS *Victory*, where she acted as Officer of the Watch. This involved meeting and greeting VIPs. On one occasion she squeezed into a no. 1 suit for the occasion. The Second Sea Lord's wife, seeing her on the gangway, intimated to her husband that it would be wise to allow Melanie to change out of no. 1s and return to her maternity clothing to avoid any unnecessary consequences. Melanie served for nine years but with a husband and a growing family she decided to leave and circumstances contrived to allow her to leave with redundancy.[13]

Another of the young girls joining Fisgard Squadron and Simpson Division in September 2003 was Jay House, who entered *Raleigh* at the age of seventeen. She was streamed ME after eight weeks and her accommodation was now in Fisgard Squadron, though still well separated from the boys. When they were due to join *Sultan* because of the numbers involved, they were split into two groups and after the now-standard MEM's course she went to sea. She passed out of *Sultan* in November 2007 as an LMEA and returned to sea. She also remembered the animosity between Artificers and the other sailors, though she believed that there was no real malice meant. To highlight how things had changed, when Jay finished her apprenticeship she had earned a foundation degree: progress indeed from the earlier years.

Other changes from when *Fisgard* was in being included there being captain's rounds only once in the eight weeks and divisions only a couple of times; indeed, there seemed to be more of this in *Sultan*, possibly because during the seventeen-week course there were MEMs doing the same course and even back classed MEMs in the same classes as MEAs. There are many old ex-Artificers who would blanch at the thought of Apprentices doing the same training as MEMs prior to going to sea and would question what skills the young Apprentices were taking with them to sea and what benefit was to be gained by the early sea time rather than the tried and tested system of old.

There were some changes to the Artificer structure. In 2004 the Charge Chief Artificer was redefined as Warrant Officer Class 2.[14] This was a move that had been advocated for some considerable time and addressed the strange limbo of the Charge Chief being senior to the other CPO Artificers in matters technical but having no higher substantive rate than any other Chief Petty Officer, though seniority over non-technical CPOs was normally ensured by the fact that the Artificer would have reached CPO long before his non-technical equivalent. This was only a temporary expedient and with the advent of the Engineering Technician it would lapse with time. It was formally abolished in 2014.[15]

In the same year, 2004, there was the final nail in the coffin for the Artificer cadre with the announcement of the introduction of the Engineering Technician. This was reported in the *Fisgardian* magazine in 2006, where an article by Lt D W Morris RN was reproduced:

> On 19 May 2004 the Navy Board endorsed the development of proposals for the biggest and most important change to the Engineering Branch for a generation.
> The last major change to the ME Department was ME Branch Development (MEBD) in 1994 which has led to a significant reduction in specialisations within the General Service (GS) streams (the submarine (SM) Service has retained the electrical and mechanical streams). While a large number of the specialisations of the past have been rationalised, a significant legacy population exists, with a variety of backgrounds, some of whom find it difficult to fit into the

emerging structure and to cope with the wider employment now envisaged.

This means that key weaknesses exist in the engineering departments onboard ships and submarines which must be addressed to allow them to contribute effectively to future operations.

The situation is also made worse by a serious shortfall in artificer numbers, leading to doubts that the structure is sustainable in the medium term. A shortfall in GS Weapon Engineering Artificers (WEA) numbers is already having an effect and gapping in the MEA(SM) community has potential for further impact.

The proposals included:

- *Combining artificers and mechanics into a single stream career path with the title of "Engineering Technician" from able rate to Warrant Officer 1.*
- *Spreading professional training across the career which is linked closely with the competence required at sea for each rate, instead of the heavily front-loaded regime which is currently the case for artificers.*
- *Aligning rates and competency levels so that the Petty Officer Engineering Technician (POET) becomes the rate at which Operational Capability (OC) is delivered (i.e. Section Head level) with CPOs becoming system level diagnosticians and group heads.*
- *All POETs to be skilled but only those who have sufficient academic ability would earn a Foundation Degree (FD).*
- *Provision of opportunities, as now, for promotion of technicians to the Officer Corps.*

Work on implementing these proposals is now nearing completion and the first Engineering Technicians (Marine Engineer) (ET(ME)) will be coming through the gates of HMS Raleigh in May 2006 and will commence the Vesting Day for the transition to ET is 31 Mar 2007 when all personnel on the trained strength serving ashore will re-categorise to ET. Personnel serving in surface ships will transfer in accordance with the Fleet Roll-out Programme which has already commenced, and submariners will transfer on Vesting Day. At this point Junior Rate Mechanics will re-categorise to ET(ME) and LET(ME). Senior Rate Mechanics will not be obliged to transfer to the ET branch but can do so should they wish and provided they have sufficient time left to serve. Senior Rate Artificers will also re-cat to ET (with preserved rights for advancement to CPO) but Junior Rate Artificers will remain MEAs and LMEAs until advanced to PO when they will become POETs. There will therefore be ME Artificers in the RN until 2010.

Promotion in the ET branch will be purely by selection ensuring that the correct numbers of people of sufficient calibre are in the right rates. A new system of streamlined promotion is being introduced in tandem with the ET branch which is designed to focus on demonstrable proficiency rather than the "time-based" criteria of today.

There will also be three selection boards per year as opposed to the current one per year meaning that once qualified for the next higher rate, personnel will only have to wait a maximum of four months before being considered for selection. This will also ensure that the higher calibre rating who would have become an artificer today will still have the opportunity to move quickly through the ranks. Those ETs who show sufficient qualities will be identified for promotion to officer, as happens today from the artificer branch.

In the surface flotilla the able rate ET(ME) will be common (i.e. both mechanically and electrically trained), and capable of being employed across all sections of the ME Department at sea in much the same capacity as the MEM of today. The LET(ME), however, will be considerably more capable than the common LMEM, able to undertake a draft to any section in the department but will have the necessary capacity to act as Deputy Section Head when required. In the submarine service the ET selected for LET will specialise mechanical or electrical during his LET professional training depending on aptitude, service requirement and personal preference.

He will then be employed in appropriate sections thereafter in his career. Submariners will also receive nuclear operating training as part of their professional packages following selection and will not be able to gain promotion unless they are nuclear trained.

The professional qualifying courses for LET will amount to approximately 1 year compared to the 6 months previously given to the LMEM.

The POET will be the OC deliverer as the Section Head and, as such, will receive specific training as part of the POET professional training depending on which section he is to head up onboard. Depending on their academic calibre and recommendations, those selected for POET will also be given the opportunity to undertake an extra module of academics in order to gain a Foundation Degree.

The professional qualifying courses for POET will be between 18 months and 2 years depending on specialisations and being selected to complete the Foundation Degree.

Those who transfer from MEM to ET will be given enabling training to bridge the gap between the two branches. The extra training will usually occur as part of the professional training received following selection for LET and POET.[16]

This met with a robust response from the editorial team of the *Fisgardian*, who were aghast at the proposals, as were many serving and retired Artificers, who saw it as a complete betrayal of the Artificer ethos and expected that the outcome of the proposals would not be beneficial, as indeed proved to be the case.

Editorial Response

Having been assured last year that the new Engineering Technicians would undergo a full apprenticeship, the above statement was read with dismay.

The complete absence of the word Apprentice and the second bullet-point under the heading "The proposals included" indicate that the new Marine Engineering Technicians will not undergo a long formal continuous Apprenticeship. A subsequent request for confirmation of this elicited the claim that they will undergo a "Modern Apprenticeship".

Assuming that this new scheme of training will also apply to Engineering Technicians of the Weapons and Air Engineering specialisations, it seems that the MOD has finally abandoned formal technical apprenticeships in favour of a re-hash of the old "Mechanician" scheme.

It is a great pity that the MOD have decided to abolish the front-loaded apprenticeship scheme at the very time that the value of such apprenticeships has received fresh support from industry. Indeed, Sultan has begun to train civilian youths, as apprentices for private firms, by the well-proven method of fast-tracking young naval practical engineers to a responsible charge position. The abolition of the RN Apprenticeship scheme and the honourable title Apprentice removes the last of several distinctions proudly deserved and enjoyed by a highly trained elite for over a hundred years.

This reactionary move is likely to have an adverse effect on recruiting from the Tiffy's traditional academic and intellectual source, the top 25% of the nation's youth.[17]

There are several other salient points to make about the proposals. It is difficult to see how Mechanics, whether senior or junior rates, could suddenly be deemed to be able to act as an Artificer of old; the mention of the provision of "enabling training to bridge the gap between the two branches". There is no mention of the fact that, if these Mechanics were not considered of the right calibre academically to be an Artificer candidate, how they would be able to cope with this "enabling training". Those who show the required academic ability would be given a fast-track route to promotion; is that not the route the Artificer had always followed? And to gear the knowledge base to what is required for a particular job or draft seems to show a lack of foresight for the unexpected defect that often occurs at the most inopportune moment when a ship is far from any support. Where is the initiative to cope with the unexpected to come from?

That as early as 2004 the lack of craft training was apparent is highlighted in another article from the *Fisgardian*:

The Artificer is Dead – Long Live the Artificer?
By Bryan Marshall (1952 Series 14)

> *What's in a name?*
> *That which we call a rose*
> *By any other name would smell as sweet*
> *(Romeo and Juliet)*

Well, Shakespeare was right there, but the important point to this utterance is that the flower itself is unchanged, whatever its name. So, when we reflect on our proud title – Artificer – is it apt to morn its passing from the Naval lexicon. After all, along with "Artisan" (remember that?), is "Artificer" merely an archaic word that recalls Britain's 19th Century industrial might: a title that has no place – or recognition – in today's hi-tech world? Or, more to the point, does its abolition go hand-in-hand with the loss of indispensable and fundamental skills? We all spent many hours in workshop training imbibing esoteric craft skills and producing intricate and high-quality Test Jobs. But, once qualified, how many of us actually made such complex items? Some branches, e.g. ERAs, Shipwrights, more than others, e.g. REAs, "Fleeties", is probably the answer.

Was all that training an expensive insurance policy by their Lordships, as well as a bolstering by our branch of our professional elitism? These can be difficult questions for us to consider objectively.

Frank Wootton (1943 Ark Royal) has expressed his views in forthright style in a letter intended for "Navy News": "The newly classified Technician bears no resemblance to the concept of the Artificer, as envisaged by Jackie Fisher over a hundred years ago."

He adds: "In today's Fleet, the maintenance philosophy is based on 'repair by replacement'". (but was that not often the case even fifty years ago?).

On the question of our modern-day successors' title of Technician, Frank believes that this belittles them, and their need for "considerable diagnostic and technical expertise to fulfil their tasks." After all, nowadays "Technician" is all too frequently used where our readers would use the term "Mechanic" – this is all part of a trend to "talk-up" job titles e.g. Assistant Sales Manager = shop assistant!

Elsewhere in this issue is David Prideaux's graphic account of his and his family's encounter with the Boxing Day 2004 Tsunami. This links in with a well written account, by Lieutenant Stirling Patch, of the Royal Navy's response to this disaster with the sending of one of its Fleet Support Units (FSU) (full article in "Royal Naval Engineering Review"). After an initial deployment to Sri Lanka, the FSU was then sent to assist the Maldives by providing a surge capacity to the State Electricity Company (STELCO), thus returning normal power to the islands. In his conclusion, Lt. Patch states:

"The original plan identified twenty-two generators across thirteen islands that required repair. The UN estimated that it would take six weeks for the FSU and STELCO to achieve this. The combined teams actually repaired thirty-nine generators" (of which more later), "and installed a further four across eighteen islands, all within ten days".

"Everybody worked hard in hot, humid and unpleasant conditions, but morale remained high throughout the deployment because they never lost sight of the tragedy that had befallen the people they were there to help. The experience provided a great deal of satisfaction in the knowledge that they had made some significant improvements to the lives of people in both Sri Lanka and the Maldives."

One of the "lessons brought back from the experience… should be heeded: Engineering at a grass root level needs to be both encouraged and regularly exercised lest we become too reliant on repair by replacement." (The Editor of the Review's endorsement is – "a lesson to factor into the new ET skills set")

Now, the description by Lt. Patch of the repairs carried out makes fascinating reading:

"A triage routine was quickly established, with the prime mover, generator and switchboards being worked on simultaneously. The engine and generator electrical components were stripped-down and the bulk of the dry sand and salt removed by blowing through with compressed air. The various parts of the generators were then washed with a cocktail of petrol and domestic washing powder (Genclean was not available). This was applied using a diesel pressure washer with a spill pick-up from a bucket. The components were again washed with fresh water to remove any residue. Once the readings were acceptable, the various parts were varnished as required and cooked again to dry them. The heating and drying method devised by STELCO engineers was ingenious. An 'oven' was constructed from a flat sheet of aluminium rolled into a cylinder, roughly twice the size of a standard oil drum, with a flat aluminium sheet lid.

Halogen floodlights were used as the heat source, being suspended inside the oven over the components to be dried. This method did not fail once (as it could be repeated if necessary) and all components were found to be electrically sound on completion. This simple design also allowed for the oven to be easily dismantled and moved to the next island. Improvisation became the norm. as the only tools available were those brought from the UK and a few belonging to the Maldiveans. The documentation had been swept away or was in a foreign language and spare parts were virtually non-existent… any possible source of spares was exploited, including stripping-down old washing machines for washers, plundering rubber sheeting from rubbish tips to make gaskets and, especially, scavenging from dumped engines designated beyond repair! It was from a rubbish tip that the team recovered and recycled some old filters that had been removed during a previous service routine. The team also came to realise that, initially, the STELCO and the RN engineers were operating at opposite ends of the engineering spectrum. **Because of a lack of craft training and an 'upkeep by exchange' mentality, the RN engineers were at a disadvantage in one particular skill area. Simply, they had lost sight of their grass roots 'make it work' engineering ethos**" *[Editor's emboldening].*

"Quickly adjusting, and realizing the Maldiveans were learning from the RN in equal measure, the joint teams flourished, with both teams being highly complimentary of the skills and working practices of their counterparts."

So, it would seem that all is not lost. There is clearly recognition that those fundamental skills, of which we are so conscious, are still necessary in the RN of today, and we can only hope that they are brought back into the curriculum, as proposed.

Finally, it is noteworthy that Lt. Patch joined the Royal Navy in 1976 as a Junior Marine Engineering Mechanic, subsequently qualifying as an Artificer, and then commissioned from the rank of WOMEA. He and the FSU well deserve full praise for their efforts and initiative in difficult conditions, upholding the finest traditions of the Royal Navy.[18]

Late in 2005 Steve Nelson joined Fisgard Squadron in 053 entry, the second to last entry of Artificer Apprentices. His entry consisted of two groups, one of thirty-seven including two WEMs and another of the same size. They were not immediately categorised but carried out naval general training. He remembered standing out from the crowd, by virtue of the different beret badge, the red badge being worn exclusively by Artificers. While there was not the same opportunity for the age-old sprogging, there remained the same amount of ribald rivalry amongst the Apprentices.

He remembered that there was very little skill of hand training, even on his return from sea, certainly not on anything like the level of the period before the 1970s but submariners seem to have had rather more workshop training, making a pillar drill as a test job. The workshops were very much winding down and this was very evident to all the trainees and instructors; indeed, the next class (061) would be the final class of Apprentices. While Apprentices were still issued with toolboxes, they were of the compartmentalised variety, with a space for each tool clearly defined. This of course meant there could be no individuality as of old where any amount of "useful" tools would be added by the owner throughout his career.[19]

Once 061 Class started on its journey, there were no more Artificers; the Royal Navy put its faith in the Engineering Technician. The final class of Weapons Engineering Artificers passed out of HMS *Collingwood* on 27 February 2009 and the final class of Marine Engineering Artificers passed out of HMS *Sultan* on 12 February 2010.

These two events did not pass by unnoticed by old Artificers, as was recorded in the *Fisgardian* magazine:

Friday 27th February 2009 – A historic day in the story of Artificer Apprentices. Several Fisgard Association members were invited to attend Divisions at HMS Collingwood to witness the end of an era. Several Fisgard Association members were invited to attend Divisions at HMS Collingwood to witness the end of an era. After a continuous period of 106 years the final group of Artificer Apprentices were to receive their Certificates of Apprenticeship from the First Sea Lord, Admiral Sir Jonathan Band Gathering at the foot of HMS Collingwood's parade ground, (a mere shadow of its earlier acres) at 0700 on a cold Friday morning we were met by WO Bob Mitchell, an Artificer from 803 entry, and now the key figure in the training scheme. Bob briefed us on the day's programme, and showed us to our allotted seats for the parade. The Association was greatly honoured by your Secretary being invited by Commodore Kirby to share the saluting dais with the First Sea Lord. The passing out class, WESA 061C, comprised 11 persons, one of whom was "excused marching" (Times haven't changed that much!).

It was a surprise to note that the platoon included both square and fore and aft rigs, with Petty Officers, leading hands and ordinary rates all marching together. This is a result of ratings transferring to the apprenticeship class at different stages in their naval career. It was revealed that one apprentice had started his career in the army, and another transferred from the RAF. The platoon looked strange to those of us more used to uniformity in the class photographs we have seen over the years. The sun shone brightly as the Royal Marine band played, and the guard marched onto the parade ground. The 1st Sea Lord carried out his inspection of guard and apprentices. There were also platoons comprising Chief, 1st and 2nd Class Artificers, and a platoon formed from officers who had started their careers as apprentices. On completion of the inspections, and before the march past, Warrant Officer Bob Mitchell read an eulogy to the passing of the Artificer Apprentice, which I include here:

First Sea Lord, Cdre Kirby, Ladies and Gentlemen I am WO1 Mitchell the Weapon Engineering Systems Artificer Course Manager. It seems like yesterday that, at 16 years and three weeks of age I walked through the gates of HMS Fisgard in Torpoint to become a 803 Series Artificer Apprentice. After four years and nine months of training I marched off this Parade Ground with my head held high and I have been immensely proud to serve for over 28 years as an Artificer in the Royal Navy. With that sense of vision, purpose and leadership, that are the hallmarks of our First Sea Lords, back in 1903 Admiral Sir Jackie Fisher, concerned that the Royal Navy might otherwise be overtaken in seagoing technical expertise by the Imperial German Navy, introduced a scheme for the training of Boy Artificers, which, in his words, "…would prove second to none. How right he was! His vision has endured for 106 years and you men and women of WESA 061C are privileged to bring an extraordinary era to a close. March off with pride flanked this morning by fellow artificers of all ranks and ages who are proud to celebrate a glorious past with you and proud to train your successors, the Engineering Technicians, who will take us to the future as a Royal Navy which continues to be Ready to Fight and Win.

Thus the parade ended, and the various platoons marched smartly past the dais– the end of a long tradition. However, the event was far from complete, as the gathering proceeded to the Millennium Hall for the presentation of certificates. Each Apprentice received their Certificate of Apprenticeship from the First Sea Lord. Bob Mitchell introduced each apprentice, in an informal manner, before they stepped up to be presented with their awards. They were witnessed by friends and families, and others from Naval associations, such as the Royal Naval Engineers Benevolent Society and ourselves.

The Apprentices of WESA 061C receiving their Certificates were:

POWEA Archer,
WEA/A Briggs,
LWEA Bannerman,
WEA/A Duffy,
LWEA Fenwick,
WEA/A Gent,
WEA/A Jones,
LWEA Kinder,
WEA/A Ramos,
WEA/A Rollason and
POWEA Turnill.

The day was not exclusively for the Apprentices, as Collingwood undertakes a range of training, including leadership courses which were once the domain of Royal Arthur at Corsham and diving courses. Thus the presentation ceremony lasted some time! On completion of the awards ceremony, all were invited to move to the gymnasium, where a variety of static displays had been assembled, including an Artificers' stand which relied heavily on photographs "borrowed" from the Fisgard Association web site! There's initiative!

A buffet lunch was provided for the passing out classes and their assembled guests During lunch the First Sea Lord mingled with the gathering, and spent a considerable time speaking with our group, and of course posing for photographs! In conclusion in has to be said that although the passing of the Artificer Apprenticeship is a sad occasion, the requirements of the modern fleet cannot justify the manpower or expense of such an extended course. The role of the maintainer will now be carried out by Technicians, who will receive ever greater degrees of training as they progress through their Naval careers, and specialist training elements to suit their future requirements. I should like to thank Commodore Kirby and Warrant Officer Bob Mitchell for their kindness in allowing the Fisgard Association to take part in this historic occasion.[20]

Among this passing out class was one Garry Jones, who had a somewhat unusual path into the Royal Navy as an Artificer Apprentice, having served over eight years in the RAF, having two Good Conduct Badges and a medal, which made him stand out from the crowd. This was his novel method of entry:

I began the process in 2005 whilst serving on the Tactical Communications Wing at RAF Brize Norton. I had asked my girlfriend to marry me and was reluctant to move her away from her home in Lee on the Solent. My Warrant Officer at the time suggested that I consider transferring to the RN.

When I initially applied, I was informed that I could expect to join the RN in Autumn 2006 as an Engineering Technician. The Navy had stopped recruiting Artificers by this time. I was disappointed but decided to press on anyhow.

In January 2006 I was deployed to Al Udeid air base in Qatar, supporting OP TELIC. Whilst there I was contacted by the RN and asked if I wished to join as an Artificer. The last entry was already at HMS Raleigh but would complete phase one training shortly after I was due to return to Brize Norton. The WE Branch Manager had decided that I would not pose a training risk as I was already employed in an RAF technical branch.

01 Mar 2006 I attended a three day induction course at HMS Raleigh where I was given a new service number (D262206G) before joining Class WEA 061 at HMS Collingwood the following week. As far as I know, I am the last person to join the RN as a WEA.[21]

Garry had a few more words to add about his transfer from the RAF and subsequent entry into the RN:

I joined the RAF 26 Aug 97 and was a Junior Technician (Eng Tech EL) at the time of my transfer.

I had considered transferring service in 2002 when I worked alongside the Navy in the Falkland Islands at JCUFI and even visited an AFCO to enquire but ultimately resolved to stay in the RAF. I hadn't really enjoyed my time up to that point. I was serving at RRH Portreath, there weren't many people my own age and the expected camaraderie was non-existent but I was soon posted to TCW at RAF Brize Norton.

TCW was more to my liking, hundreds of people my own age and 6 to 8 months a year spent deployed on operations or exercises. I may even have stayed if I hadn't met a girl from Lee on the Solent whom I had asked to marry me. Not wishing to move her away from her family, I planned to leave the RAF after 9 years and join Hampshire Constabulary but WO Unsworth at TCW convinced me that I belonged in the military and that as a Plymouth native, I should transfer service to the RN.

The RAF and the Navy share many similarities but are also fundamentally different in their attitudes. It was a culture shock but a welcome one. The Navy had a sense of fun and fair play. Matelots felt a sense of pride and belonging that was somewhat looked down upon in the RAF.

Drill was a chore. I'm 6ft 3in and arrived at HMS Collingwood having never been taught Navy Drill. Worst Right Hand marker on divisions and I'm not much better today.

The three day induction course was a paper work exercise so I had wait until my 6 month initial sea training to learn how to be a proper Matelot.[22]

There may well be many ex-Artificers who would take issue with the suggestion that the level of training that the ET will receive could in any way match the skill and resourcefulness of the Artificer.

A similar report on the *Sultan*'s passing out parade also appeared in the *Fisgardian*:

Friday 12 February 1000 hours and around 150 ex Artificer Apprentices were assembling at HMS Sultan to witness the final passing-out parade of the Navy's remaining Artificer Apprentices. The temperature was just above freezing and a cold breeze was blowing. The establishment had extended a welcome to the Fisgard Association, the Old Caledonian's Artificer Apprentice Association and the RN Engineer's Benevolent Trust to be their guests for the day.

Around 35 or so hardy souls, including six of your committee members, volunteered to take part in the March-Past. They assembled at Vulcan Gate, met by WO Benmasaud to be briefed about their role in the Ceremonial Divisions. By 1015 the remainder of us ex-Tiffs took our seats at the Parade Ground alongside the dais.

Ceremonial Divisions took their usual course and this involved our intrepid band of members standing in the cold for over an hour but finally they marched past the Admiral as the last platoon. They acquitted themselves admirably. They may not have been the best platoon at marching but they definitely were not the worst.

After the parade we were able to warm up with a cup of tea or coffee before being taken on a tour of the Skill of Hand (SOH) training group. This included (Electrical Training Group) Free Running areas, the Machine Shop (Fitting and Turning, Technical Drawing) and Allied Trades (Welding, Coppersmith, Sheet metal, GRP, Wood).

On completion of the tour we proceeded to the Gym for a very welcome hot buffet lunch. Here we were able to talk to the VIPs, the Artificer passing out classes and their families. Whilst at lunch Rear Admiral Burgess, (1945 Rodney), addressed the gathering reminding the passing out classes that they had a fine tradition to live up to and to accept the challenges of the future.

After lunch various tours were arranged for those who wished to update themselves with the RN and in particular ME training. Also included was a visit to the Artificer's Museum The day ended with an address by Captain Watts and we departed after a cold, but nevertheless enjoyable, day.[23]

So after 142 years Artificers were no more. Those who served as Artificer are still proud to remember their roots and they will always be Fisher's "Second to None", ready to provide the highest levels of skill, improvisation and knowledge in any situation and under any conditions, whether in peace or war, far from outside help or assistance and with fortitude and good humour in the knowledge that they were the best. A band of brothers and, latterly, sisters proud to call themselves "Tiffies".

From this day to the ending of the world,
But we in it shall be rememberèd-
We few, we happy few, we band of brothers.[24]

Endnotes

• • •

Introduction

1 Henry Shore, "A Fin-de-Siècle Tragedy: or, The Death and Burial of Seamanship", *United Service Magazine*, XXIII (1901).

2 Geoffrey Penn, *Up Funnel, Down Screw! The Story of the Naval Engineer* (London: Hollis & Carter, 1955), 13.

3 Edgar C. Smith, *A Short History of Naval and Marine Engineering* (Cambridge: Cambridge University Press, 1937), 53.

4 J.H. Briggs, *Naval Administrations 1827–1892* (London: Sampson, Low, Marston & Co, 1897), also quoted in Penn, *Up Funnel*, 13–14.

5 Penn, *Up Funnel*, 15.

6 Ibid, 117.

7 Ibid, 18.

8 Courts Martial Registers. *ADM 194/42 Royal Naval and Royal Marine Officers and Ratings, 1812–1855*, The National Archives, and Walton, Officers or Engineers?, 193.

9 Penn, *Up Funnel*, 35.

10 Admiralty Order in Council, 19 July 1837, *Engineers and Engineer Boys, Regulations for,* The National Archives.

11 A.W.H. Pearsall, et al., *The First Engineers, 1837*, British Naval Documents 1204–1960, Naval Records Society (1993), 414, 706.

12 ADM 11/49. *Inside front cover Memorandum, Admiralty 24 July 1837 and Regulations as to the Examination of Engineers in Her Majesty's Service*, The National Archives,

13 Penn, *Up Funnel*, 38.

14 Ibid, 33.

15 Ibid, 38.

16 Tony Chamberlain, *"Stokers – the Lowest of the Low?" A Social History of Royal Navy Stokers 1850–1950* (PhD Diss., University of Exeter, 2013), Title.

17 Chamberlain, *"Stokers – the Lowest of the Low?"*, Abstract.

18 Penn, *Up Funnel*, 58.

19 Report, *Mechanics Magazine* (1845), 331.

20 Penn, *Up Funnel*, 59.

21 Ibid, 59.

22 Ibid, 59.

23 E.P. Halstead, *The Screw Fleet of the Navy* (London: Simpkin, Marshall & Co., 1850), 1–2.

24 RNM 1994/435, 11. *Journal of Francis Wheeler, Engineer, 1855–1862*, National Museum of the Royal Navy.

25 Penn, *Up Funnel*, 47.

26 Ibid, 48.

27 Ibid, 61.

28 J. MacFarlane Gray, Annual General Meeting Address, *Transactions of the Institute of Marine Engineers* (1890–1891), 20.

29 Penn, *Up Funnel*, 51.

30 Ibid, 61.

31 Ibid, 23.

32 Ibid, 23.

33 Walton, *Officers or Engineers?*, 181.

34 H Orpen, *The Origin, Evolution and Future of the Personnel of the British Royal Navy*, Transactions of the Royal United Services Institution, November 1902, 33.

35 Denis Griffiths, *Steam at Sea, Two Centuries of Steam-Powered Ships* (London: Conway Maritime Press, 1997), 137.

36 ADM 1/6060, *Navy Department Correspondence and Letters 1840–1913, In-letters and Papers: 1860–1869.* Admiralty January–March, The National Archives.

37 PC 2/368 *Privy Council Registers, VICTORIA, Vol 149,* The National Archives.

38 PC 2/380, *Privy Council Registers, EDWARD VII, Vol 1,* The National Archives.

39 PC 2/439, *Privy Council Registers, GEORGE V, Vol 34,* The National Archives.

40 PC 2/628, *Privy Council Registers, GEORGE VI, Vol 8,* The National Archives.

41 PC 2/655, *Privy Council Registers, GEORGE VI, Vol 20,* The National Archives.

42 PC 2/674, *Privy Council Registers, GEORGE VI, Vol 36,* The National Archives.

43 ADM 7/941, *Scheme for Entry, Training and Employment of Officers, Men and Boys for the Royal Navy,* 21 November 1902, The National Archives.

Chapter One

1 P.M. Rippon, *Evolution of Engineering in the Royal Navy, Volume 1, 1827–1939* (Tunbridge Wells: Spellmount, 1988) 111.

2 PC 2/268, *Privy Council Registers, VICTORIA, Vol 49,* The National Archives.

3 Cooper Key Report, House of Commons, *UK Parliamentary Papers,* Command

Papers, C1647, 1877.

4 Rippon, *Evolution of Engineering in the Royal Navy*, 51.

5 Penn, *Up Funnel*, 96.

6 Report, Four Generations, The Harcourt Family at Cowplain, *Hampshire Telegraph*, 13 July 1928.

7 Ibid.

8 ADM 139/287/28612, *Royal Navy Continuous Service Engagement Books*, The National Archives.

9 Ibid.

10 Ibid.

11 Ibid.

12 Ibid.

13 Ibid.

14 Ibid.

15 Report of Court Martial, *Naval & Military Gazette and Weekly Chronicle of the United Service*, 16 February 1876.

16 Information from family history research by Mrs Kirsty Rixon-Curtis, 3rd great-granddaughter of Michael Harcourt.

17 Report, Four Generations, *Hampshire Telegraph*, 13 July 1928.

18 D.W. Barrett, *J.E. Barrett, The Story of W J Barrett 1845–1946* (printed privately), 3.

19 Ibid, 3.

20 Ibid, 3.

21 Ibid, 4.

22 Ibid, 6.

23 Ibid, 7.

24 Ibid, 7.

25 Ibid, 8.

26 Anthony Carew, *The Lower Deck of the Royal Navy 1900–1939. Invergordon in Perspective* (Manchester: Manchester University Press, 1981), 1.

27 Carew, *Invergordon in Perspective*, 2.

28 Ibid, 2.

29 Ibid, 12.

30 Admiralty Circular 288, *Introduction for Training Afloat on Board HMS Illustrious*, 23 February 1857.

31 Harry Dickinson, *Educating the Royal Navy, Eighteenth and Nineteenth-Century Education for Officers* (New York: Routledge, 2007), 66.

32 Cooper Key Report, House of Commons, *UK Parliamentary Papers*, Command Papers, C1647, 1877.

33 Dickinson, *Educating the Royal Navy*, 185. Cooper Key Report, v.

34 Dickinson, *Educating the Royal Navy*, 187.

35 Cooper Key Report, Para. 8, v.

36   Ibid, Para. 64, v.
37   Ibid, Para. 47, ix.
38   Ibid, Para. 84, xiv.
39   Ibid, Para. 86, xiv.
40   Ibid, Para. 101, xv.
41   Ibid, Para. 103, xvi.
42   Ibid, 29 October 1875, 144.
43   Ibid, 29 October 1875, 146.
44   Ibid, 29 October 1875, 140.
45   Ibid, 29 October 1875, 140.
46   Penn, *Up Funnel*, 105.
47   PC 2/286 *Privy Council Registers, VICTORIA, Vol 67*, The National Archives. Penn, *Up Funnel*, 108.
48   Penn, I, 108.
49   D.W. Barrett, *J.E. Barrett, The Story of W J Barrett 1845–1946*, 15.
50   ADM 188/63/74860, *Royal Navy Continuous Service Engagement Books*, The National Archives. D.W. Barrett, J.E. Barrett, *The Story of W J Barrett 1845–1946*, 20.
51   An expression indicative of joining a ship at the last possible moment because of a sudden and unexpected appointment to it.
52   D.W. Barrett, *J.E. Barrett, The Story of W J Barrett 1845–1946*, 50.
53   Ibid, 43a.
54   Penn, *Up Funnel*, 109.
55   Dickinson, *Educating the Royal Navy*, 192.
56   Dickinson, *Educating the Royal Navy*, 193.
57   An Undistinguished Naval Officer, 83, quoted in Penn, *Up Funnel*, 115.
58   ADM 234/983, *Admiralty Order in Council*, 18 May 1897, The National Archives.
59   Article, *Fisgardian*, Issue 37, May 2015, 14.
60   Penn, *Up Funnel*, 151.
61   Ibid, 126.
62   Ibid, 127.
63   A.J. Marder (ed.) *Fear God and Dread Nought: The Correspondence of Admiral of the Fleet Lord Fisher of Kilverstone (Volume I)*. (London: Oxford University Press, 1961), 333. Also William S. Jameson, *The Most Formidable Thing, the Story of the Submarine from Its Earliest Days the End of World War I* (London: Hart-Davis, 1965), 75–76.
64   R. Bacon, *From 1900 Onwards Volume 2* (London: Hutchinson, 1940) p 377.
65   Patrick A. Moore, *The Greenie, The History of Warfare Technology in the Royal Navy* (Stroud: Spellmount, 2011), 101.
66   Moore, *The Greenie*, Admiralty Circular, N8258/1901.
67   Moore, *The Greenie*, Order in Council N14305/1913, 102.

Chapter Two

1 Letter from Rear Admiral Sir Reginald Custance (DNI) to Vice Admiral Sir Cyprian Bridge (C-in-C China Station), 9 June 1902, *Papers of Admiral Sir Cypian Arthur George Bridge*, National Maritime Museum, BRI/15.

2 ADM 7/941, *Scheme for Entry, Training and Employment of Officers, Men and Boys for the Royal Navy,* 21 November 1902, The National Archives.

3 ADM 7/941, *Scheme for Entry, Training and Employment of Officers,* The National Archives.

4 Dickinson, *Educating the Royal Navy,* 198.

5 Geoffrey Till et al., *The Engineer Question 1902*, British Naval Documents 1204–1960, Naval Records Society (1993), 515, 972.

6 Ibid, 973.

7 Speech to the House of Lords, 8 May 1903, *Hansard*, vol. 122, cc 155–91.

8 House of Lords, 8 May 1903, Hansard.

9 Ibid.

10 Ibid.

11 Marder, *From the Dreadnought to Scapa Flow,* 267, quoted in Leggett, Shaping the Royal Navy, 259.

12 House of Commons Debate, 22 February 1906, *Hansard*, vol. 152 cc 495–6.

13 Letter to the Editor, *The Spectator*, 19 May 1906, 15.

14 P.K. Kemp, *The Fisher Papers Vol II*, Naval Records Society, 1964, 128.

15 Till, *The Engineer Question 1902*, British Naval Documents 1204–1960, 515, 973.

16 PC 2/392, *Privy Council Registers, EDWARD VII, Vol 13,* The National Archives.

17 David Eaton *et al., Second to None. 100 Years of the Artificer Apprentice* (Waterlooville: BAE SYSTEMS Ltd, 2003), 4.

18 ADM 7/941, *Scheme for Entry, Training and Employment of Officers,* The National Archives.

19 Geoffrey Lowis, *Fabulous Admirals* (London, Putnam & Co Ltd, 1957), Chapter VI.

20 ADM 188/435/271276, *Shipcott, Lionel Gordon, Official Number: 271276*, The National Archives.

21 ADM 273/15/161, *Royal Naval Air Service: Registers of Officers Service,* The National Archives.

22 *London Gazette*, 25 May 1920.

23 *London Gazette,* 18 January 1922.

24 ADM 188/436/271978, *Frew, Sidney Oswell, Official Number: 271978*, The National Archives.

25 Cecil Reginald Percival Bennett, *Memoirs of a Boy Artificer,* Courtesy of Alan Bennett, Commodore RN (Retd.), 22.

26 Bennett, *Memoirs of a Boy Artificer,* 23.

27   Ibid, 23.
28   Ibid, 24.
29   Ibid, 24.
30   Ibid, 25.
31   Ibid, 25.
32   Ibid, 26.
33   Ibid, 29.
34   Ibid, 32.
35   Ibid, 32.
36   Moore, *The Greenie*, 32.
37   Ibid. ADM 12553/1910, 102.
38   Ibid, 102.

Chapter Three

1   Noah Webster, *A Dictionary of the English Language, Vol 1* (London, Black, Young and Young, 1832).
2   Penn, *Up Funnel*, 153.
3   Bennett, *Memoirs of a Boy Artificer*, 38.
4   Ibid, 43.
5   Penn, *Up Funnel*, 152
6   Ibid, 153.
7   Ibid, 154.
8   Ibid, 157.
9   *London Gazette*, 3 March 1915.
10   Ibid.
11   Penn, *Up Funnel*, 161.
12   Bennett, *Memoirs of a Boy Artificer,* 47.
13   Ibid, 47.
14   Ibid, 48.
15   Ibid, 48.
16   Ibid, 48.
17   Ibid, 49.
18   Ibid, 49.
19   Ibid, 51.
20   Ibid, 51.
21   Richard Osborne, *Voices From the Past, The Battle of Jutland* (Barnsley: Frontline Books, 2016), 10.
22   Nicholas Jellicoe, *Jutland The Unfinished Battle* (Barnsley: Seaforth Publishing, 2016), 109.
23   Osborne, *Voices From the Past,* 10.
24   Jellicoe, *Jutland The Unfinished Battle*, 103.
25   Arthur J. Marder, *From the Dreadnought to Scapa Flow: The Royal Navy in the*

Fisher Era, 1904–1919, 5 vols (London: Oxford University Press, 1961–1970).

26 Jon Tetsuro Sumida, A Matter of Timing, The Royal Navy and the Tactics of Defensive Battle, 1912–1916, *The Journal of Military History*, vol. 67, no. 1 (Jan 2003), 86.

27 Jellicoe, *Jutland The Unfinished Battle,* 136. Nicholas A. Lambert, "Our Bloody Ships" or "Our Bloody Systems"? Jutland and the Loss of the Battlecruisers, 1916, *The Journal of Military History*, vol. 62, no. 1 (Jan 1998), 30–31. Holger Herwig, Jutland: Acrimony to Resolution, *Naval War College Review, Washington* (Autumn 2016), 151.

28 Osborne, *Voices From the Past,* 130.

29 Ibid, 131.

30 Ibid, 216.

31 Alfred Temple Patterson (ed.), *The Jellicoe Papers Volume I,* The Naval Records Society, 1968, 265.

32 Lambert, "Our Bloody Ships" or "Our Bloody System?", 31.

33 Patterson (ed.), *The Jellicoe Papers,* 271.

34 Bennett, *Memoirs of a Boy Artificer,* 51.

35 Ibid, 52.

36 Ibid, 52.

37 Ibid, 53.

38 Ibid, 55.

39 ADM 336/29/697, *Service Record of Whitworth, Muriel, Rating: Artificer, Service Number: G6702,* The National Archives.

40 Article, *Fisgardian,* Issue 34, Spring 14, 1.

41 *The London Gazette,* 19 October 1920, 10081.

42 CSC 10/4661, *Artificer Apprentice in HM Navy, Examination, Tables of Marks and Results, 7 April 1921,* The National Archives.

Chapter Four

1 Holy Bible, Exodus 35:35.

2 Admiralty Circular 121, printed in *The Navy List,* 1853.

3 Anthony Carew, The Invergordon Mutiny, 1931: Long-Term Causes, Organisation and Leadership. *International Review of Social History* (Aug 1979), 159, accessed 2 March 2017.

4 John B. Hattendorf et al. (eds), *Pay and Allowances 1919,* British Naval Documents 1204–1960, Naval Records Society (1993), 521, 986.

5 Carew, *Invergordon in Perspective,* 153.

6 Carew, *Invergordon in Perspective,* 110.

7 Carew, *Invergordon in Perspective,* 111.

8 Ibid, 116.

9 Ibid, 116.

10 Ibid, 118.

11 Ibid, 120.
12 ADM 182/19, *Admiralty Fleet Order No. 36576, December 22, 1920*, The National Archives.
13 Carew, *Invergordon in Perspective*, 138.
14 David Eaton et al. (eds), *Second to None, 100 Years of the Artificer Apprentice* (Waterlooville: BAE SYSTEMS Ltd, 2003), 5.
15 John A. Gurr, *In Peace and War, A Chronicle of Experiences in the Royal Navy, 1922–1946* (Worcester: Square One Publications, 1993), 1.
16 Gurr, *In Peace and War*, 5.
17 Ibid, 8.
18 Carew, *The Invergordon Mutiny*, 1931, 163.
19 ADM 182/42, *Admiralty Fleet Order 2858/59, October 3, 1925*, The National Archives.
20 Carew, *The Invergordon Mutiny*, 1931, 164.
21 Ibid, 163.
22 Ibid, 164.
23 The Effects of the Pay Cuts, 1931, British Naval Documents 1204–1960, Navy Records Society, 527, 998.
24 Carew, *The Invergordon Mutiny*, 1931, 166.
25 Ibid, 166.
26 Carew, *Invergordon in Perspective*, 138.
27 Ibid, 141.
28 Ibid, 141.
29 David Eaton et al. (eds), *Second to None*, 34.
30 Penn, *Up Funnel*, 165.
31 Bennett, *Memoirs of a Boy Artificer*, 172.
32 Ibid, 174.
33 Ibid, 177.
34 Ibid, 177.
35 Moore, The Greenie, 288.
36 David Eaton et al. (eds), *Second to None*, 38.
37 Ibid, 35.
38 Ibid, 39.
39 Ibid, 40.
40 Gurr, *In Peace and War*, 14.
41 Ibid, 14.
42 Ibid, 15.
43 Ibid, 17.
44 ADM 363/174/60, *Gurr, John Arthur, Official Number M37091*, The National Archives.
45 Gurr, *In Peace and War*, 26.
46 Ibid, 27.

Chapter Five

1   Bliss Carman (ed.), *The World's Best Poetry, Tubal Cain, Charles Mackay* (Philadelphia: John D. Morris, 1904).
2   Gurr, *In Peace and War,* 31.
3   Bennett, *Memoirs of a Boy Artificer,* 220.
4   Ibid, 222.
5   Gurr, *In Peace and War,* 36.
6   David Eaton et al. (eds), *Second to None,* 41.
7   Ibid, 41.
8   Ibid, 40.
9   Carew, *The Invergordon Mutiny,* 1931, 172.
10 Ibid, 173.
11 Alan Ereira, *The Invergordon Mutiny, A Narrative of the Last Great Mutiny in the Royal Navy and How It Forced Britain off the Gold Standard in 1931* (London: Routledge & Kegan Paul, 1981), 49.
12 Ereira, *The Invergordon Mutiny,* 55.
13 Ibid, 55.
14 David Eaton et al. (eds), *Second to None,* 40.
15 Gurr, *In Peace and War,* 46.
16 Ibid, 48.
17 Article, *Portsmouth Evening News,* 11 December 1931.
18 Bennett, *Memoirs of a Boy Artificer,* 223.
19 Ibid, 223.
20 Ibid, 223.
21 Ibid, 225.
22 Ibid, 230.
23 Ibid, 233.
24 Gurr, *In Peace and War,* 52.
25 Ibid, 3.
26 Ron Calverley, e-mail to the author, 30 September 2018.
27 Ibid.
28 Ibid.
29 Gil Harding, *HMS Caledonia, The Apprentices' Story* (printed privately, 1986), 12.
30 Ibid, 13.
31 Ibid, 14.
32 Ibid, 17.
33 Ibid, 21.
34 Ibid, 21.
35 Ibid, 22.
36 Article, *Fisgardian,* Issue 23, Autumn 2008, 17.
37 Ibid, 26.

38   Ibid, 32.
39   Gurr, *In Peace and War,* 131.

Chapter Six

1   Bliss Carman (ed.), *The World's Best Poetry.*
2   Ron Calverley, e-mail to the author, 11 October 2018.
3   Ibid.
4   Ibid.
5   Ibid.
6   Ibid.
7   Ibid.
8   Ibid.
9   Ibid.
10   Ibid.
11   Ibid.
12   Ibid.
13   Ibid.
14   Gil Harding, *HMS Caledonia, The Apprentices' Story,* 36.
15   Ibid, 37.
16   Ibid, 43.
17   David Eaton et al. (eds), *Second to None,* 14.
18   Paul Bass, e-mail to the author, 16 March 2018.
19   Ibid.
20   Ibid.
21   Gil Harding, *HMS Caledonia, The Apprentices' Story,* 69.
22   Ibid, 76.
23   Gurr, *In Peace and War,* 136.
24   Ibid, 169.
25   Ibid, 181.
26   Ibid, 200.
27   Ibid, 207.
28   Article, *Fisgardian,* Issue 32, Spring 2013, 20.
29   Article, *Fisgardian,* Issue 35, Autumn 2014, 8.
30   David Eaton et al. (eds), *Second to None,* 54.
31   Ibid, 82.
32   Gil Harding, *HMS Caledonia, The Apprentices' Story,* 75.
33   David Eaton et al. (eds), *Second to None,* 15.
34   Gurr, *In Peace and War,* 213.
35   Ibid, 219.
36   Ibid, 274.
37   Gil Harding, *HMS Caledonia, The Apprentices' Story,* 75.
38   David Eaton et al, (eds), *Second to None,* 15.

39   Ibid, 17.

40   Ibid, 19.

41   Gil Harding, *HMS Caledonia, The Apprentices' Story*, 246-274, first published in 'British Machine Tool Engineering' January-June 1945

42   Frank Wootton, Letter to *Fisgardian*, Issue 4, 1999, 7.

Chapter Seven

1   Bliss Carman, (ed), *The World's Best Poetry, Tubal Cain, Charles Mackay,* (Philadelphia: John D. Morris, 1904).

2   Phillip Payton, *The Story of HMS Fisgard* (Redruth: Dyllansow Truran1983) 47.

3   David Eaton et al, (eds), *Second to None*, 72.

4   Stuart Latham Bateson, *ADM 196/124/94,*The National Archives.

5   Elinor Francis Romans, *Selection and Early Career Education of Executive Officers in the Royal Navy c1902-199*, PhD Diss., University of Exeter, 2012.

6   David Eaton et al, (eds), *Second to None*, 69.

7   Ibid, 72.

8   Gil Harding, *HMS Caledonia, The Apprentices' Story*, 129.

9   Ibid, 130.

10   !bid, 131.

11   Ibid, 137.

12   Article, *Fisgardian*, Autumn 2011, 9.

13   Article, *Old Caledonia Artificer Apprentices Association*, Newsletter, Spring 2011.

14   Gil Harding, *HMS Caledonia, The Apprentices' Story*, 147.

15   Ibid, 150.

16   Article, *Fisgardian*, Autumn 2003, 15.

17   Ibid, Autumn 2005, 18.

18   Harding, *HMS Caledonia, The Apprentices' Story*, 174.

19   Article, *Fisgardian*, Autumn 2007, 20.

Chapter Eight

1   William Shakespeare, *Hamlet*, Act 3, Scene 4, 202-209.

2   Harding, *HMS Caledonia, The Apprentices' Story*, 179.

3   Ibid, 179.

4   Article, *Fisgardian*, Autumn 2004, 19.

5   PC 2/763 *Privy Council Registers, ELIZABETH II, Vol 39,* The National Archives.

6   David Eaton et al, (eds), *Second to None*, 75.

7   Article, *Fisgardian*, January 2016, 13.

8   Stuart Wakefield, e-mail to the author, 4th January 2018.

9   Article in *Navy News May 1966*, quoted in, Harding, HMS Caledonia, The Apprentices' Story, 199.

10   Stuart Wakefield, e-mail to the author, 25th May 2018.
11   Stuart Wakefield, e-mail to the author, 25th May 2018.
12   Ibid.
13   Mike Doyle, e-mail to the author, 19th June 2018.
14   Ibid.
15   Ibid.
16   Ibid.
17   Ibid.
18   Ibid.
19   *DCI(RN) 415/65* and *DCI(RN) 140/66*.
20   Harding, *HMS Caledonia, The Apprentices' Story,* 207.
21   Mike Doyle, e-mail to the author, 19th June 2018

Chapter Nine

1   Bliss Carman, (ed), *The World's Best Poetry, Tubal Cain, Charles Mackay,* (Philadelphia: John D. Morris, 1904).
2   Ministry of Defence, *DCI (RN) 923/70.*
3   Ministry of Defence, *DCI (RN) 329/85.*
4   INF 14/427/2, 31st July 1970, *The Last Tot,* The National Archive.
5   Mike Doyle, e-mail to the author, 19th June 2018.
6   Ibid.
7   Ibid.
8   Ibid.
9   Ken Enticknap, e-mail to the author,18th September 2018.
10   Harding, *HMS Caledonia, The Apprentices' Story,* 209.
11   Roger Bateman, e-mail to the author, 24th August 2017.
12   Ibid.
13   Mike Doyle, e-mail to the author, 19th June 2018.
14   Ibid.
15   Ibid.
16   Ibid.
17   Ibid.
18   Harding, *HMS Caledonia, The Apprentices' Story,* 211.
19   Mike Doyle, e-mail to the author, 19th June 2018.
20   Ibid.
21   John Newell (Commodore RN Rtd) e-mail to the author, 16th June 2018.
22   Ibid
23   Stephen Gosden, (Captain RN Rtd), e-mail to the author, 3rd August 2018.
24   Ibid.
25   Dick Hobbs, (Captain RN Rtd), e-mail to the author, 12th August 2018.
26   Ibid.
27   Mike Doyle, e-mail to the author, 19th June 2018.

28   Ibid.
29   Ibid.
30   Defence Council Instructions, *DEFE 45/105*, The National Archive.

Chapter Ten

1   Rudyard Kipling, *Traffics and Discoveries, 1904*,(London: Penguin Group, 1988).
2   Robert Mitchell, *From recorded interview in HMS Collingwood*, 14th November 2018.
3   Eric Mitchell, *Fisgardian*, Issue 46, May 2018, 9.
4   Peter Bellamy, e-mail to the author, 5th December 2018.
5   Commodore John Newel RN Rtd, e-mail to the author, 16th June 2018.
6   Chris Parry, *Down South, A Falklands War Diary* (London: Penguin Group, 2012), 215.
7   Citation for award of Queens Gallantry Medal to MEA(M)1 Kenneth Enticknap, D113547S, *Supplement to the London Gazette,* 8th October 1982, 12842. Quoted in Max Arthur, Above All Courage, The Falklands Front Line: First Hand Accounts.(London: Book Club Associates, 1985), 32.
8   Eric Mitchell, *Fisgardian*, Issue 46, May 2018, 9.
9   Peter Hennessy and James Jinks, *The Silent Deep, The Royal Navy Submarine Service since 1945* (London: Penguin Random House, 2016), 407.
10   Mike Simpson, *Fisgardian*, Issue 28, Spring 2011,5.
11   Captain Matt Bolton RN, e-mail to the author, 1st August 2018.
12   Captain Mike Rose RN, e-mail to the author, 13th July 2018.
13   Commodore Mark Cameron RN, e-mail to the author, 6th July 2018.
14   Captain P J Towell OBE MA MBA CEng CMarEng FIMarEST Royal Navy Royal Navy Website, accessed 20 May 2018, https://www.royalnavy.mod.uk/-/media/royal-navy-responsive/documents/profiles/towell-peter.pdf.
15   Captain Bill Oliphant RN Rtd, e-mail to the author, 7th September 2018.
16   Bill Oliphant, e-mail to the author, 29th October 2018.
17   Ibid.
18   Ibid.
19   Commander Andy Donaldson RN, *From recorded interview in HMS Collingwood*, 14th November 2018.
20   Ministry of Defence, *DCI(RN) 96/83*. 1 April 1983.
21   Matt Bolton, e-mail to the author, 1 August 2018.
22   Ibid.
23   Ian Dickinson, e-mail to the author, 21 October 2018.
24   David Eaton et al. (eds), Second to None, 77.
25   Peter Bellamy, e-mail to the author, 5 December 2018.
26   HMS Fisgard, *Fisgard Finale Programme,* 13 August 1983.
27   Harding, *HMS Caledonia, The Apprentices' Story*, 213.
28   Ibid, 216.

29 David Eaton et al. (eds), *Second to None,* 28.

30 House of Commons Debate, 8 March 1984, *Hansard*, vol. 55 cc 1083–90.

31 Ibid.

32 Ibid.

33 John Newell, e-mail to the author, 16 June 2018.

34 Peter Bellamy, e-mail to the author, 9 October 2017.

35 WO1 ET (ME) Steven Drayton, *From Recorded Interview in HMS Sultan,* 25 June 2018.

36 HMS Fisgard, *Fisgard Magazine 1981*, Summer 1981.

37 Commander Jonathan Pearce RN, *From Recorded Interview in HMS Collingwood*, 14 November 2018.

38 Ibid.

Chapter Eleven

1 Bliss Carman (ed.), *The World's Best Poetry, Tubal Cain, Charles Mackay* (Philadelphia: John D. Morris, 1904).

2 Peter Bellamy, e-mail to the author, 5 December 2018.

3 CPO ET (ME) Dawn Jennings, *From Recorded Interview in HMS Sultan,* 25 June 2018.

4 Derek Nadine, e-mail to the author, 8 December 2018.

5 Derek Nadine, e-mail to the author, 8 December 2018.

6 Jef Webster, e-mail to the author, 16 September 2018.

7 Ian Cook, e-mail to the author, 20 October 2018.

8 CPO ET (WE) Helen Robson, *From Recorded Interview in HMS Collingwood*, 14 November 2018.

9 Ibid.

10 Harding, *HMS Caledonia, The Apprentices' Story*, 243.

11 John Newell, e-mail to the author, 16 June 2018.

12 Jef Webster, e-mail to the author, 16 September 2018.

13 Ibid.

14 Moore, *The Greenie,* 222.

15 Harding, *HMS Caledonia, The Apprentices' Story*, 244.

16 CPO ET (ME) Jumper Collins, *From Recorded Interview in HMS Sultan,* 25 June 2018.

17 CPO ET (ME) Andrew Grimes, *From Recorded Interview in HMS Sultan,* 25 June 2018.

18 Stephen Galloway-Kirkland, e-mail to the author, 31 August 2018.

19 Ibid.

Chapter Twelve

1 J. VanAmersfoort, *Traces of an Alexandrian Orphic Theogony in the Psuedo-Clemuintines* (Leiden, E.J. Brill, 1981), 17.

2   WO1 ET (WE)Andy Bibb, e-mail to the author, 24 June 2018.
3   Andy Bibb, e-mail to the author, 24 June 2018.
4   John Newell, e-mail to the author, 16 June 2018.
5   Andy Bibb, e-mail to the author, 24 June 2018.
6   Ibid.
7   Ibid.
8   Ibid.
9   Ibid.
10 Ibid.
11 Ibid.
12 Darren Hawkins, *From Recorded Interview in HMS Collingwood*, 14 November 2018.
13 Melanie Ward, *From Recorded Interview in HMS Collingwood*, 14 November 2018.
14 Ministry of Defence, *DCI(RN) 146/03.*
15 Ministry of Defence, *DIN 01-027.*
16 Article, *Fisgardian*, Spring 2006, 8.
17 Ibid.
18 Article, *Fisgardian*, Autumn 2006, 4.
19 CPO ET (ME), Steven Nelson, *From Recorded Interview in HMS Sulta*n, 25 June 2018.
20 Article, *Fisgardian*, Autumn 2009, 20.
21 CPO ET (WE) Garry Jones, e-mail to the author, 26 November 2018.
22 Garry Jones, e-mail to the author, 28 November 2018.
23 Article, *Fisgardian*, Spring 2010, 1.
24 William Shakespeare, *Henry V*, Act IV, Scene iii. *William Shakespeare, The Complete Works* (London, Collins, 1979), 576.

Bibliography

• • •

Admiralty Circular 121, printed in *The Navy List*, 1853.

Admiralty Circular 288, *Introduction for Training Afloat on board HMS Illustrious*, 23 February 1857.

Admiralty Order in Council 19 July 1837, *Engineers and Engineer Boys, Regulations for*, The National Archives.

ADM 1/6060, *Navy Department Correspondence and Letters 1840-1913, In-letters and Papers: 1860-1869*. Admiralty January–March, The National Archives.

ADM 139/287/28612, *Royal Navy Continuous Service Engagement Books*, The National Archives.

ADM 234/983, *Admiralty Order in Council, 18 May 1897*, The National Archives.

ADM 7/941, *Scheme for Entry, Training and Employment of Officers, Men and Boys for the Royal Navy*, 21 November 1902, The National Archives.

ADM 188/435/271276, *Shipcott, Lionel Gordon, Official Number: 271276*, The National Archives.

ADM 273/15/161, *Royal Naval Air Service: Registers of Officers Service*, The National Archives.

ADM 188/436/271978, *Frew, Sidney Oswell, Official Number: 271978*, The National Archives.

ADM 336/29/697, *Service Record of Whitworth, Muriel, Rating: Artificer, Service Number: G6702*, The National Archives.

ADM 182/19, *Admiralty Fleet Order No. 36576, December 22, 1920*, The National Archives.

ADM 182/42, *Admiralty Fleet Order 2858/59, October 3, 1925*, The National Archives.

ADM 363/174/60, *Gurr, John Arthur, Official Number M37091*, The National Archives.

ADM 196/124/94, *Stuart Latham Bateson*, The National Archives.

Article, *Fisgardian*, Autumn 2003.

Article, *Fisgardian*, Autumn 2004.

Article, *Fisgardian*, Spring 2006.

Article, *Fisgardian*, Autumn 2007.

Article, *Fisgardian*, Issue 23, Autumn 2008.

Article, *Fisgardian*, Autumn 2009.

Article, *Fisgardian*, Autumn 2011.

Article, *Fisgardian*, Issue 32, Spring 2013.

Article, *Fisgardian*, Issue 34, Spring 2014.

Article, *Fisgardian*, January 2016.

Article, *Old Caledonia Artificer Apprentices Association*, Newsletter, Spring 2011.

Article, *Portsmouth Evening News,* 11 December 1931.

Arthur, Max, *Above All Courage, The Falklands Front Line: First Hand Accounts* (London: Book Club Associates, 1985).

Bacon, R., *From 1900 Onwards Volume 2* (London: Hutchinson, 1940).

Barrett, D.W., Barrett, J.E., *The Story of W J Barrett 1845-1946* (printed privately).

Bass, Paul, e-mail to the author, 16 March 2018.

Bateman, Roger, e-mail to the author, 24 August 2017.

Bellamy, Peter, e-mail to the author, 5 December 2018.

Bennett, Cecil Reginald Percival, *Memoirs of a Boy Artificer,* courtesy of Alan Bennett, Commodore RN (Retd.).

Bibb, Andy, WO1 ET (WE), e-mail to the author, 24 June 2018.

Bolton, Matt, Captain RN, e-mail to the author, 1 August 2018.

Briggs, J.H., *Naval Administrations 1827-1892* (London: Sampson, Low, Marston & Co, 1897).

Calverley, Ron, e-mail to the author, 30 September 2018.

Cameron, Mark, Commodore RN, e-mail to the author, 6 July 2018.

Carew, Anthony, *The Lower Deck of the Royal Navy 1900-1939. Invergordon in Perspective* (Manchester: Manchester University Press, 1981).

Carew, Anthony, The Invergordon Mutiny, 1931: Long-Term Causes, Organisation and Leadership. *International Review of Social History* (Aug 1979), 159, accessed 2 March 2017.

Carman, Bliss (ed.), *The World's Best Poetry, Tubal Cain, Charles Mackay* (Philadelphia: John D. Morris, 1904).

Chamberlain, Tony, *"Stokers – the Lowest of the Low?" A Social History of Royal Navy Stokers 1850–1950* (PhD diss., University of Exeter, 2013).

Citation for award of Queens Gallantry Medal to MEA(M)1 Kenneth Enticknap, D113547S, *Supplement to the London Gazette*, 8 October 1982.

Collins, Jumper, CPO ET (ME), *From Recorded Interview in HMS Sultan*, 25 June 2018.

Cook, Ian, e-mail to the author, 20 October 2018.

Cooper Key Report, House of Commons, *UK Parliamentary Papers*, Command Papers, C1647, 1877.

Courts Martial Registers. *ADM 194/42 Royal Naval and Royal Marine Officers and Ratings, 1812-1855*, The National Archives.

CSC 10/4661, *Artificer Apprentice in HM Navy, Examination, Tables of Marks and Results, 7 April 1921*, The National Archives.

Dickinson, Harry, *Educating the Royal Navy, Eighteenth and Nineteenth-Century Education for Officers* (New York: Routledge, 2007).

Dickinson, Ian, e-mail to the author, 21 October 2018.

Donaldson, Andy, Commander RN, *From Recorded Interview in HMS Collingwood*, 14 November 2018.

Doyle, Mike, e-mail to the author, 19 June 2018.

Drayton, Steven, WO1 ET (ME), *From Recorded Interview in HMS Sultan*, 25 June 2018.

Eaton, David, et al. (eds), *Second to None, 100 Years of the Artificer Apprentice* (Waterlooville: BAE SYSTEMS Ltd, 2003).

Enticknap, Ken, e-mail to the author, 18 September 2018.

Ereira, Alan, *The Invergordon Mutiny, A Narrative of the Last Great Mutiny in the Royal Navy and How It Forced Britain off the Gold Standard in 1931* (London: Routledge & Kegan Paul, 1981).

Galloway-Kirkland, Stephen, e-mail to the author, 31 August 2018.

Gosden, Stephen (Captain RN Rtd), e-mail to the author, 3 August 2018.

Griffiths, Denis, *Steam at Sea, Two Centuries of Steam-Powered Ships* (London: Conway Maritime Press, 1997), 137.

Grimes, Andrew, CPO ET (ME), *From Recorded Interview in HMS Sultan*, 25 June 2018.

Gurr, John A., *In Peace and War, A Chronicle of Experiences in the Royal Navy, 1922-1946* (Worcester: Square One Publications, 1993).

Halstead, E.P., *The Screw Fleet of the Navy* (London: Simpkin, Marshall & Co., 1850).

Harding, Gil, *HMS Caledonia, The Apprentices' Story* (printed privately, 1986).

Hattendorf, John B., et al. (eds), *Pay and Allowances 1919, British Naval Documents 1204–1960*, Naval Records Society (1993): 521.

Hawkins, Darren, *From Recorded Interview in HMS Collingwood*, 14 November 2018.

Hennessy, Peter and Jinks, James, *The Silent Deep, The Royal Navy Submarine Service since 1945* (London: Penguin Random House, 2016).

Herwig, Holger, Jutland: Acrimony to Resolution, *Naval War College Review, Washington* (Autumn 2016).

HMS Fisgard, *Fisgard Finale Programme*, 13 August 1983.

Hobbs, Dick (Captain RN Rtd), e-mail to the author, 12 August 2018.

Holy Bible.

House of Commons Debate, 22 February 1906, *Hansard*, vol. 152 cc 495–6.

House of Commons Debate, 08 March 1984, *Hansard*, vol. 55 cc 1083–90.

INF 14/427/2, 31 July 1970, *The Last Tot*, The National Archive.

Jellicoe, Nicholas, *Jutland The Unfinished Battle* (Barnsley: Seaforth Publishing, 2016).

Jennings, Dawn, CPO ET (ME) *From Recorded Interview in HMS Sultan*, 25 June 2018.

Johnson, Oliver, Class Warfare and the Selborne Scheme: The Royal Navy's Battle over Technology and Social Hierarchy, *The Mariner's Mirror* (2014) 100:4, 422–433, DOI: 10.1080/00253359.2014.962327.

Jones, Garry, CPO ET (WE), e-mail to the author, 26 November 2018.

Kipling, Rudyard, *Traffics and Discoveries, 1904* (London: Penguin Group, 1988).

Lambert, Nicholas A., "Our Bloody Ships" or "Our Bloody Systems"? Jutland and the Loss of the Battlecruisers, 1916, *The Journal of Military History*, vol. 62, no. 1 (Jan 1998).

Letter from Rear Admiral Sir Reginald Custance (DNI) to Vice Admiral Sir Cyprian Bridge (C-in-C China Station), 9 June 1902, Papers of Admiral Sir Cypian Arthur George Bridge, *National Maritime Museum*, BRI/15.

London Gazette, 3 March 1915.

London Gazette, 19 October 1920.

Lowis, Geoffrey, *Fabulous Admirals* (London, Putnam & Co Ltd, 1957).

MacFarlane Gray, J., Annual General Meeting Address, *Transactions of the Institute of Marine Engineers* (1890–1891), 20.

Mackay, Ruddock F., *Fisher of Kilverston* (Oxford: Clarendon Press, 1973).

Marder, Arthur J., *Fear God and Dread Nought: Correspondence of Admiral of the Fleet Lord Fisher of Kilverstone, vol. 1854–1904* (London: Jonathan Cape, 1952).

Marder, Arthur J., *From the Dreadnought to Scapa Flow: The Royal Navy in the Fisher Era, 1904-1919, 5 vols.* (London: Oxford University Press, 1961–1970).

Ministry of Defence, *DCI(RN) 415/65*.

Ministry of Defence, *DCI(RN) 140/66*.

Ministry of Defence, *DCI (RN) 923/70*.

Ministry of Defence, *DCI (RN) 329/85*.

Ministry of Defence, *DCI(RN) 96/83*, 1 April 1983.

Ministry of Defence, *DCI(RN) 146/03*.

Ministry of Defence, *DIN 01-027*.

Mitchell, Robert, *From Recorded Interview in HMS Collingwood*, 14 November 2018.

Moore, Patrick A., *The Greenie, The History of Warfare Technology in the Royal Navy* (Stroud: Spellmount, 2011).

Nadine, Derek, e-mail to the author, 8 December 2018.

Nelson, Steven, CPO ET (ME), *From Recorded Interview in HMS Sultan*, 25 June 2018.

Newell, John (Commodore RN Rtd) e-mail to the author, 16 June 2018.

Parry, Chris, *Down South, A Falklands War Diary* (London: Penguin Group, 2012).

Patterson, Alfred Temple (ed.), The Jellicoe Papers Volume I, The Naval Records Society, 1968.

Pearsall A.W.H., et al., *The First Engineers, 1837*, British Naval Documents 1204–1960, Naval Records Society (1993).

Penn, Geoffrey, *Up Funnel, Down Screw!* (London: Hollis & Carter, 1955).

Oliphant, Bill, Captain RN Rtd, e-mail to the author, 7 September 2018.

Orpen H, The Origin, Evolution and Future of the Personnel of the British Royal Navy, *Transactions of the Royal United Services Institution*, November 1902, 33.

Osborne, Richard, *Voices From the Past, The Battle of Jutland* (Barnsley: Frontline Books, 2016).

Payton, Phillip, *The Story of HMS Fisgard* (Redruth: Dyllansow Truran, 1983).

PC 2/268, *Privy Council Registers, VICTORIA, Vol 49*, The National Archives.

PC 2/368 *Privy Council Registers, VICTORIA, Vol 149*, The National Archives.

PC 2/380, *Privy Council Registers, EDWARD VII, Vol 1*, The National Archives.

PC 2/439, *Privy Council Registers, GEORGE V, Vol 34*, The National Archives.

PC 2/628, *Privy Council Registers, GEORGE VI, Vol 8*, The National Archives.

PC 2/655, *Privy Council Registers, GEORGE VI, Vol 20*, The National Archives.

PC 2/674, *Privy Council Registers, GEORGE VI, Vol 36*, The National Archives.

PC 2/763 *Privy Council Registers, ELIZABETH II, Vol 39*, The National Archives.

Pearce, Jonathan, Commander RN, *From Recorded Interview in HMS Collingwood*, 14 November 2018.

Report, Four Generations, The Harcourt Family at Cowplain, *Hampshire Telegraph*, 13 July 1928.

Report of Court Martial, *Naval & Military Gazette and Weekly Chronicle of the United Service*, 16 February 1876.

Rippon, P.M., *Evolution of Engineering in the Royal Navy, Volume 1, 1827-1939* (Tunbridge Wells: Spellmount, 1988).

RNM 1994/435, 11. *Journal of Francis Wheeler, Engineer, 1855-1862*, National Museum of the Royal Navy.

Robson, Helen, CPO ET (WE), *From Recorded Interview in HMS Collingwood*, 14 November 2018.

Romans, Elinor Francis, *Selection and Early Career Education of Executive Officers in the Royal Navy c1902-199* (PhD Diss., University of Exeter, 2012).

Rose, Mike, Captain RN, e-mail to the author, 13 July 2018.

Scheme for Entry, Training and Employment of Officers, Men and Boys for the Royal Navy, 21 November 1902, *The National Archives*, ADM 7/941.

Shakespeare, William, *William Shakespeare, The Complete Works* (London, Collins, 1979).

Shore, Henry, "A Fin-de-Siècle Tragedy: or, The Death and Burial of Seamanship", *United Service Magazine*, XXIII (1901).

Smith, Edgar C., *A Short History of Naval and Marine Engineering* (Cambridge:

Cambridge University Press, 1937).

Speech to the House of Lords, 8th May 1903, *Hansard*, vol 122, cc155-191.

Sumida, Jon Tetsuro, A Matter of Timing, The Royal Navy and the Tactics of Defensive Battle, 1912–1916, *The Journal of Military History*, vol. 67, no. 1 (Jan 2003), 86.

The Effects of the Pay Cuts, 1931, British Naval Documents 1204–1960, Navy Records Society, 527,998.

Till, Geoffrey, Grove, Eric, Sumida, Jon, The Engineer Question 1902, British Naval Documents 1204–1960, Naval Records Society (1993).

Towell, P.J., Captain OBE MA MBA CEng CMarEng FIMarEST Royal Navy, Royal Navy Website, accessed 20 May 2018, https://www.royalnavy.mod. uk/-/media/royal-navy-responsive/documents/profiles/towell-peter.pdf.

VanAmersfoort, J, *Traces of an Alexandrian Orphic Theogony in the Psuedo-Clemuintines* (Leiden, E.J. Brill, 1981).

Wakefield, Stuart, e-mail to the author, 4 January 2018.

Walton, Oliver C., *Social History of the Royal Navy, 1856-1900: Corporation and Community* (PhD Diss., University of Exeter, 2003).

Ward, Melanie, *From Recorded Interview in HMS Collingwood*, 14 November 2018.

Webster, Jef, e-mail to the author, 16 September 2018.

Webster, Noah, *A Dictionary of the English Language, Vol 1* (London, Black, Young and Young, 1832).

White, Alan, The Way We Were, *Marine Engineering Review*, IMarEST, September 2009.

Wootton, Frank, *Letter to Fisgardian*, Issue 4, 1999.